PLANTS OF THE WORLD

THE LOWER PLANTS

Plants of the World

THE LOWER PLANTS

K. B. Boedijn
translated by A. J. Pomerans

*with 157 color plates
and 383 illustrations in black and white*

E. P. DUTTON & Co. INC.   NEW YORK 1969

PLANTS OF THE WORLD: The Lower Plants

English translation Copyright © 1968 by E. P. Dutton & Co. Inc.,
New York, and Thames & Hudson Ltd., London
Published in The Netherlands 1965 under the title *Lagere Planten*
Copyright © 1965 by W. Gaade
Library of Congress catalog card number: 66–25815
Produced by W. Gaade, The Hague/Chanticleer Press, New York

Printed in The Netherlands by A. Sijthoff N.V., The Hague

Contents

Acknowledgments

The colour plates are from photographs by Professor W. Rauh of the Institute of Systematic Botany, Heidelberg University, with the following exceptions:

Plates 148, 149, 150, E. Günther
Plate 37, X. Misonne
Plates 94, 137, W. Schacht
Plates 43, 44, 49, 52, 63, 65, 68, 69, 71, 76, 78, 89, 92, 97, 100, 105–7, 109, 111, 112, 114–17, 122, 129, 131, 133, 138, 141–3, 145, 146, 151, 154–7, H. Schrempp
Plates 75, 79, 113, W. Schulz
Plate 73, D. van der Sijde
Plate 128, Vinton Richard
Plates 42, 48, 67, 127, 132, Professor H. C. D. de Wit, Agricultural College of Wageningen, the Netherlands

Plate 51, Wortman
Plates 46, 66, 72, 74, Dr. W. Bötticher

All the drawings are by the author.
The black and white plates are from photographs by Professor W. Rauh, with the following exceptions:

Figs. 220, 225, 232, 369, 373, 380, R. Fischer
Figs. 371, 382, E. Günther
Figs. 239, 376, W. Schacht
Fig. 5, Dr. C. van der Scheer
Figs. 205, 232, H. Schrempp
Figs. 27, 130, 167, 186, 199, 201, 204, 209, 211, 212, 214, 217–19, 222, 226, 227, 231, 244, D. van der Sijde
Figs. 221, 343, 353, Professor H. C. D. de Wit

Introduction

In Volumes I and II of this series, we examined the life of higher plants in all their rich variety. Though they are far more conspicuous than the 'lower plants', it is true to say that the latter are no less profuse or interesting, and that many, for instance bacteria and fungi, are of great economic importance.

All extant plants are descended from earlier forms. However, in the course of evolution they have diverged so considerably that it is extremely difficult to determine their precise interrelationship, the more so as entire families and tribes have disappeared – fossils of the older forms are few and far between. As a result, 'family trees' do little more than provide the criteria for classifying plants by their level of organization. When applying these criteria, we make a number of assumptions; for instance, we suppose that green algae are the direct ancestors of club mosses, that club mosses are the ancestors of ferns, and ferns of gymnosperms. On the 'lowest rung' of the ladder, modern botanists place bacteria and blue-green algae, the latter, it has been suggested, being derived from colourless green and brown flagellates. Though we know a number of intermediate types between green flagellates and green spermatophytes, only a few groups of existing plants can be fitted into the scheme running from Chlorophyta (green algae), through Bryophyta (mosses) and Pteridophyta (ferns), to Gymnospermae (naked-seeded plants) and Angiospermae (covered-seeded plants). Several groups have ended up as lateral offshoots, among them diatoms, brown algae, red algae and water ferns.

As in the first two volumes, we shall trace the family tree from the bottom upwards. In other words, we shall be making a mighty leap downwards from the orchids and palms, with which we ended Volume II, to the bacteria, and then climb up again to the forms that provide us with a bridge to the gymnosperms, the plants with which we began Volume I.

Among the rich variety of plant forms, it is possible to discover a number of common characteristics. The most general of these is that all plants are built up of tiny cells and that they grow by cell division. All cells, moreover, reflect an identical structural plan, and the simplest plants of all – bacteria, blue-green algae and flagellate algae, consist of only a single cell.

Further general principles emerge from a study of reproduction. Asexual reproduction, by the division of single cells, cell complexes, or entire organs, occurs throughout the plant kingdom. More important in the life of most plants is sexual reproduction, i.e. the fusion of two sexual cells (gametes) into a zygote and its subsequent division into daughter cells. This process occurs from the lowest algae (and presumably even from the bacteria) to the highest plants, though the associated processes become more complicated as we climb up the evolutionary ladder. In sexual reproduction, an essential part is played by the cell nucleus and its chromosomes. Every species has a characteristic number of chromosomes, and that number is doubled whenever two gametes fuse into a zygote. Were this duplication continued indefinitely, normal reproduction would, of course, become impossible. However, a basically simple process ensures that the number of chromosomes in the cell remains constant. Once the gametes have joined into a zygote, the chromosome number is halved by a process known as meiosis, or reduction division, which may take place at any time after fusion. In most cases, the zygote develops into a plant with a double (diploid) complement of chromosomes, and it is only as the plant matures that special cells with a reduced number of chromosomes are formed. The resulting cells with a single (haploid) set of chromosomes do not generally produce gametes, but grow up into haploid plants. This change between haploid and diploid phases is known as 'antithetic alternation of generations'. The phases can be of varying duration in different plants; in other words meiosis can occur at different intervals after the formation of zygotes. In special cases (e.g. in many green and brown algae), both generations are equivalent and not externally distinguishable, in other cases (e.g. in green and flagellate algae) the diploid phase may be exceedingly short, or there may be only a very brief haploid generation (e.g. in some brown algae and mosses). Sometimes the two phases are so distinct that the haploid and diploid generations are easily mistaken for two different plants – a case in point is the genus *Cutleria* (brown algae). Reproduction and alternation of generations in lower plants are so varied that we shall often have to refer to them in our discussion of the individual groups.

Striking similarities between all groups of plants are also found in their metabolic behaviour, so much so that we can speak of uniformity in this sphere. Thus the agents accelerating metabolic processes, i.e. the catalysts, are identical in all plants, indeed in all living organisms, and so are the basic foods.

We have been stressing the similarities, but it should be remembered that even the so-called lower plants are so diverse in structure and represent such vastly different levels of development that they are a much more heterogeneous group than the higher plants. Thus lower plants comprise organisms ranging in size from less than 0.2 micron = two ten-thousandths of a millimetre (e.g. cocci) to 100 metres (e.g. *Macrocystis*). Some are among the simplest of all organisms (e.g. yeasts); others are highly differentiated (e.g. red algae and ferns). Again, some of the simpler types can barely be distinguished from simple animals, whereas the vast majority leave us in no doubt as to their real nature. Lower plants occur as plankton in lakes, rivers and oceans and also in the air. Some species are as much at home in the snow and alpine ice as they are in dry deserts. They may inhabit the soil or other plants and animals. Some of them are truly ubiquitous; others are dependent on very special conditions.

Many lower plants assimilate atmospheric CO_2 with the help of the pigment chlorophyll, much as higher plants do; others employ different pigments. Several families, and indeed an entire group, the fungi, live without any pigments, they are saprophytes or parasites, and as such feed on dead or living organisms.

Quite obviously, so motley a crew cannot be fitted into a single system without difficulties. At the moment the uncertainties are still so large that speculation among taxonomists remains rife. The system we shall be using in this book is based largely on external characters, and must be considered a sort of showcase for the display of all those untold forms that do not fit into the world of flowering plants, namely:

Viruses and bacteriophages

Bacteriophyta	Bacteria
Cyanophyta	Blue-green algae
Pyrrophyta	Brown flagellate algae
Euglenophyta	Euglenoid algae
Chrysophyta	Yellow algae
Chlorophyta	Green algae
Phaeophyta	Brown algae
Rhodophyta	Red algae
Mycophyta and Lichenes	Fungi and Lichens
Bryophyta	Mosses
Pteridophyta	Ferns

It should be emphasized right from the start that viruses and bacteriophages (or phages for short) cannot be considered living organisms in the accepted sense of the word. For many years, biologists remained unclear about their true nature, often claiming that viruses were 'primitive forms' or precursors of living organisms. Today we know that no other organisms are descended from them.

Like living organisms, viruses consist of protein and nucleic acids, these being organic compounds capable of self-duplication inside chromosomes, where they are responsible for transmitting the hereditary material and also constitute the master templates for the construction of proteins. In addition, most viruses contain enzymes. However, their organization is so rudimentary that they cannot be considered as living organisms. To begin with, reproduction can only take place within the living cells of the host organism. Because viruses completely alter the normal development of the host cell – which they force to produce new viruses – they cause diseases in plants, animals, man and even in bacteria. Hence their name of *virus*, which is simply the Latin for 'poison'.

Modern biologists believe that viruses and phages are either strongly reduced forms of earlier, bacterium-like organisms, or that they have originated in parts of the genetic equipment of higher animals, i.e. in genes or chromosome sets that broke free from living cells. Some, such as the tobacco mosaic disease virus, can even be produced in crystallized form. By far the largest number of viruses are sub-microscopic – thus the virus causing tobacco necrosis measures 17 millionths of a millimetre (millimicrons, or mμ); that causing foot and mouth disease only 8 – 12 millimicrons.

Hence the sudy of viruses had to await the invention of the electron microscope. Under it, they appear as small spheres (e.g. the foot and mouth disease virus), rods (e.g. the tobacco mosaic virus), or cubes (e.g. the smallpox virus); many bacteriophages have a spherical or polyhedral 'head' and a rod-shaped or filamentous 'tail'.

Plant virus diseases include tobacco mosaic, which causes the leaves of young plants to become spotted with light areas, and potato leaf-roll which, *inter alia*, manifests itself in the reduction of the number of tubers. Pod disease on cocoa plants can be diagnosed by the abnormally short pods. Mosaic disease of the cucumber causes the leaves to become irregularly mottled and somewhat wrinkled. Virus disease in hop helps to stunt the entire plant. Witches' broom, too, is often caused by virus infection.

Since viruses also attack and kill the larvae and pupae of insects, they may be used in biological pest control, for instance against the clothes moth.

Virus diseases of warm-blooded animals include cow-pox, sheep-pox, cattle-plague, swine-plague, foot and mouth disease, hydrophobia, myxomatosis and psittacosis. In man, the following are just a few of the diseases that may be attributed to viruses: influenza, measles, German measles, mumps, some forms of pneumonia, herpes, infantile paralysis, yellow fever, smallpox, and encephalitis. It would seem that some types of cancer in warm-blooded animals and men are also due to viruses.

Great though the pathological importance of viruses may be, they are neither living organisms nor, as far as we can tell, the ancestors of living organisms. Because they contain nucleic acids, however, they share the basic elements of all living organisms. Since many phages can be grown on bacteria, they are now widely used in the study of hereditary processes. Indeed, viruses may well hold the key to the origins of life itself.

THE PROKARYOBIONTS:
plants without a distinct nucleus

This group includes the bacteria (Bacteriophyta) and the blue-green algae (Cyanophyta). All are unicellular organisms or else made up of very few cells only. They differ from all other plants in that their cells lack a distinct, i.e. morphologically identifiable, nucleus. Instead, the desoxyribonucleic acid, the substance responsible for genetic processes and normally located in the nucleus, is scattered over the entire cell or at least over a region round the centre of the cell. Since this region lacks a nuclear membrane, biologists speak of a nuclear equivalent. Its presence is readily demonstrated by chemical means, but structures corresponding to the chromosomes of other organisms have not so far been discovered among prokaryobionts, and this despite great efforts. However, genetic experiments suggest that here, too, the genes are aligned linearly and that bacteria, in particular, have a single 'chromosome', the so-called lineome.

In other respects, too, the cells of prokaryobionts are more simply constructed than those of other plants. To begin with they lack special pigment cells (chromatophores) with a distinct membrane; what pigments blue-green algae and bacteria do have (and only a minority of bacteria have any) are simple lamellated structures, distributed freely throughout the protoplasm. Mitochondria (morphologically autonomous units within the cell, which are important sources of cellular energy) are also missing in prokaryobionts, though some blue-green algae have been found to contain mitochondria 'equivalents'.

For the rest, blue-green algae and bacteria are quite distinct groups. Even a cursory observation will show that most bacteria are entirely devoid of pigments, while lack of pigment is rather the exception among blue-green algae.

Most organisms now existing are dependent on oxygen which, as we know, was not freely available during the early period of the earth's existence. It had first to be produced by the pigment-carrying plants. Hence the earliest plants must either have lived without oxygen, obtaining their energy from other sources as many (anaerobic) organisms still do to this day, or else they must have contained special pigments enabling them to produce their own oxygen supplies. Blue-green algae might well have fallen into the second category, though it is too early to pronounce on this point with any certainty.

In our treatment of the lower plants, we shall follow the common practice of beginning with the bacteria which, in many respects, seem to be the most simply organized of all, so much so that many botanists consider them as reduced forms that have undergone secondary simplification.

1 BACTERIOPHYTA
Bacteria

Bacteria are ubiquitous organisms. This is largely because they are so diminutive (of the order of 1 micron = 0.0001 cm.) that even the slightest breath of air scatters them far afield. Moreover, they are capable of multiplying at a phenomenal rate: under suitable conditions, all bacteria can split into two every twenty minutes or so. Hence a single bacterium is capable of producing 10^{24} descendants within twenty-four hours, weighing altogether some 3000 kg., whereas a single bacterium weighs only 10^{-15} gm. (i.e. a million-millionth of a milligram). Luckily, this fantastic rate of multiplication is only a theoretical possibility. Bacteria also owe their ubiquity to their marked ability to withstand heat, cold, dryness and radiation in the form of thick-walled resting spores. Thus the spores of the anthrax bacillus can withstand boiling at 100°C for ten minutes; phosphorescent bacteria can withstand temperatures of –190°C for weeks, and the spores of soil-dwelling bacteria will germinate after decades of storage under dry conditions. However, the majority of bacteria are highly dependent on temperature conditions – the most widespread species can only develop and reproduce between 0°C and 45°C. Pathogenic species have specialized to body temperatures (38°C – 40°C); heat-loving (thermophilous) species do not grow below 45°C and prefer temperatures of from 50°C to 65°C – they do not, however, die until the temperature rises to about 80°C. At temperatures of from 80° to 100°C most bacteria die.

Bacteria are highly specialized organisms. This may seem to contradict what we have just said, but the contradiction is merely apparent. They are ubiquitous, simply because they exist in so vast a variety of forms. Different bacteria live in arid deserts, in tropical swamps, in regions of permanent snow and in the ocean, among the roots of plants and inside their tissues, in the intestines of worms, insects and mammals, in mineral oil and in milk, indeed even in the organic fluids produced by modern chemists. They may be harmless like those inhabiting our mouth or most of those in our intestine, or extremely harmful – like the agents of bubonic plague, cholera, typhus, tuberculosis, pneumonia or tetanus. Many cause great damage by helping to putrefy our food and drink. Others again help to maintain the fertility of our soil, or are essential to the fermentation of vinegar, cheese and other edible products; bacteria supply us with vitamins (B_{12}), mild antibiotics, butyl alcohol and swamp ore. They cause such strange phenomena as blue milk, phosphorescence in fishes or the bleeding of holy wafers. Indeed, they can even start fires, by causing the self-combustion of hay.

We have seen that their small size is responsible for the wide scattering of bacteria, but it has other consequences as well. One of these is that an untold number of bacteria can be crowded into a tiny space. No less than 200,000 million relatively large bacteria, 1 micron in diameter and 5 microns in length, can be crowded into 1 cubic centimetre. Even poor, sandy soils will be found to contain several hundreds of thousand of bacteria per c.c., and 1 c.c. of rich humus contains 100 million to 5000 million bacteria. One cubic metre of air in a large industrial city holds from 300 to 1,500 bacteria; in living quarters and stables the number is far greater, in the country it is far less. Needless to say, bacteria occur in every conceivable type of water. Effluents are particularly rich in them (about 1 million per c.c.); spring water, on the other hand, may contain less than 100 bacteria per c.c. The health authorities in most countries consider 200 bacteria per c.c. of drinking water the permissible upper limit. Bacteria orginated in the soil, from which they later spread to other environments: water, air, plants, animals and man. Thus the number of micro-organisms (chiefly bacteria) counted in Linzer Untersee (a mountain lake) was found to be 50–90 per c.c. at a depth of 0–33 m., but up to 400,000 per c.c. in the bottom ooze. In the soil itself, the number of bacteria decreases with depth; thus a pasture containing 10 million bacteria per gram of earth at a depth of 1 cm. will only contain 1 million at a depth of 30 cm. and 200,000 at a depth of 75 cm. Bacteria are exceedingly numerous in the ocean deeps; mud samples from the Philippine Trench (depth 10,000 m.) were found to contain up to 1 million bacteria per gram.

In the air, the number of bacteria decreases with height; it is greater in the tropics than at the poles, in summer than in winter. Bacteria have been found even in the stratosphere – at a height of more than 6 miles and at a temperature of $-55°$ C. The bacterial flora of the air is unusual in that it contains a particularly high proportion of pigmented types (47 per cent as compared with only 7 per cent in the mud).

Plants, animals and man have already been mentioned as bacterial hosts; the bacteria can take the form of harmless epiphytes, or of dangerous parasites and disease-producing organisms. One species – *Bdellovibrio bacteriovorus* – even lives as a parasite on other bacteria. More frequently, however, bacteria live on plants, animals and men as symbionts, deriving advantages from the host but bestowing benefits as well. A number of interesting species have entered into cyclical symbiosis with animals or plants: they are transmitted directly from the parent host to the offspring (e.g. in the vegetative reproduction of lichens). Symbiotic associations often involve interesting adaptations. Thus *Bacterium coli*, which lives in the intestine of man, helps in the digestion of food and in the suppression of putrefying bacteria; and in ruminants, bacteria break down cellulose inside the paunch, and probably play an important part in the nitrogen metabolism. Among the most fascinating symbiotic associations of all are those between bacteria and termites. Many termites harbour flagellates in their baggy intestine, where the symbionts not only break down wood splinters, but apparently harbour specific bacteria in their turn. If that is so, the latter undoubtedly play some part in the decomposition of cellulose, and we would have a case of double symbiosis – a true miracle of mutual adaptation.

In addition, bacteria can also form symbiotic associations with Protozoa (e.g. *Amoeba, Paramecium*).

As a further result of their small size, bacteria have an unusually fast metabolic rate. Thus, *Azotobacter*, a soil bacterium, has 2000 times the rate of respiration measured in the leaves or roots of higher plants. As a result, they can react extremely quickly to changes in environmental conditions.

This brings us to the main role of bacteria (and other micro-organisms) in the metabolism of nature: the break-down of complex organic substances into simple inorganic substances. Without this contribution we should all be suffocated by the gases exuded by animals and plants. Just as green plants use sunlight to synthesize their food, so micro-organisms use the energy stored in oxygen to break down organic matter. In that way the solar energy stored by plants is liberated once again.

Bacteria play a particularly crucial role in the carbon cycle. Carbon is found on earth in the most diverse combinations. The greatest percentage is fixed in the form of mineral carbonates and plays no part in the metabolism of plants and animals; the formation of mineral carbon compounds in the course of geological time merely leads to the depletion of atmospheric carbon supplies. (The deficit is partly reversed by the increase in atmospheric carbon dioxide resulting from volcanic activity.) For metabolic purposes, therefore, we have to rely on the carbon supply in the air, on organic carbon compounds, and dissolved carbon in the sea. Now, estimates suggest that the available supply of atmospheric carbon dioxide is only enough to satisfy the needs of existing plants for thirty-five years, so that, in the absence of micro-organisms, life on earth might well become extinct. As it is, soil microbes produce an annual 4000 kg. of carbon dioxide per acre of forest or agricultural land.

Even more important is the contribution of bacteria to the nitrogen cycle, for while green plants can derive their carbon supplies from atmospheric carbon dioxide, they are unable to make use of the much more abundant atmospheric nitrogen. (There are some exceptions which we shall mention later.) Hence they must absorb their nitrogen through the roots from mineral salts in the soil. Now, such salts are far less evenly distributed in the soil than carbon dioxide in the atmosphere; moreover, most of these salts are deficient in nitrogen. Nitrogen in the soil is largely produced during thunder storms: lightning helps to synthesize nitric acid from atmospheric nitrogen, oxygen and water, and this is washed down by the rain. The nitrogen supply in the soil is, however, augmented by the activity of bacteria living in the root nodules, particularly of leguminous plants (*Bacterium radicicola*), and capable of building up atmospheric nitrogen, carbon dioxide, hydrogen and oxygen into protein. This is a truly remarkable feat which, as we know today, is also performed by various free-living soil bacteria, blue-green algae, yeasts, and mycelium-forming fungi. Root bacteria make the nitrogen available to their host plants; without it the Leguminosae could barely exist, let alone survive on poor soils. Experiments have shown that lupins grow twelve times more profusely in the presence of *Bacterium radicicola* than in its absence.

The moment an organism dies – be it a tree or a bacterium, a man or an amoeba – putrefying bacteria spring into action. Special types such as *Bacterium vulgare*, *B. coli*, *B. prodigiosum*, *Bacillus subtilis*, *B. putrificus*, *B. mycoïdes*, *B. mesentericus*, *B. tumescens* and *Pseudomonas fluorescens* – to mention but a few – see to the breakdown of proteins. The nitrogenous end product of their activity is ammonia, which other bacteria transform into nitrites (e.g. *Nitrosomonas europaea*) or nitrates (e.g. *Nitrobacter winogradskyi*), thus making the nitrogen freshly available to plants. In this way the nitrogen cycle is closed, and with it the energy cycle: green plants need solar energy to build up their protein, and this energy, as we saw, is released step by step as bacteria break the protein down again.

Nitrogen-fixing bacteria, moreover, play a part in the formation of soil from rock. Since they make few demands on the substrate, they can settle among stones which they dissolve in acids. Dead bacteria become mixed with this inorganic debris, with the result that small quantities of 'soil' are formed, on which lichens and mosses, and sometimes other plants, can take root.

Similar to the action of soil bacteria is that of bacteria on dead organisms in rivers, lakes and oceans. They remove these organisms so efficiently that under natural conditions the water remains clear and clean. They can deal with the effluent men have been pouring into rivers in ever-increasing quantities and as a result of their activity the 'germ' content sinks from more than a million per c.c. at the source of pollution to a few thousands per c.c. only a few kilometres down river. Typical waste-water bacteria

are found in the order Chlamydobacteriales (e.g. *Cladotrix dichotoma* and *Clonothrix fusca*). However, such vast quantities of waste are being poured into rivers by modern civilization that the system of natural purification often breaks down. Hence many local authorities have been forced to filter the waste before it is released into rivers, lakes and oceans. This, too, is done with the help of bacteria. For years, sewage has been treated by the activated sludge method: an aeration tank is filled with sludge and brought into contact with a suspended floc of bacteria and other micro-organisms which oxidize it. The oxygen content of the sludge is maintained by diffusion of air bubbles or mechanical mixing. During this procedure two valuable by-products are released, namely methane, a gas with a high calorific value, and dry sludge which can be used as a fertilizer. The excess activated sludge can moreover be used as a source of vitamin B_{12}.

Another cause of grave concern to municipal authorities is the disposal of solid waste. Many towns simply burn their 'welfare middens', but a far better procedure is to transform them into compost. Here, too, bacteria assist in the process: modern techniques help to turn waste into humus within twenty-four hours. In this way the refuse of civilization can be restored to nature by way of gardens and fields.

Surprisingly enough, bacteria can even attack man-made substances that do not exist in nature. This is often regrettable, for instance when cable insulations are attacked. More often than not, however, it is a true blessing, for instance when insecticides and weed-killers, which are being used on an ever-vaster scale, are removed from the soil by bacterial action – the unimpeded accumulation of such substances would otherwise have the most deleterious effects on civilized life.

Other bacterial effects are far more difficult to determine. In particular, we know very little of the part bacteria play in geological processes. They probably help in the formation of carbon deposits inasmuch as they dissolve the cellulose of plant remains, but do not affect the more resistant lignin. Bacteria may well have been involved in the formation of iron, manganese and copper ore deposits, both by precipitation with hydrogen sulphide (produced by putrefying bacteria and by *Sporovibrio desulfuricans*, which lives on sulphates and releases ample quantities of H_2S), and also by the oxidation of bivalent iron compounds into the more passive tervalent iron compounds. (This reaction supplies the so-called iron bacteria with vital energy.) It is even conceivable that bacteria may have played a part in laying down the Chilean saltpetre deposits. Moreover they were undoubtedly involved in the formation of mineral oil deposits by the breakdown of plankton and other pelagic organisms.

In the industrial sphere, again, bacteria are used in the production of various fuels. Thus special plants have been constructed to exploit the ability of *Bacillus amylobacter* and *B. acetobutylicus* to turn sugar into butyl alcohol and acetone by fermentation.

No less important is the action of bacteria in the manufacture of various foods and drinks. Thus *Streptococcus lacti*, *S. cremoris* and the so-called aromatic streptococci help in the production of sour milk, buttermilk, yoghurt and the less well-known kumys and kefir of the steppes. Bacteria are essential to the maturing of many cheeses: they help to convert remnants of milk sugar into lactic, butyric, formic and propionic acids, together with traces of alcohol, which combine with the acids into esters, important aromatic substances. In addition, cheese bacteria produce amino acids and ammonia compounds which break down the proteins. Finally the carbon dioxide released during these processes exerts the pressure to which many cheeses owe their holes.

Pickled gherkins and similar preserves involve the anaerobic action of lactic-acid bacteria. In the manufacture of vinegar, on the other hand, air must be freely available; the starting substance, generally wine or beer, is stirred up in large vats, allowed to drip on to beech chips and, during the process, exposed to the action of *Bacterium xylinum*, *B. xylinoides*, *B. orleanense* and other bacteria.

Bacterial reduction plays a large part in the fermentation of tobacco, coffee, tea and cocoa. The individual processes involved have not yet been fully investigated.

Several bacteria (*Bacillus amylobacter*, *B. felsineus*, *B. asterosperus*, *B. mesentericus*, and *B. subtilis*) play a part in the retting of flax and hemp: they help to reduce the central, chiefly pectinic, layer between the fibres and the stem into acids.

All these beneficial effects are less well known than the more harmful ones. Now the 'useful' activities are generally those which help to break down materials; hence we must not be surprised to learn that bacteria also attack substances in which their presence is most unwelcome. Let us take the case of milk once more. While still in the cowshed, milk becomes suffused with deleterious bacteria. Most of them belong to the *coli* group, but pathogenic bacteria, too (e.g. *Bacterium pyogenes*, *B. coli*, *B. abortus Bang*, *Mycobacterium tuberculosis*, *Streptococcus agalactiae*), can find their way into milk – there may be up to one million such bacteria per c.c. To counteract this type of infestation, Pasteur developed the special technique bearing his name: milk is heated to $62° - 65°$ C for 30 minutes, or at $71° - 74°$ C for a few minutes, or again at $85°$ C for a very brief time. This process, known as 'pasteurization', does not give milk the unpleasant taste associated with boiling, and is simply a special case of sterilization by direct heating in dry air or hot steam; it helps to preserve foodstuffs in general by eliminating putrefying bacteria for a limited period of time. Bacteria can also be attacked with many other well-known and tried methods. A degree of protection can be obtained by ordinary cooking methods, i.e. by boiling food and conserving it in air-tight jars. Foods can also be preserved in salt (salt meat or herrings), in vinegar (pickled cucumbers, etc.) by smoking (kippers), by treatment with chemicals (benzoic acid, formic acid, boric acid, hexamethylentretamin, hydrogen peroxide, etc.), and finally by dehydration and deep freezing. All these methods deprive the putrefying bacteria of their basic needs, or at least inhibit their normal development and reproduction.

A special problem is posed by pathogenic bacteria that find their way into food yet survive preservation methods, particularly by those that develop anaerobically, i.e. in the absence of oxygen. One of these is the extremely dangerous *Clostridium botulinum*, which causes the meat poisoning known as botulism – one hundredth of a milligram of the poison is fatal to man. Others belong to the *Salmonella* group which numbers several hundred species. They cause acute inflammation of the intestine, which may last a week and even longer. Salmonella poisoning may occasionally prove fatal to man. These bacteria are particularly prevalent in ducks' eggs.

So far we have been discussing the action of bacteria in breaking down dead inorganic and organic substances – all the bacteria involved were saprophytes. But now we come to bacteria that attack living cells and tissues, damaging them directly or by the secretion of toxins. Pathogenic bacteria attack men, animals and plants. In general, different species cause different diseases; many can even be divided into sub-species or varieties with distinct pathogenic properties. The pathogenic agents are not the parasites themselves but their enzymes or metabolic products – host-specificity is often determined by very small differences in enzyme systems or other factors. Some are obligate parasites, i.e. they can only live in association with their host, and are accordingly difficult to grow in the laboratory. Others are facultative parasites, i.e. they are normally free-living or exist as saprophytes inside their host, but can become pathogenic under certain circumstances.

Plant diseases caused by bacteria (bacterioses) are quite common, but not nearly as prevalent or devastating as bacterial infections in animals and man. Some of the best-known plant bacterioses are potato blight (caused by *Bacterium phytophtorum*) and potato scab (caused by *Streptomyces scabies*); less well-known is the bacterium causing soft rot in carrots, radishes and onions (*Bacterium carotovorum*). Tomatoes are attacked by *B. michiganense*, and tobacco leaves may become infected with an eruptive disease caused by *B. tabacum*. Hyacinth bulbs may be destroyed on a wide scale by hyacinth rot (caused by *Xanthomonas hyacinthi*); black venation in cabbage is caused by *B. campestris* and 'fatty degeneration' in beans by *X. phaseoli*. Crown and root galls of various fruit trees are caused by *Bacillus tumefaciens*; tumour in olive trees by *B. oleae* and tumour in the Aleppo pine by *Pseudomonas pini*.

Parasitic bacteria may be disseminated by wind, water or insects. Varieties of the same species of plant often differ in their susceptibility to bacterial attack, hence growers generally prefer the breeding of resistant strains to bactericidal campaigns involving expensive and often far less effective chemicals. Chemotherapy is at best suited to long-living plants such as fruit trees. Sometimes more indirect measures prove effective as well; potato scab, for instance, can be suppressed by the use of vegetable manure which encourages the growth of harmless bacterial competitors.

One of the many bacteria pathogenic to animals was the first to be identified and studied as such, when Robert Koch discovered the anthrax bacillus in 1876. Koch introduced the method, used to this day, of growing the bacteria in a sterilized solution of gelatine or agar-agar to which has been added a food solution similar to that on which bacteria feed normally. The bacteria are then stained for better recognition. Koch was also the first to take a microphotograph of such organisms, and hence to show that the agent of anthrax was the rod-shaped *Bacillus anthracis*. With this discovery, he ushered in three decades of intensive hunting for pathogenic bacteria in animals and man; dozens have since been discovered and vanquished.

To show just how many diseases bacteria can cause in animals, we shall examine the case of the pig. One of the most fearful diseases in these animals, red murrain, is caused by *Erysipelothrix muriseptica*, a bacterium that prefers to attack pigs 3 to 12 months old. Another disease of pigs, a kind of pneumonia, caused by *Pasteurella suiseptica*, has become less common. Like other domestic animals, pigs can also suffer from salmonellosis (caused by *Salmonella cholerae suis*). Pigs also contract tuberculosis, diphtheria, anthrax, and brucellosis. Some diseases of the pig have recently become more prevalent, among them snuffle disease and oedema disease. Here the agents are not yet fully known, so that they need not necessarily be bacterial. Bacteria also attack other domestic animals, including poultry, in which they cause chicken cholera and poultry spirochaetosis. Needless to say, wild animals suffer from bacterial diseases as well. Here we shall merely mention rat plague (*Pasteurella pestis*) which can have such fatal consequences for man, and which is carried from rat to rat by a louse. Even the invertebrates, for instance insects, can be plagued with bacterial diseases. These may prove advantageous or detrimental to man. Thus when young bees are attacked by *Bacillus larvae* they fall prey to foul-brood, and cause severe losses to bee-keepers. Silkworms are attacked by similar organisms. On the other hand, bacteria can be used to fight caterpillar infestations and particularly to eradicate bombycid and geometrid moths in forests. To that purpose, the bacteria are grown in isolated cultures and scattered over the infested area. In other cases of biological warfare, individuals of the harmful species are infected with bacteria and then released, whereupon they infect others.

In man, bacteria have been causing great suffering for millennia, spreading plague (*Pasteurella pestis*), leprosy (*Mycobacterium leprae*), cholera (*Vibrio comma*), typhoid (*Salmonella typhosa*), typhus (*Rickettsia prowazekii*), and causing the deaths of millions, particularly during famine and war. The discovery of the causative agents ushered in an eradication campaign that has now been almost completed with the introduction of hygienic and therapeutic measures.

Another devastating bacterial disease is tuberculosis, whose agent, *Mycobacterium tuberculosis*, was also discovered by Robert Koch (1882). Tetanus is caused by *Clostridium tetani*; gas gangrene by various saprophytic bacteria of the genus *Clostridium*; diphtheria by *Corynebacterium diphtheriae*; syphilis by *Treponema* (= *Spirochaeta*) *pallidum*; dysentery by various species of *Shigella*, and pneumonia by *Diplococcus* (= *Pneumococcus*) *pneumoniae*. As we have said, even normally harmless bacteria can become pathogenic, for instance *Bacterium coli* which lives as a saprophyte in the colon of man may cause peritonitis and infections of the urogenital system.

To round off this dark chapter in the life of these tiny plants, we must mention that all the harbingers of death can be attacked with as many 'useful' bacteria. We are, of course, referring to the use of antibiotics. The first of these to be discovered was a fungus of the genus *Penicillium* and not a bacterium – in 1928 Fleming found that its metabolic products (penicillin) inhibit the growth of pathogenic bacteria or even kill them. In his subsequent search for other, and possibly better, antibiotics, Waksman (1944) was led to the discovery of streptomycin, a metabolic product of *Streptomyces griseus*, a bacterium. Waksman's discovery was the starting point of many intense studies, which continue to this day. As a result, modern medicine can boast a whole armoury of antibiotics, obtained partly from species of *Streptomyces* and partly from species of *Bacillus*. Thus

aureomycin is produced by *S. aureofaciens*, chloramphenicol by *S. venezuelae*, neomycin by *S. fradiae*, streptothricin by *S. lavendulae*, terramycin by *S. rimosus*, and bacitracin by a strain of *Bacillus subtilis*, first isolated from the healing lesion of a compound fracture in a 7-year-old girl. Another bacillus, *B. polymyxa*, yields polymixin, and a further strain of *B. subtilis* yields subtilin. *B. brevis* yields four antibiotics all at once, namely tyrothricin, tyrocidin, gramicidin and gramicidin-S. It would take us too far afield to mention the rest; all we can add here is that the action of different antibiotics varies considerably, both in specificity and in effect. Thus albomycin, a metabolic product of a fungus, has proved to be effective in inhibiting the growth of pathogenic bacteria if administered in dilutions no greater than one part to sixty million.

The biochemical action of antibiotics is not yet fully understood. It probably occurs during specific parts of the metabolic process, for instance by blocking the flow of certain enzymes or by inhibiting certain reactions.

Many antibiotics are still obtained by biological methods, although on a large scale and with complicated apparatus. Others can now be synthesized.

Far more exciting from the purely biological point of view is the fact that certain bacteria can apparently be used directly in the struggle against disease. Naturally, these new methods must be treated with great circumspection. It has, for instance, been suggested that if various species of *Clostridium* are injected into the blood of cancer victims, they will start to compete for food with the proliferating cancer cells. This method is still being studied, so that it would be presumptuous to pronounce on its possible efficacy. However, we do know that the agent of typhoid fever, *Salmonella typhosa*, has been effectively used to combat certain mental disorders and syphilis. Paralysis, too, has been combated with a living organism, albeit an animal and not a bacterium (*Plasmodium vivax*).

After this discourse on the prevalence of bacteria, their uses and dangers, we must briefly return to their cell structure. Nowadays bacterial cytology increasingly employs not only the classical methods of microscopic analysis, staining and cultivation, but also biophysical and biochemical techniques. In

16

particular, ultra-centrifuges working at from 15,000 to 150,000 revolutions per minute are now used to separate cell wall from protoplasm, with the result that it has been possible to determine the precise composition of the former, and with it the structural differences between various species of bacteria and indeed their differential absorption of stains. The method promises to settle such questions as to why certain substances immunize some and not other bacteria. In general, the bacterial cell wall is a highly complex structure, built up of sugars, fats, proteins, acids, etc. In general, the wall is 10 – 20 microns thick (= 10⁻⁵ mm.). Just as centrifugation helps to isolate the walls, so enzymatic dissolution can be used to isolate the protoplasts, and even to keep them growing and dividing. True, the cells lose their shape, and become spherical – clear proof that their profile is determined by the walls. Naturally the wall performs other tasks as well, for instance protecting the bacterium against external dangers. Photographs taken with the electron microscope have revealed the fine structure of the cell wall, showing that, in *Spirillum*, for instance, it consists of two layers, and that many bacteria secrete a special capsule or ring of mucus.

The study of the cell interior has made comparable progress during the last few years. Biologists have learned to distinguish between certain regions of the protoplast, for instance a highly membranous outer zone, grain-like structures containing phosphates, and the nuclear equivalent. As we have said, genetic studies suggest that the latter contains a single 'chromosome' in which the 'genes' are arranged in line. In more recent times, hybridization experiments have provided incontrovertible proof that bacteria can reproduce sexually – in fact several cases of actual copulation have been observed under the electron microscope. In this process the lineome, and hence the genetic characters, are transferred from one individual to the next.

All these advances have shown that bacteria have much in common with other living organisms and have helped to fit them progressively into the general framework. As a result, the very concept of 'organism' has become much sharper.

Many bacteria are actively motile – they propel themselves by means of flagella, attached singly or in

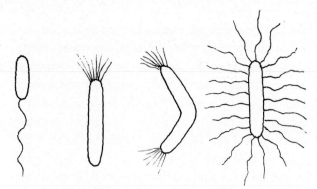

Fig. 1 Bacteria with various types of flagella (highly magnified)

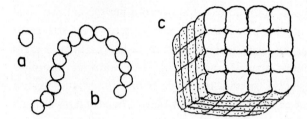

Fig. 2 *a*: Unicellular *Coccus*; *b*: chain of *Streptococci*; *c*: bale-shaped *Sarcina* colony (highly magnified)

Fig. 3 *Bacillus*; right, *Bacillus* with endospore (highly magnified)

Fig. 4 Left, *Vibrio*; centre, *Spirillum*; right, *Spirochaete plicatilis* (highly magnified)

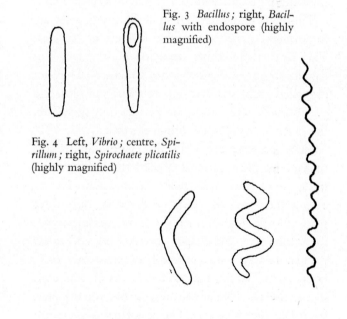

tufts at either end; sometimes they cover the entire surface of the bacterium, which is then said to be peritrichous. Generally the flagella are longer, and sometimes much longer, than the cell body. Thus *Nitrosomonas* has a body length of 1 micron but flagella measuring 30 microns. The flagella are, however, extremely thin (10 – 50 mμ), and the electron microscope has shown that they consist of 2 – 3 fibrils. Chemically speaking, flagella are made up of contractile protein. They are not attached to the cell

17

wall, but pass through it into the protoplasm. Microscopic studies suggest that the flagellum works roughly like the screw of a ship. As the 'screw' rotates so the bacterium rotates as well – in the opposite sense. This is particularly obvious in the case of larger bacteria, for instance in various species of *Spirillum* which have a tuft of flagella at either end, while the cell itself is twisted like a corkscrew. The flagella can propel the bacterium in either direction. Their motor force is tremendous: at forty flagellar 'revolutions' per minute, a ten-micron *Spirillum* can move forward at the rate of 100 microns per second. To rival this feat a swimmer would have to cover 100 yards in less than 6 seconds (when in fact he usually takes more than 50 seconds). Their extreme mobility enables bacteria to escape from 'unpleasant' stimuli and to discover pleasant ones. Thus bacteria in need of oxygen will gather at the water surface or collect round air bubbles, while bacteria with photosynthesizing pigments will congregate in well-lit places.

The nature and arrangement of the flagella are important criteria in the classification of bacteria. This task is sometimes impeded by the fact that flagella are extremely transitory structures. They are discarded at the slightest unfavourable stimulus, and are normally active at certain periods only (generally the juvenile stage) in the life of the cell.

Since bacteria are only just visible under the microscope, their external appearance provides relatively few clues for their classification. Hence, despite their vast physiological diversity, only three main morphological forms can be distinguished: spherical cocci, rod-shaped bacilli and corkscrew spirilla. Bacteria with a normally constant form may, under special circumstances, form cells of abnormal shape, the so-called involution forms, for instance, from *Bacterium radicicola*. The abnormal cells are not generally capable of reproduction but may, under favourable conditions, give rise to normal cells. Under unfavourable conditions, for instance when attacked, many bacteria are capable of forming large, misshapen cells, the so-called 'large bodies'. These, too, may revert to the normal form. Sometimes they become stabilized into the so-called L-forms, extremely varied and irregular bodies combined into colonies by a plasma-like matrix. Such forms resemble the pathogenic PPLO (pleuro-pneumonia-like organisms), and are also known as mycoplasma (see p. 21). Their nature and taxonomic position is still highly uncertain. Many students place them half-way between bacteria and viruses, but all such interpretations remain highly speculative.

Numerous bacteria are able to form durable resting stages. These are called spores when they originate from part of the cell content, and cysts when the whole cell is involved in their formation; both types are far more resistant to external influences than metabolically active cells. Luckily, only relatively few pathogenic bacteria can form such resting stages – else the fight against bacterial diseases in man and animals would be infinitely more difficult.

By now, the reader will have gathered that it is far more difficult to split up the Bacteriophyta into classes, orders and families than other divisions of the plant kingdom. Nor does the classification of bacteria fully reflect the relationship between their various taxons. Opinions on these relationships are still divided; the system used in this book is therefore one of convenience only. Even our remarks on the relationship between bacteria and other divisions, e.g. the blue-green algae, must be considered as having a purely hypothetical character. In general, however, bacteria can be distinguished by the structure of their cell (nuclear equivalent, chromoplasts) and the form of their flagella (the flagella of bacteria consist of two to three fibrils while those of all other organisms consist of 9 fibrils).

In the following classification, we largely follow Bergey (1957) and Hawker (1962). This gives us eleven orders, or rather order-like groups, of which the first two, the Pseudomonadales and the Eubacteriales, are more closely interrelated than the rest.

Order
PSEUDOMONADALES

The Pseudomonadales are spherical, rod-shaped or spiral bacteria. The cell is rigid, and often bears one or two polar flagella. This order includes the green and red sulphur bacteria (Thiorhodaceae and Chlorobacteriaceae), marked by the presence of bacteriochlorophyll and carotenoids. They live in the absence of oxygen (anaerobically) and exploit light as a source of energy. Many use hydrogen sulphide as a source

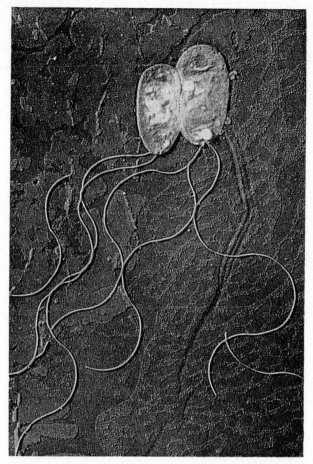

Fig. 5 *Pseudomonas fluorescens* (x 30,000)

of hydrogen. The order also includes many coloured bacteria capable of using organic sources of hydrogen (the Athiorhodaceae) and others whose pigments do not enable them to exploit light energy. Some (the Methanomonadaceae) obtain their energy from the oxidation of carbon monoxide or methane or even from the oxidation of molecular hydrogen. The order also includes the unpigmented sulphur bacteria (Thiobacteriaceae), which are able to oxidize sulphur compounds. Many species store the resulting sulphur inside their cell, others store it outside. As a result, sulphur bacteria can be found in the most unexpected places, for instance in the Black Sea where they occur at the contact surface between the oxygenated top layer and the stagnant bottom layer rich in hydrogen sulphide.

The order further includes the nitrite- and nitrate-forming bacteria which we mentioned in connection with the nitrogen cycle (see Vol. I, p. 308). A whole series of other soil bacteria (Pseudomonadaceae) also

belongs here, among them the agent of blue pus (*Pseudomonas aeruginosa*); the agent of hyacinth rot (*Xanthomonas hyacinthi*); and also the vinegar bacterium (*Acetobacter*). Of great biological interest are the luminous bacteria (*Photobacterium*) which cause meat or fish to glow in the dark. The Pseudomonadales also include the Caulobacteriaceae, a family of rod-shaped aquatic bacteria which occur singly and are attached by small stalks to water plants, etc. The Siderocapsaceae include the iron bacterium *Ferrobacillus ferrooxydans*, which derives energy from the oxidation of bivalent into tervalent iron.

The Spirillaceae, finally, are a family of flagellate and spiral aquatic or parasitic organisms, and include the agent of cholera (*Vibrio comma*). Some spirilla have a length of 0.1 mm. and are thus among the largest bacteria, though they are also exceedingly thin (0.002 – 0.003 mm.).

Order

EUBACTERIALES

This order comprises 13 known families. Their cells are rigid, spherical or rectilinear. Eubacteriales cannot photosynthesize food.When flagella are present, they are invariably peritrichous, i.e. they cover the entire cell. Most bacteria we have mentioned in our general discussion belong to this order. Important members include *Azotobacter* (Azotobacteriaceae) which lives freely in the soil and is able to fix atmospheric nitrogen, and *Bacterium radicicola* (= *Rhizobium radiciola*; Rhizobiaceae). Among the family Enterobacteriaceae, special mention must be made of the genus *Escherichia*, many species of which inhabit the human intestine (e.g. *E. coli* = *Bacterium coli*), and also of the genus *Serratia* which includes *S. marescens* (= *Bacterium prodigiosum*), the cause of 'blood spots' on cereals. We have already met the genus *Salmonella* as the cause of bacterial food poisoning. The genera *Pasteurella* and *Brucella* belong to the family Brucellaceae; these can cause plague and other fatal diseases in man and animals. Special mention must also be made of the genera *Bordatella* (the cause of whooping cough) and *Haemophilus* (the influenza bacillus which occurs in association with the influenza virus). The Micrococcaceae, a family which includes the genus *Staphylococcus*, are occasionally responsible for the

19

pollution of milk; many species are, however, completely harmless. *Sarcina* is morphologically interesting – its cells divide in three planes to produce rectangular cell packets. *Streptococci* are generally associated with the formation of pus; they are also responsible for scarlet fever, pneumonia and acute tonsillitis. *Lactobacillus* is important in the formation of lactic acid, and the Propionibacteriaceae play a part in the formation of numerous ferments and acids, for instance those responsible for the typical aroma of various cheeses. *Cellulomonas* plays an important role in the break-down of cellulose in the soil. The Bacillaceae are another important family in this order. They are capable of forming highly resistant spores, and include such important proteolytic species as *B. putrificus*. The genera *Bacillus* and *Clostridium* include the pathogenic *B. anthracis* (anthrax), *B. alvei* (foul-brood), *C. tetani* (tetanus) and *C. botulinum* (botulism). We conclude this section with a useful species, namely *C. acetobutylicum* which is used industrially in the production of butyl alcohol.

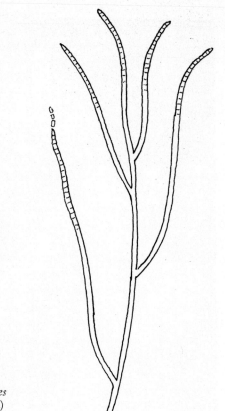

Fig. 6 *Actinomyces*
(highly magnified)

Order
ACTINOMYCETALES

This order includes the agent of tuberculosis (*Mycobacterium tuberculosis*) and also *M. leprae*, the cause of leprosy. *Corynebacterium diphtheriae*, the cause of diphtheria, also belongs here, and so does *Streptomyces scabies*, the cause of potato scab. *Actinomyces bovis* causes chronic inflammation in animals and man (actinomycosis). 'Friendly' organisms in this order include the sources of various antibiotics (see p. 16). Actinomycetes are also well-known as nitrogen-fixing symbionts; thus *Streptomyces alni* lives in symbiotic association with the alder tree. Actinomycetes are widely distributed in the soil, causing its characteristic smell.

The family Actinomycetaceae and, to a lesser extent, the rest of this order, have a strong structural resemblance to fungi. They, too, form a unicellular mycelium (plant body) composed of filaments (hyphae) which are, however, much thinner than the hyphae of fungi (0.5 – 1.0 micron). The cells are, moreover, devoid of a nucleus, so that we are justified in treating this group as bacteria rather than fungi. Members of the family Mycobacteriaceae

bear a much closer resemblance to 'normal' bacteria. Their cells branch out into stubs so that they look very similar to the 'involution stages' of *Bacterium radicicola*. Actinomycetaceae, on the other hand, form vegetative bodies measuring several centimetres. They also have the unusual ability to form spores by the division of their hyphae. This, too, is highly reminiscent of the fungi, but is, in fact, no more than a remarkable case of parallel development.

Order
CHLAMYDOBACTERIALES

This order includes *Leptothrix ochracea*, a bacterium responsible for the formation of meadow ore, an early source of iron, together with other iron-loving species, for instance *Crenothrix polyspora* which can foul up water pipes, and *Spaerotilus natans*, which forms a white skin, particularly on effluents.

The cells of Chlamydobacteriales are characteristically composed of threads surrounded by a delicate sheath. Normally the threads are unbranched, but during rapid growth a few cells are pushed out of line, to produce 'false' branches by growth and division. Moreover, the cells of the thread can live a free and independent existence, and multiply by the production of independent fragments. In addition, Chlamydobacteriales produce motile zoospores which later become sessile.

Order
BEGGIATOALES

Side by side with iron bacteria, we often find various species of filamentous sulphur bacteria capable of oxidizing sulphites. The best-known genus is *Beggiatoa*. Beggiatoales closely resemble algae, for which reason they are often considered to be blue-green algae that have lost their pigment.

Order
MYXOBACTERIALES

The systematic position of this order is, if anything, even more uncertain than that of the last. The Myxobacteriales are rod-shaped cells devoid of flagella, 5 – 14 microns in length and 1 micron in diameter, whose movement resembles a crawl, probably produced by contraction waves passing through the cell. They generally live together in large groups and, under suitable conditions, form orange or blue 'fruiting bodies'. These contain spores approximately 1 micron in diameter, which are scattered abroad and germinate. In this respect the Myxobacteriales bear a strong resemblance to the Myxomycetes or Slime Fungi, also feeding on decaying plant remains and on rotting wood or compost. They are able to break down cellulose by means of special enzymes, before digesting the end products.

Order
SPIROCHAETALES

This order includes *Treponema pallidum*, which, as we saw, is the causative agent of syphilis; together with other pathogenic bacteria, and a number of harmless types.

Spirochaetes are unusual in that they lack flagella yet can move about rapidly. Their cells are very elongated, sometimes attaining a length of 500 microns, twisted into spirals, and surrounded by a flexible wall. The order is usually divided into two families of which the Spirochaetaceae are generally harmless, while the Treponemataceae include many pathogenic agents.

Orders
HYPHOMICROBIALES, CARYOPHA-NALES and MYCOPLASMATALES

Very little can be said about these three orders. The Hyphomicrobiales generally reproduce by budding; the filamentous Caryophanales have particularly conspicuous granules in their protoplasm; the Mycoplasmatales resemble the 'large bodies' of Eubacteriales. Since they were discovered in connection with pneumonia and pleurisy they have become known as pleuro-pneumonia-like organisms (PPLO). More recently it has been suggested that they are also involved in leukaemia.

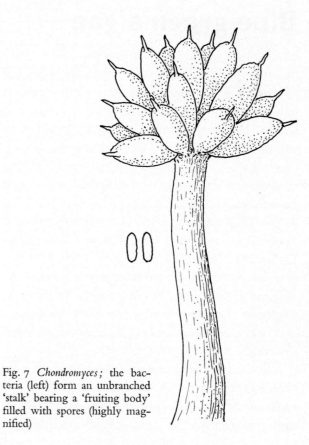

Fig. 7 *Chondromyces;* the bacteria (left) form an unbranched 'stalk' bearing a 'fruiting body' filled with spores (highly magnified)

RICKETTSIALES

This order, too, is relatively unknown. Like viruses, the Rickettsiales are host-dependent, causing various fevers, including epidemic typhus (*Rickettsia prowazekii*). Rickettsiae are very small organisms (*R. prowazekii* measures 3 to 4 ten-thousandths of a millimetre) but not small enough to pass through bacterial filters.

Our discussion so far has shown that the Bacteriophyta embrace a vast variety of forms and account for a host of metabolic processes. Thus while some forms cannot live without oxygen others cannot live with it; some are highly resistant to temperature changes; others are extremely sensitive to them;

some are autotrophic while others are obligate parasites. Bacteria use every conceivable source of energy: sunlight, organic substances, including alcohol, and also such diverse inorganic sources as hydrogen sulphide, iron oxide or molecular hydrogen.

All this, and the fact that bacteria lack a proper nucleus, suggests that they are survivors from the distant past, when things on earth were quite different, with much smaller supplies of oxygen and different conditions of light and temperature. In fact, however, it seems highly probable that the bacteria that flourished then were not the same as 'ours', though some of their properties have undoubtedly been handed down to their distant descendants. Not surprisingly, bacteria are among the oldest known fossils – in 1965, bacteria were identified in specimens of Pre-Cambrian rock, i.e. in rock going back some 2000 million years.

2 CYANOPHYTA
Blue-green algae

On moist rock faces and walls, on ledges, walls and flowerpots, in hothouses, and even on the walls of public lavatories, we can often find thin layers of blue or black, which sometimes have a gelatinous consistency. Rivers and river banks often display large, shaggy accumulations of the same colours; in irrigation ditches they may appear as a tough browny-green deposit. Finally, we may find the surface of ponds and pools covered with a bright green, blue or brown skin, the so-called water-bloom. All these phenomena are caused by blue-green algae, which are said to represent some of the oldest of extant plants. Ernest Haeckel, for instance, suggested that *Chroococcus*, a unicellular blue-green alga, was the simplest and most ancient of all living organisms.

And, in fact, blue-green algae have an extremely simple organization. *Chroococcus* has a spherical cell surrounded by a multi-layered membrane which, in turn, is protected by an outer integument. Inside the

membrane, the cell can divide several times, to give rise to numerous daughter cells, each surrounded by a multi-layered membrane of its own. In this way, entire colonies of interlocking cells may develop. Much the same thing happens with other genera in the order Chroococcales, e.g. with *Gloeocapsa* (*Pl. 5, p. 50*). *Merismopedia* is a delight to behold under the microscope: colonies of small round cells are fitted into rectangular plates as cell division proceeds in a single plane. Round cells are also found in *Nostoc* (*Pl. 1, p. 49*), a member of the order Hormogonales. *Nostoc* cells are strung together like a rosary, with the individual threads or trichomes intertwined and contorted inside a hyaline or coloured sheath. The filaments of Oscillatoriaceae look quite different: here the cells are unbranched and heaped up like stacks of coins. In the family Scytonemataceae, again, the trichomes have false branches of the kind we first met in the Actinomycetales and Chlamydobacteriales. A similar structure

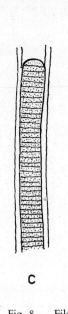
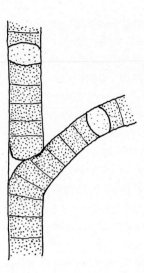
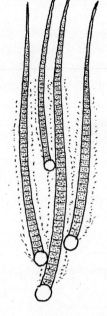

Fig. 8 Filamentous blue-green algae; *a: Oscillatoria; b: Phormidium; c: Lyngbya* (highly magnified)

Fig. 9 *Scytonema:* false branching (highly magnified)

Fig. 10 *Rivularia* (highly magnified)

is found in the family Rivulariaceae, except that each of the branches terminates in a hair. Stigonemataceae, finally, may form true branches. *Spirulina*, a relative of *Nostoc*, deserves special mention, because here the filaments are twisted into spirals. In *Microcoleus* (Oscillatoriaceae) several threads are surrounded by a common sheath.

In the Cyanophyta, every cell is capable of storing reserve materials during unfavourable conditions, of surrounding itself with a thicker membrane and of surviving as a resting stage (cyst). In addition, whole threads, often with branches, can also become encysted, and survive as hormocysts for up to 90 years. Normally, however, pieces of the thread break away, crawl off and grow into independent trichomes. This type of motion is said to depend on the secretion of mucus from pores in the membrane. No known blue-green alga is provided with flagella,

nor has sexual reproduction ever been observed among these organisms. Instead, unicellular species in the order Chamaesiphonales split up their cell contents into several spores (endospores), which later germinate.

Blue-green algae can be roughly divided as follows:

Order: CHROOCOCCALES (unicellular; spherical)

Order: PLEUROCAPSALES (prostrate and erect threads)

Order: CHAMAESIPHONALES (one to two-celled plants; production of endo-spores)

Order: HORMOGONALES (threads generally surrounded by special sheaths; production of cysts and hormocysts)

(a) NOSTOCINALES (all threads identical; no true branches)

(b) STIGONEMATINALES (threads different – prostrate and erect; true branching)

The system is still being completed, and quite recently (1963) a new family was discovered – its unicellular members live as symbionts inside unicellular algae.

Their inner cell organization suggests that blue-green algae have a very long history (see p. 10). One

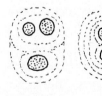

Fig. 11 *Chroococcus;* cells surrounded by mucilaginous membrane (highly magnified)

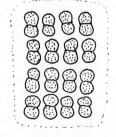

Fig. 12 *Merismopedia;* plate of cells (highly magnified)

23

of their pigments, chlorophyll, is found throughout most of the plant kingdom. In addition, they contain various yellow, red or orange carotenoids, together with the characteristic blue phycocyanin; many also contain phycoerythrin, a red pigment normally associated with red algae. The pigments are present in different proportions in different species, with the result that the colour of 'blue-green' algae may range from blue through red, yellow and brown to black. Some species of the genus *Oscillatoria* have the remarkable capacity of adapting their pigment to the prevailing light conditions: colonies that have been exposed to red light for some time look green, those exposed to green light look red, those exposed to violet light look grey-blue, those exposed to orange light look red, those exposed to blue light look brown, and those exposed to normal daylight look grey. This capacity is called chromatic adaptation. Blue-green algae are unique in that they can even use the infra-red range of the spectrum as a source of energy. Some species have lost their pigments; all of these live as symbionts or parasites in the intestine of mammals (e.g. species of *Oscillatoria* in the intestine of guinea pigs), or else at ocean depths to which no light can penetrate in any case. Another remarkable phenomenon is the ability of blue-green algae to cope with abnormal atmospheres – species of *Oscillatoria* enclosed in evacuated vials for a period of eight years were found not only to be alive but to have built up an atmosphere consisting of 46 per cent oxygen and 54 per cent nitrogen. Some species, for instance *Oscillatoria caerulescens*, can withstand a high concentration of hydrogen sulphide; hence their association with sulphur bacteria. Moreover, like many bacteria, a number of blue-green algae are able to fix atmospheric nitrogen – this makes them excellent partners in symbiotic associations.

Thus symbiotic blue-green algae may act as chloroplasts, for instance in the alga-like fungus *Geosiphon pyriforme*. Recently it has even been suggested that the chloroplasts of red algae are derived from symbiotic blue-green algae – this assumption seems to be corroborated by current studies with the electron microscope. Blue-green algae also enter into symbiotic associations with higher fungi to form lichens, which are generally

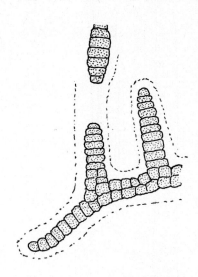

Fig. 13 *Stigonema*: true branching, with young colony (top) sliding out of mucilaginous sheath (highly magnified)

treated as independent species. The fungal partners are mostly Ascomycetes and, more rarely, Basidiomycetes. A particularly interesting association is that between *Anabaena*, a genus related to *Nostoc*, and the water fern *Azolla*: the alga congregates in the air sacs on the underside of the leaf. The same genus also found in symbiotic association with *Cycas*, a gymnosperm (*Pl. 2, p. 49*). Here the alga inhabits a certain zone of the root, which it transforms into a 'coral root', with typical short and thick ramifications. A species of *Nostoc*, finally, inhabits the roots of *Gunnera* (Myrtales). As a curiosity, we might also mention that South American Indians treat *Nostoc commune* as a food. A species of *Nostoc* may well have been involved in the Biblical manna, which is usually thought to have been a lichen. This is borne out by the fact that this species is capable of shrivelling into a paper-thin structure, only to swell up again after rains.

In the past, there were many stories of so-called gelatinous meteorites. These were, in fact, *Nostoc* colonies which are practically invisible when dry but can suddenly take up water and swell up to the size of a fist, with the result that the uninitiated think they must have dropped out of the sky. Blue-green algae can colonize recently cooled, and previously bare, volcanic surfaces – this happened, for instance, over the entire surface of the volcanic island of Krakatoa in 1885. They owe their ability to form

24

such dense associations and to survive arid conditions to their capacity for utilizing atmospheric carbon dioxide and nitrogen as food. Hence they can act as soil-forming pioneers, not only on lava but also on the foreshore on oceans and lakes. In deserts, we often find blue-green algae on the underside of loose stones, where the plants are protected from direct sunlight and also profit from the moisture preserved beneath the stones.

Many blue-green algae are adapted to life at very high temperatures. Thus *Phormidium lanulosum* (Oscillatoriaceae) occurs in water at 85 °C both in the thermal springs near Padua and also in the geysers of Yellowstone Park. Nor are Cyanophyta averse to water with very high salt concentration. Thus *Microcoleus chthonoplastes* forms dense colonies in salt lakes and even helps in the production of table salt – the salt deposits on top of the algal layer are easy to rake off. In water with a high calcium content, the metabolic activity of blue-green algae often leads to the production of deposits of calcareous tuff – a layer several millimetres thick may be formed within a single week. This is the origin of the Travertine deposits in the Abruzzi region of Italy or of the snow-white terraces of Yellowstone Park. But while some blue-green algae produce rocks, others dissolve limestone, seriously endangering marble monuments and statues. As a preventative, the stone is usually capped with copper – the copper salts dissolved by the rain run down the stones and prevent the spread of algae.

In fresh water, species living attached to stones or crawling in the sand and mud exist side by side with planktonic species forming floating communities. Mucilaginous species often associate into a solid mass resembling frogs' spawn (e.g. *Microcystis*, *Gomphosphaeria*, *Coelosphaerium*, *Oscillatoria* and *Aphanizaomenon*). Many species, including *Cladrocystis aeruginosum*, develop gas bladders, thus increasing the floating power of the slimy colonies. Their fantastic rate of reproduction enables some species to cover large lakes with water-bloom within a few hours. In one case, 11,000 *Oscillatoria* threads were counted in 1 c.c. of water. *Aphanizaomenon kaufmannii* (Nostocaceae) causes the phenomenon known as 'green Nile', and it is thanks to the presence of *Oscillatoria erythrea* that the Red Sea obtained its name and colour. The organisms responsible for water bloom are said to secrete antibiotic substances which inhibit the growth of rivals, thus disturbing the normal biological equilibrium. Moreover these organisms are poisonous to fishes and some are also said to cause poisoning in cattle. On the other hand, the water bloom on Lake Chad is collected by the natives and used as a food.

The primitive organization of blue-green algae, the absence of a clear nucleus, of clearly differentiated choroplasts and mitochondria, their resistance to many external influences, and their soil-pioneering activities – all these justify the belief that they may have been numbered among the first living creatures on earth. In any case, there is no doubt that blue-green algae are a very ancient group, with fossils going back to the Pre-Cambrian.

THE KARYOBIONTS: plants with a clearly separated and differentiated nucleus

All the plants in this group have one, and occasionally more than one, nucleus. Every cell division is preceded by a nuclear division during which the chromosomes are distributed to the daughter cells. Karyobiont cells also include other independent 'organelles', among them mitochondria and plastids. The flagella constitute yet another distinct element; in all cases investigated so far, they are built on the same pattern: two inner, surrounded by a circle of nine outer, double fibres. Karyobiont flagella thus differ characteristically from the much simpler flagella of bacteria. In their metabolism, too, karyobionts rather resemble the higher algae, mosses, ferns and seed-bearing plants.

In all these groups we also find that individuals follow much the same pattern of general development. Needless to say, there are a number of exceptions, and it is precisely these that enable us to classify given species as 'primitive' or 'derived'. Thus unicellular structure is considered a primitive character, and so, in multi-cellular organisms, are the lack of cell differentiation and reproduction by spores or by gametes that cannot be distinguished from ordinary vegetative cells. Aquatic life, too, is considered a primitive character, as is a life cycle during which the chromosomes in the cell nucleus are preserved in the single (haploid) number. Organisms with a single set of chromosomes are known as haplonts, those with a double set are called diplonts. A change in the number of chromosomes occurs during sexual reproduction, i.e. when two sexual cells (gametes) fuse to form a resting cell (zygote). In the most primitive karyobionts the zygote remains the only cell with a double (diploid) set of chromosomes. During the subsequent division of the zygote, the chromosomes are shared out among the two daughter cells, so that the number of chromosomes becomes reduced to the haploid set (meiosis or reduction division). In more 'highly' developed, generally multicellular, karyobionts, for instance in green algae, reduction division does not occur immediately after the formation of the zygotes;

instead, each of the daughter cells receives the double set of chromosomes, so that the daughter cells are diploid as well. They do not immediately form gametes but produce gonospores, during the formation of which reduction division occurs, restoring the single number of chromosomes. The sex of the gonospores is often decided during this process, with the result that haploid male and female plants are formed. These produce gametes in turn, and it is deemed yet another primitive character when the male and female gametes are externally indistinguishable (isogametes), and a derived character when they are not (anisogametes). Dissimilarity between gametes can be so extreme that the males are small and motile, while the females are large and immobile. In that case we have a male spermatozoid and a female ovum – and the plants in question are known as oogamous.

Many groups of algae and lower fungi cover the entire spectrum from isogamy to oogamy; in mosses, ferns and seed-bearing plants oogamy has become the general rule.

Another major evolutionary trend is reflected in changes of nuclear phase and in the alternation of generations. We already know what is meant by the term haplont, *viz.* an organism whose cells have a single set of chromosomes. We also speak of the haplont as the haploid generation, and of the diplont as the diploid generation. We also learned that, in flagellate algae, the diploid generation is found exclusively in the zygote; the haploid and diploid nuclear phases are thus of unequal duration – for practical purposes, we can say they live perpetually in the haploid phase, the more so as they can also reproduce in it. The same relationship between nuclear phases is also found in more highly developed algae, for instance in *Ulothrix*. However, the group to which this genus belongs (the Confervae) also includes genera in which both nuclear phases are of equal duration, for instance *Cladophora*, whose two generations are, moreover, indistinguishable.

Good examples of a shift in the relative importance of the two generations are provided by the brown algae. In many genera, e.g. *Cutleria*, the diploid generation takes second place to the haploid. In *Dictyota* and *Cladophora* the haploid and diploid phases are of equal duration; in *Laminaria*, finally, the haplont is almost completely ousted by the diplont. Among fungi, we can observe a similar shift from haploid to diploid dominance; it can also be followed as we proceed from the mosses through the ferns to seed-bearing plants. Thus what we normally call mosses are all haplonts, their diploid generation being represented by the inconspicuous spore capsules. The opposite is the case with ferns: the familiar plants are all diplonts; here the haploid generation consists of tiny, delicate plants lying flat on the ground where they are hidden between mosses and leaf litter. Seed-bearing plants, finally, from grasses to the mightiest trees, are all diplonts; their haploid generation is microscopically small and enclosed in special organs. It is most instructive to follow the development of the special structures in which gonospores and gametes are formed in the course of the haplont-diplont path. In the most primitive plants, the container is the unicellular organism itself. But even in the Confervae (e.g. *Ulothrix*) every cell is capable of becoming a gonospore container (gametangium). Step by step, however, these containers become more specialized and distinct from the rest of the plant (in higher algae, mosses and ferns, for instance, they take the form of antheridia, archegonia and sporangia), and lie embedded in special organs (e.g. the pollen sacs and ovules of seed-bearing plants). The fact that the haploid and diploid generations are represented by distinct individuals in algae, mosses and ferns but combined in one and the same individual in some fungi and in many seed-bearing plants, presents the student with special problems and complications.

Hand in hand with this trend in the alternation of generation goes a transformation of the vegetative body of karyobionts. This path leads from unicellular organisms (e.g. flagellate algae), through the loose association of a few independent cells (e.g. *Gonium pectorale* = 4 cells), to more complicated aggregates of spherical cells (*Pandorina*, *Eudorina*, and *Volvox* with 5,000–25,000 cells), and on to cells joined into filaments (e.g. *Ulothrix* or *Cladophora*). From the filamentous forms are derived both the flat types (e.g. *Ulva*, a green alga) and also the three-dimensional forms involving fairly complex combinations of filaments into vegetative tissues (e.g. some brown algae, red algae and fungi). The form of the vegetative body: unicell, cell association, filament, flat thallus, web tissue or true vegetative tissue, is ultimately dependent on the manner in which the cells divide during growth. Thus in most lower forms (unicellular organisms, cell associations, filaments) every one of the cells is capable of division, but in several filamentous forms only the apical cell has retained that capacity. Here we first meet the cell that plays so important a role in the growth of all higher plants. If the apical cell divides in one direction only, the result is a thread; if it divides alternately to the right and left and the resulting cells continue the same process, the result is a surface (of the kind found in many algae and mosses). An apical cell capable of dividing in three planes gives rise to a three-dimensional vegetative body by way of primary meristems, i.e. groups of undifferentiated cells capable of division.

As the vegetative body grows in length and depth the plant has to solve metabolic and structural problems that do not occur in small organisms. The solution is provided by firm cell walls and the introduction of conductive tissue. These problems are particularly acute for plants that have left the water for the uncertain support of the air. For them, the evolution of firm cellulose walls studded with lignin, of complicated conductive tissues, and the division of the vegetative body into an underground root system topped by branches, were essential prerequisites to their development on land. The transformation from aquatic to terrestrial life was thus a transformation from prostrate or floating plant body (Thallophyte) into erect root- and branch-bearing plant body (Cormophyte). Algae and fungi belong to the first type; most ferns have become cormophytes, and mosses occupy an intermediate position.

There is little doubt that the development from the small and puny *Ulothrix* to the mighty oak was due, at least in part, to the emergence of diploidy, a *sine qua non* of sexual reproduction and a guarantee of ever-new combinations of characters – only with diploidy could natural selection begin to play its full part.

3 ALGAE

The first six divisions of karyobionts are generally combined under the heading of true algae. These do not form a phylogenetically homogeneous group, though all of them have probably sprung from a common root. They often resemble one another in external appearance, in inner structure, in evolutionary trends, in distribution and in environmental demands. Most of them are aquatic and, together with the fungi, constitute the vast mass of Thallophytes. Their sizes range from the microscopic (e.g. flagellate algae) to the gigantic, for some of them are 1000 ft. in length, surpassing even the largest of terrestrial plants. In their organization, algae range from haploid unicellular plants to diploid multicellular organisms with true tissue. An intermediate group is constituted by multicellular algae with filamentous or flat thalli or with false tissue composed of thread fragments. The higher forms have moreover, developed special tissues and, particularly, tissues associated with reproductive processes (precursors of the pericarp), anchorage (holdfast organs as precursors of true roots) and conduction. The algae are thus pioneers of all the organs found in cormophytes (shoot, root, central axis, vascular bundles, sexual organs, etc.). The classification of some algal groups seems well-founded, particularly that of the red algae (Rhodophyta), brown algae (Phaeophyta), green algae (Chlorophyta), and more recently, that of the yellow algae (Chrysophyta), a group including such apparently dissimilar genera as *Vaucheria*, *Synura* and *Biddulphia*.

On the other hand, the combination of various brown flagellates into the division Pyrrophyta is not universally accepted. The small division of Euglenophyta (euglenoid algae), too, may well have to be re-arranged. By and large, therefore, biologists have failed to establish a truly satisfactory natural system of classifying algae.

All amateur microscopists are familiar with *Euglena viridis*, a flagellate alga with a prominent 'eyespot' (*Fig. 18*). *Euglena* has variously been classified as a rotifer, a moss and an alga, receiving no less than seventeen different generic names. That this was more than mere pedantry is perhaps best illustrated by the case of a relative of *E. viridis*, namely *E. gracilis*, which occurs in four distinct forms, designated by the Greek letters alpha, beta, gamma and delta. Alpha is a normal cell containing numerous chloroplasts, paramylum (starch) bodies, and an eyespot (stigma). In the presence of light, it can live on mineral substances, though it fares much better if its diet is supplemented with organic matter, for instance with sugar. Beta may be described as a colourless stage of alpha; it arises when alpha is grown on organic media in the dark. However, the moment the culture is exposed to light, the cells turn green again – even after years of darkness. More interesting still is the gamma form. When grown in the light and on organic media, the cells gradually lose their pigment and turn saprophytic. If they reproduce by division, one of the daughter cells inherits all the colourless chloroplasts, while the second receives none. The latter then gives rise to the delta form, which lives saprophytically in the presence or absence of daylight, but never turns green. Thus while beta can always adapt itself to light, delta and all its descendants are permanently saprophytic. The new form obtained experimentally can barely be distinguished from naturally occurring *Astasia* individuals. Quite generally speaking, unicellular flagellates can exist in two forms: with or without chlorophyll. Hence there is some justification in the old belief that several groups of fungi are derived from colourless flagellates, indeed that the entire animal kingdom is descended from them. In any case, it is difficult to say with any degree of certainty whether flagellate algae are plants or animals.

In this connection we might mention that one distinguishing characteristic of plants is their relatively large surface area: gaseous exchanges and food absorption take place through the 'skin'. In animals on the other hand, gaseous exchanges and food absorption are controlled by internal body surfaces, with the result that the ratio of body surface to body volume is always smaller. The body of animals is more like that of a sphere, that of plants more like a cylinder (axis) or even a flattened cylinder (leaf). During their development from unicellular to multicellular organisms, plants traverse the path: unicellular organism → cellular thread → cell surface → shoot → leaf. Their tendency to assume a spherical shape is rudimentary in the extreme: unicellular organism (*Chlamydomonas*) → multicellular organism (*Gonium* = 4 cells, *Pandorina* = 16 cells, *Eudorina* = 64 cells) → hollow sphere (*Volvox* = 5000–25,000 cells).

Just as the organization of algae is extremely varied, so also are their vital needs and habits. Algae are found on the bark of trees, the walls of houses, on rock faces, in thermal springs, in snow and ice, in swirling mountain rivers, in dirty pools and in the ocean deeps; attached to sea cliffs, in symbiotic association with other plants or as parasites. Even so, most of them are aquatic, congregating together as important constituents of plankton, and helping to turn the surface of lakes green, brown, yellow or red. Similarly at sea, masses of algae often cause the waves to turn brown and provide fishes with unequalled feasts. Most of these organisms are too small to be identified as plants by the layman, but some leave him in no doubt as to their nature, for instance the sea-lettuce (*Ulva*) and many brown seaweeds. Very occasionally a finely chiselled branch of a red alga will be washed up as well. The larger species of algae are particularly prevalent on rocky coasts with a slight gradient, where they form distinct vegetation at different levels. Thus high (5–6 metres) above the littoral zone, in the so-called elittoral, we often observe dark bands of blue algae, followed by a band of *Bangia fuscopurpurea* (filamentous red algae), and another of *Fucus platycarpus* (brown algae). Where the elittoral zone merges with the littoral, there is a predominance of green algae, particularly of *Enteromorpha compressa* and *Ulva lactuca* (sea-lettuce).

Occasional bands are also formed by the paper-thin red alga *Porphyrus*, whose thallus is only one cell thick. The littoral zone is particularly rich in brown algae (*Fucus vesiculosus*). With its ramified and extremely pliable thallus, and studded with air bladders, this alga is tossed to and fro by the waves while remaining firmly attached to cliff or pier by means of a basal disk. Very similar in shape and habit is *Ascophyllum nodosum*. Finally, between the fronds of *Fucus serratus* in the lower littoral, we find the red alga, *Ceramium rubrum*, whose pale red thallus resembles a finely branched network of arteries. These algae, living as they do in the tidal zone, have to cope with a host of special environmental problems: they are exposed to constant mechanical assault by the waves, and to 12-hourly recessions of the salt water and hence to exposure to the air, the sun and rain. Special problems are also posed on flat coasts. Here sea water forms puddles during the ebb tide, which evaporate fairly quickly, particularly in summer, with the result that the salt concentration is greatly increased. Again, if it should rain, the salt concentration may drop considerably, so that these algae must be able to withstand considerable and sudden fluctuations. As we go down into the sublittoral zone, i.e. into that part of the coast which is generally covered by the sea, we find first *Plocamium coccineum*, a finely branched red alga, followed by *Corallina officinalis*, which forms a crust on pebbles. Delightful to watch are the brown seaweeds *Laminaria hyperborea* and *L. saccharina*, whose very long and highly ramified thallus fronds rise on short stalks, the claw-shaped bases of which help to keep them attached to the rocks. Like *Fucus*, they often occur in large colonies. In the same zone, we also find *Chorda filum*, a string-shaped brown alga whose whip-like vegetative body is particularly well suited to riding the waves. Related to *Laminaria* are a number of giant seaweeds particularly prevalent on the east coast of South America. They include the genus *Macrocystis* which, as we saw, can attain a length of several hundred yards. Not quite so gigantic (150–300 feet) are the genera *Nereocystis* found on the coast of New Zealand; *Pelagophycus* (Alaska and California), and *Pelagocystis* and *Durvillea* (New Zealand). *Nereocystis*, incidentally, can reach its full length (150 feet) within a single year. The upper end of this plant bears a bladder up to 10 feet in length, which is edible. But let us return to temperate shores. Here, in the sublittoral zone, at depths of from 6–12 metres, we find such red algae as *Polyides rotundus*, *Delesseria sanguinea*, *Furcellaria fastigiata* and *Lithothamnion polymorphum*, together with isolated brown algae, for instance *Demarescia aculeata*. This zonal distribution is typical of all rocky coasts and although the abundance of certain species may differ from place to place and zone to zone, the sequence green, brown and red algae is generally constant. The reason is that sunlight, from which algae derive their vital energy, is increasingly filtered as it travels to the sea bottom. At a depth of only one metre the surface light intensity is reduced by 50 per cent, and depending on whether the water is turbid or clear, complete darkness sets in at a depth of from 15–200 m. The longer, red rays are less penetrating than the shorter blue and green rays, and since it is light of a complementary colour that is most strongly absorbed, brown and red algae predominate at the greater depths. The main algal population is generally concentrated in the top 15–25 metres. In particularly clear waters, plants may be found deeper down as well – in exceptional cases down to 150 m. Along many coasts, however, the water is so turbid that the algal population is limited to the top metre.

The algae we have just been describing are all epilithic, i.e. they are attached to stones. Others prefer wooden substrates, and are called epixylic. They generally grow on the bottom of boats, on floats, piers and sluices, etc., and include green algae of the genera *Ulva*, *Enteromorpha*, *Ulothrix* and *Cladophora*; brown algae of the genera *Ectocarpus* and *Fucus*; and red algae of the genus *Bangia*. Others again live attached to plants or animals and are called epiphytic or epizoic. In general, epiphytic algae are not very fussy in their choice of hosts, but in individual cases host-specialization may be very marked – thus *Lithosiphon pusillus* can only live on *Chorda filum*, a brown alga.

Certain algae (e.g. *Lithophyllum dentatum*) are found exclusively on sea urchins; some even simulate the ambulacral feet of their hosts. Moreover, certain blue-green and green algae inhabit the fur of sloths thus helping to camouflage these animals.

Unlike sessile algae, freely-floating algae are generally microscopic in size and consist of a single or, at most, a few cells. They constitute the nanoplankton, that tremendously important link in the food chain linking fishes to man. For that reason, the study of plankton and its seasonal changes and migrations is an important branch of deep-sea fishing. Many nanoplanktonic algae are flagellates and can respond actively to light and chemical stimuli (oxygen); others have special floating devices. By their sive are found macroplanktonic algae, which include such large forms as *Sargassum bacciferum* (seagrass).

While some algae prefer warm water, others are adapted to life in cold seas. Thus diatoms and flagellates regularly form brown layers in the drift ice of the Antarctic. Measurements have shown that the metabolic output of this type of plankton is thirty times higher than that of all others.

Aerophytic algae have to exist under entirely different conditions. Their number includes the unicellular, green *Chroococci* which live on the bark of trees, where they may have to survive prolonged droughts, and such filamentous forms as *Vaucheria*, *Oedogonium* and *Ulothrix*.

Of particular interest is the association of algae with other algae or with different organisms. In these the algae can act as parasites, as for instance *Polysiphonia fastigiata*, a red alga which attacks the brown alga *Ascophyllum nodosum*, or *Cephaleuros*, a green alga which attacks tea and coffee plants. More often than not, however, algae reward their hosts with certain advantages, i.e. they enter into symbiotic association with them. Such associations are particularly interesting when the host is an animal – a case in point is the association of *Chlorellae* with Hydrozoa, Bryozoa or Protozoa. Brown algae, too, occur as symbionts, and as late as 1965 it was discovered that the diatom *Licmophora hyalina* forms symbiotic associations with the worm *Convoluta convoluta*. Species of *Chlorella* also inhabit the endoderm of fresh-water polyps, in which they grow and multiply apace, though some are consumed by the host. Lichens (see p. 10) are yet another important case of symbiosis between algae and, in this case, a fungal host.

Algae are already of great economic importance, and promise to become considerably more so in the future. Experts have estimated that planktonic organisms account for more than 90 per cent of all photosynthetic processes on earth. They supply the basic food of all fish and are therefore indispensable to fisheries. In addition, more than seventy species of marine algae serve man directly as food. The main users are the Japanese and Chinese, but even in the U.S.A. scientific experts are making concerted efforts to render algae palatable to man. It has become clear that some algae can be grown as crops and that their great size – *Laminaria* and its relatives grow several yards during a single vegetative period – can be increased even further in this way.

In addition, pectinic substances derived from brown and red algae are widely used as jelling agents in jams and ices; they also help to dress textile fabrics and go into soaps and creams. Surgical thread, too, is made from these substances, and so are certain artificial fibres. Japanese and Californian red algae supply agar-agar, a substance used in confectionery, and especially as a culture medium for growing bacteria. Many brown algae yield iodine; North Atlantic red algae yield the drug carragheenin; in many parts of the world algae are used as a source of soda.

Quite frequently, they are also employed as artificial fertilizers, both in agriculture and more recently in horticulture. As a curiosity, we might mention that algae provide indigestible but otherwise harmless substances which make them excellent 'fillers' for slimming cures.

In recent times there have also been attempts to cultivate unicellular algae as food. Thus the quick-growing *Chlorellae* have been used to produce rich supplies of proteins and vitamins. Work in this field, which was begun in the thirties, has long since passed the experimental stage; for many years, cultivation has been proceeding on a semi-technical, and in some cases on a large technical scale. Harvest of 20 g of dry mass per day and square metre of growing surface have been obtained, and this figure represents some twenty times the average agricultural yield. Hence we are entitled to take a hopeful view of the future of this industry, particularly when we remember that bacteria and yeasts can also be cultivated as sources of protein. The problem of rendering the crop palatable is easily solved by the methods of modern organic chemistry. In inter-planetary travel, *Chlorellae* have been envisaged not only as possible sources of food but also as sources of oxygen and as means of transforming the exhalation of the astronauts (carbon dioxide) into organic material.

PYRROPHYTA
Yellow-Brown Flagellate Algae

This division comprises some 150 genera with 1100 species. As we have pointed out, their systematic position has been questioned for very good reasons. In particular, recent investigations have shown that the armoured dinoflagellates (class: Dinophyceae) do not seem to fit in with the rest. Thus their flagella lack cilia; many of them do not store starch; they have relatively small supplies of chlorophyll *c*; nuclear division differs from that of the other classes; and their chromatophores have a different fine structure. All these distinctions show just how difficult it is to keep the taxonomic system in line with the latest discoveries. For purely practical reasons, we shall, however, continue to apply the term Pyrrophyta to the three classes Desmophyceae, Dinophyceae and Cryptophyceae.

Let us now see what all Pyrrophyta have in common – despite their many differences. Most of them are unicellular (filamentous or branched forms or colonies are the exception) and distinguished by the peculiar appearance of their reproductive cells. Most species move about by means of two flagella; a few move by means of pseudopodia (false feet) much as amoebae do; others are completely immobile. The flagella are of unequal length and are characteristically embedded in two furrows, one transverse and the second longitudinal. One flagellum provides forward motion and the other probably acts as a stabilizer, since it causes the cell to rotate. Most species are pigmented and are yellowish green, yellowish brown and occasionally red in colour. In addition to chlorophyll *a* and *c*, they contain pigments that are not found in other divisions. Forms devoid of chlorophyll contain leucoplasts, i.e. colourless plastids, and are therefore obligate saprophytes. Some Pyrrophyta have a light-sensitive spot; quite a few have a cell wall made of cellulose; others are naked. The cell wall often consists of elaborate sculptured plates, and is divided into two by a meridian groove. During reproduction, which is generally asexual, the two 'halves' may separate, whereupon each daughter cell completes the missing half. Sexual reproduction involving copulation is also known.

Pyrrophyta account for a considerable part of the

oceanic plankton and are accordingly of great economic significance. They live in warm and cold oceans where they congregate in large masses. Several produce luminous substances and are responsible for phosphorescent phenomena on the high seas. A number of species inhabit lakes, pools and ponds, among them the golden brown *Peridinium* (Dynophyceae) which prefer shady forest pools.

The Dynophyceae, which play so important a part in the food supply of fish, also include a number of poisonous species. The poisons are alkaloids and have been responsible for killing large masses of fish, for instance off the coast of Florida. A curious exception is *Gonyanlax catenata*, whose alkaloid is harmless to cod, which are able to store it, but not to man. Cod paste made out of such fish is highly poisonous.

The relatively small class of Desmophyceae includes the flagellate *Exuviella marina* (Order: Desmonodales; Family: Prorocentraceae). It occurs in all oceans and also in brackish waters. Its oval, laterally compressed cell contains two brownish plastids and a relatively large cell nucleus. A longitudinal groove divides the cell into two halves. The flagella are attached to the front end of the cell and protrude through a pore.

Its complicated floating processes make *Ornithocercus magnificus* a most unusual spectacle: it has wedge-shaped, flat processes pointing downwards and plate- and umbrella-shaped formations pointing upwards, all of them joined by vertical wings. The result is a most complicated system of gullies, in which the flow of water is probably directed by the two flagella. These are fitted into a transverse and a longitudinal groove, hidden among all the other features.

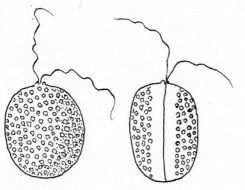

Fig. 14 *Exuviaella marina;* left, front view; right, lateral view (highly magnified)

The dinoflagellates (Dynophyceae) include the largest number of species: 1000 all told and grouped into 120 genera. All are motile, and bear a transverse and a longitudinal groove. The flagella are attached ventrally, roughly where the two grooves cross. Most species have a prominent eyespot. Some dinoflagellates lack a cell wall (Order Gymnodiniales), but are surrounded by a firm outer layer of cytoplasm; e.g. *Gymnodinium aeruginosum*, a pear-shaped fresh-water alga with blue-green chloroplasts; or the marine *Noctiluca miliaris*, which is 1–1.5 mm in length and is still treated as an animal flagellate by many taxonomists, though its reproductive cells stamp it clearly as a member of the Gymnodiniales. When present in large concentrations, *Noctiluca* is responsible for luminescence at sea.

Most dinoflagellates, however, are provided with a thick and characteristically shaped cell wall divided into plates of unequal size (Order: Peridinales). These plates often have the marked surface sculpture characteristic of, for instance, *Peridinium cinctum*. Often the cells of individual species have characteristic processes (e.g. in *Ceratium*). Moreover, this character may also vary from individual to individual and with environmental changes. Thus species inhabiting warm seas invariably have longer processes than those inhabiting colder seas. The cells of most dinoflagellates contain chlorophyll; in addition many species have carotenoids and such red pigments as phycopyrin and puridin. Occasionally blue pigments occur as well. The number of chromatophores is not constant. This class, too, includes colourless saprophytes and even species that are parasitic on fishes and invertebrates. Dinoflagellates store proteins or oils as reserve materials. Reproduction is generally by diagonal division.

All members of the class Cryptophyceae are devoid of cell walls and are surrounded by a layer of 'skin'. They have a characteristically wedge-shaped front end, and a 'gullet' that leads to the centre of the cell. The gullet is said to be associated with the potentially saprophytic habit of these organisms. Those lacking chloroplasts, as for instance the cosmopolitan *Chilomonas paramaecium* are, in any case, obligatory saprophytes. In the gullet, and sometimes elsewhere inside the cell, are found trichocysts, rod-shaped and highly refractive struc-

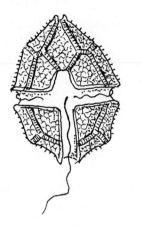

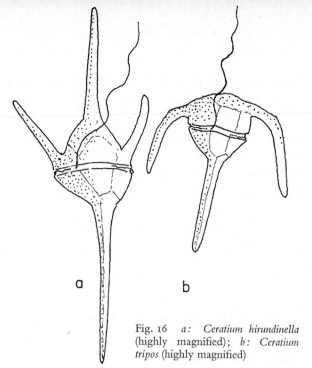

Fig. 15 Left, *Peridinium* (Dynophyceae) with plate armour (highly magnified). Right, *Gymnodinium* (Dynophyceae), lacking cell wall (highly magnified)

Fig. 16 *a: Ceratium hirundinella* (highly magnified); *b: Ceratium tripos* (highly magnified)

tures which expel threads on stimulation – a further indication of their saprophytic or even predatory habits. These algae, too, store their reserves in the form of proteins or oils. The motile forms have two belt-shaped flagella, mostly attached to the front end of the cell. The cell often bears a longitudinal furrow (e.g. *Cryptomonas*). Various Cryptophyceae live in symbiotic association with animals, for instance with corals, where they settle on certain parts of the epidermis; because of their yellow colour they are known as zooxanthellae (Greek: zoon = animal, xanthos = yellow). However, Cryptophyceae also live in symbiosis (e.g. *Chrysidella*) with Radiolaria and Foraminifera.

The last class in this division, the Chloromonadophyceae, consists of delicate-skinned, mud-dwelling algae.

EUGLENOPHYTA

Euglenoid Algae

The main genus in this division, *Euglena* (Order: Euglenales; Family: Euglenaceae) was previously mentioned in connection with the problem of distinguishing primitive animals from primitive plants. And in fact *Euglena* combines an astonishing number of characteristics associated with both groups. Its cell wall is not rigid as it is in plants, but pliable enough to allow every possible change of form. In many species, the wall has spiral markings

which, under strong magnification, prove to be rows of grains. In normal conditions, the cell is pear- or spindle-shaped and generally pointed at the rear end. A flagellum (in some species 2 or 3 flagella) is attached at the front end and continued for a short distance through the gullet, where it divides, into a spherical cavity known as the reservoir. The external part of the flagellum is generally studded with cilia on one side. At the spot where the flagellum divides it passes into a light-sensitive organ (photoceptor). Near by is the stigma, or red eyespot, so characteristic of *Euglena*. It is not yet clear how stigma and photoceptor collaborate, though it seems likely that the stigma is a kind of filter or shade-producer. The electron microscope has shown that the flagellum itself consists of eleven fibrils: two inner ones, surrounded by a spiral of nine outer ones; the entire structure is covered by a sheath. A closer study of flagellar motion has been made, not in *Euglena* itself, but in a representative of the next division, but it seems likely that the conclusions are

Fig. 17 *Cryptomonas*, example of a flagellate Cryptophycean (highly magnified)

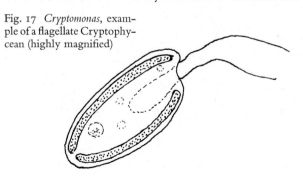

applicable to Euglenophyta as well. The flagellum works much like an oar, whereas that of bacteria acts as a propeller. *Euglena* has a system of internal cavities consisting of a large vacuole which communicates with the outside world through the gullet, and two pulsating, small vacuoles which contract and expand rhythmically. This system, which is situated in the anterior part of the cell, may be called a primitive intestine. Other remarkable organelles are the nucleus and the chloroplasts, the latter being disk- or band-shaped in *Euglena* and of varied shape in other Euglenophyta. The chloroplasts contain chlorophylls *a* and *b*, together with xanthophyll and carotenoids – all pigments found in higher plants as well. *Euglena* stores reserve materials in the form of paramylum, a special type of starch not found in other divisions. Carotene is often distributed throughout the cell. During changes in temperature, e.g. in direct sunlight, the carotene of many species, including *E. sanguinea*, travels to the cell periphery with the result that the chlorophyll becomes masked and the cell looks red. Hence massive concentrations

of *E. sanguinea* can turn the surface of ponds the colour of blood.

Most of the 155 species of *Euglena* inhabit fresh waters. They are particularly prevalent in puddles or pools polluted with liquid manure, e.g. on pig farms, where they form a green scum. If the puddles dry out, the cells form resting stages (cysts) – round structures with a thick wall – capable of withstanding long periods of drought.

Of the remaining 300 or so species, 130 belong to the extremely varied genus of *Phacus*. They are common in the plankton of stagnant and other waters. *Trachelomonas hispia* has a most conspicuous 'shell' and is one of 150 species in this genus. All three genera mentioned so far belong to the Euglenaceae family. Unlike them, members of the families Paranemaceae, Astasiaceae, Rhynchopodaceae and Rhizospidaceae are devoid of chlorophyll. In *Paranema trichophorum* a flagellum protrudes from a long and narrow gullet; only its front end is moveable. Possibly because of this fact and also because the cells are considerably flattened, this alga moves through the water with a strange sliding action. Species of *Paranema* are found in ponds and lakes throughout the world; all are saprophytes, but store paramylum as a food reserve.

CHRYSOPHYTA

Yellow Algae

The name 'yellow algae' is really a misnomer, since many species in this division are green, brown, orange and a host of other colours. However, an analysis of the pigments in them generally shows a predominance of the same components: xanthophyll, carotene, and fucoxanthin. Moreover there is a characteristic lack of chlorophyll *b*.

Many yellow algae are microscopically small; some are free-swimming, some live in colonies, some are simple filaments, and some are branched. A characteristic shared by all motile forms is the presence of two flagella of unequal length; one of these, and generally the longer of the two, is provided with two rows of cilia. This, and also the particular complement of pigments, are the reasons why some species that used to be treated as green algae have recently been reclassified as Chrysophyta (e.g. *Bo-*

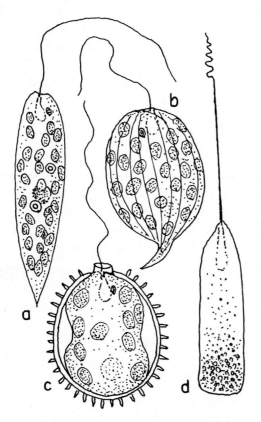

Fig. 18 *a*: *Euglena*; *b*: *Phacus pleuronectes*; *c*: *Trachelomonas hispida*; *d*: *Peranema trichophorum* (all highly magnified)

trydium and *Vaucheria*). These are admittedly larger and immobile types, but their reproductive cells are characteristically equipped with two flagella of unequal length, and one of them bears cilia.

Further common characters include the storing of leucosin or oil, but never starch, as food reserves, and the presence of cell walls rich in pectin, often fortified with silicic acid, and occasionally with calcium.

Far more so than the previous divisions, the Chrysophyta range from free-moving unicells through cell colonies to sessile multicellular organisms. At the same time, we find that sexual reproduction in this division tends to move from isogamy, common in Xanthophyceae, through anisogamy (diatoms) to oogamy (*Vaucheria*). Asexual reproduction by means of motile zoospores and immobile aplanospores occurs as well.

The genera *Botrydium* and *Vaucheria* are unusual in that, though unicellular, they are yet big enough to be seen with the naked eye, and in that each cell contains numerous nuclei. Such gigantic multinucleate protoplasts are known as symplasts, and may be considered primitive and abortive attempts to achieve a higher degree of organization – multicellular plants with one nucleus to each cell have made far greater progress in the course of evolution.

The considerably more than 10,000 species constituting the Chrysophyta (including close on 10,000 diatoms alone) are divided into nearly 300 genera, and grouped in the classes Xanthophyceae, Chrysophyceae, and Bacillariophyceae. Like the previous divisions, the Chrysophyta, too, form an independent group; within them the Bacillariophyceae (diatoms) constitute a particularly distinct section.

The Xanthophyceae (Heterokontae) are almost exclusively fresh-water and soil inhabitants. Each of their cells contains countless chromatophores in which yellow pigments predominate, though not enough to mask the green chlorophyll *a* completely. The class ranges from motile flagellate forms (Order: Heterochloridales) to immobile types (Order: Heterococcales). The Heterococcales include the family Botryococcaceae, one of whose constituent species, *Botryococcus braunii*, is depicted in *Fig. 19*. The individual immobile cells are joined radially into colonies surrounded by a mucous envelope. In

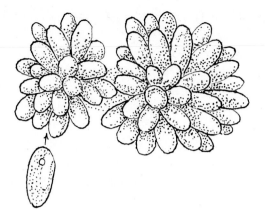

Fig. 19 *Botorycoccus braunii*, cell colony (highly magnified); lower left: single cell, at a higher magnification

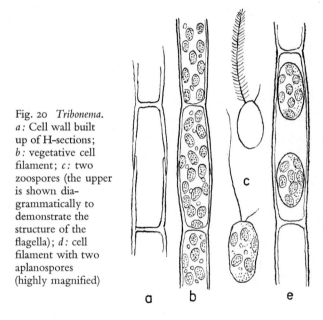

Fig. 20 *Tribonema*. *a*: Cell wall built up of H-sections; *b*: vegetative cell filament; *c*: two zoospores (the upper is shown diagrammatically to demonstrate the structure of the flagella); *d*: cell filament with two aplanospores (highly magnified)

Chariopsis borzi (Chariopsidaceae), the spindle-shaped cells are attached to water plants by gelatinous stalks. Another order, the Heterotrichales, has its cells firmly joined into branched or unbranched filaments. As in *Tribonema* (*Fig. 20*), the filaments consist of overlapping H-shaped wall sections and contain numerous disk-shaped chloroplasts. Heterotrichales can reproduce asexually by thread division, by immobile aplanospores or by motile zoospores. The zoospores have two prominent flagella of different length; the longer of the two bears cilia.

The most interesting order in this division is indubitably that of the Heterosiphonales. Here every individual consists of a giant cell with multinucleate protoplasts. *Botrydium granulatum* (*Pl. 3, p. 50*) is 1–2 mm. in length, intensely green, and pear-shaped; it congregates in large numbers on drying mud, attaching itself to the substrate by means of long and ramified rhizoids. The cytoplasm surrounds a large, central and sap-filled vacuole. Reproduction is by means of countless zoospores, or by tens of thousands of gametes produced by division of the protoplasm and released through the apex of the 'pear'. More remarkable still is the genus *Vaucheria*, species of which abound in fresh water and on moist soil, for instance in greenhouses or in flower pots. Here, long and highly branched filaments lacking septa form a dense, moss-like cushion. The protoplast is multinucleate and contains numerous disk-shaped chloroplasts ranged round a large central vacuole. In the dark, or during flooding, the protoplasm becomes concentrated in the apex of the filament, where it becomes cut off by means of a septum. The tip is then gelatinized; the apical cell (sporangium) opens up, and the protoplast oozes out to form a small sphere in the water. The nuclei in it have taken up a peripheral position and, to the observer's utter surprise, the

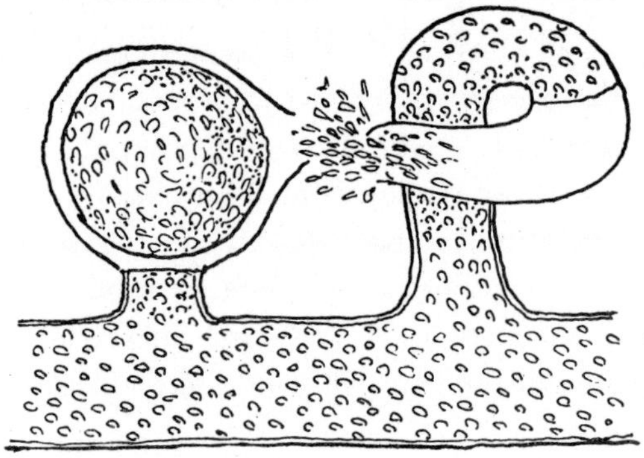

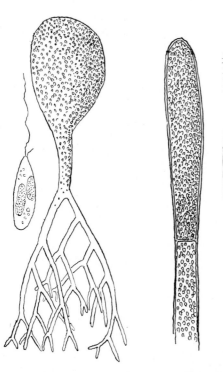

Fig. 21 *Botrydium granulatum*, showing the pear-shaped body and forking rhizoids. Left: zoospore (highly magnified)

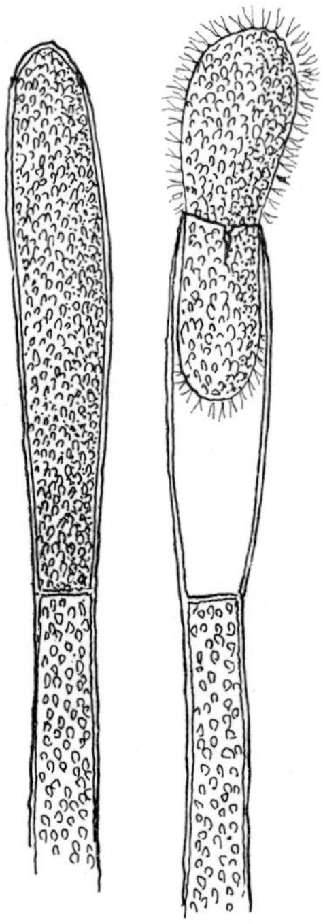

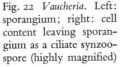

Fig. 22 *Vaucheria*. Left: sporangium; right: cell content leaving sporangium as a ciliate synzoospore (highly magnified)

Fig. 23 *Vaucheria*. Left: oogonium (female reproductive organ); right: antheridium (male reproductive organ). During fertilization the motile gametes move from the antheridium to the oogonium. (Highly magnified)

spherical protoplast sprouts pairs of flagella right round its body and begins to swim about in the water. When the botanist Unger first watched this phenomenon in 1835, he described it enthusiastically as the transformation of a plant into an animal. There is no doubt but that this motile protoplast is a zoospore, or rather a host of combined zoospores, i.e. a synzoospore. After swimming about in the water for some time, it comes to rest and germinates into a *Vaucheria* filament.

Under different external conditions, for instance in bright light or in a nutrient medium, *Vaucheria* will suddenly produce strange processes. In *Vaucheria sessilis* they arise in opposite pairs, one process becoming beak-shaped, the other elongating and spiralling towards the beak of the neighbouring process. Both structures become septate and, in the course of their further development, the beak grows into an oogonium: of its original nuclei all but one degenerate. At the same time, the special cell of the second process produces numerous motile gametes which escape through a gelatinized hole at the tip and begin to swim about by means of two unequal flagella. The second process is therefore an antheridium. In the oogonium, meanwhile, the cell wall has become gelatinized to allow the male gametes to enter and fertilize the ovum. These events usually occur between 2 and 4 a.m., and it is during this time also that increased cell division usually occurs. Not all species of *Vaucheria* bear their oogonia and antheridia on one and the same thread – many of the forty species are dioecious. Moreover the antheridia and oogonia of different species vary considerably in shape.

During the germination of the ovum, reduction division occurs at once – the resulting plant is haploid.

Many species of *Vaucheria* have their walls encrusted with lime and, when they occur in large concentrations, often give rise to tuffaceous limestone deposits. The cysts of other Heterokontae may be silicified.

The class of Chrysophyceae (golden-brown flagellate algae) comprises unicellular species, often combined into colonies. Many species are flagellate; others are sessile. These algae contain only a few chromatophores and, in addition to chlorophyll, a great deal of carotene. In this group of plants the chromatophores are often associated with pyrenoids, structures in which starch is condensed and chlorophyll is synthesized. Most species inhabit fresh water; only a few are found in the sea. A few species live in symbiosis with heterotrophic plants. A widespread unicellular motile species in this class is *Chromulina rosanoffi* (Order: Chrysomonadales; Family: Chromulinaceae) which forms golden-brown layers on the surface of greenhouse tanks and in ponds. The life cycle of *Chromulina* involves flagellate stages, cell fusion, gelatinized resting stages, silicified cysts and amoeboid stages. The cysts have a pore that is sealed by means of a 'cork'.

A species that is both colonial and motile is *Synura uvella* (Family: Synuraceae). The two flagella of each

of its cells are of equal length, and the cell wall is covered with silicified scales. This species is common in lakes and ponds, whereas the related family Coccolithophoridaceae is chiefly oceanic. Here, the cell wall contains calcium grains which help to produce attractive 'shells' of varied shape. Fresh-water and marine species are found in the genus *Dinobryon* (Family: Ochromonadaceae). The elongated cells, with two chromatophores and two unequal flagella, are cup-shaped and form colonies. Reproduction is usually by means of zoospores. However, sexual reproduction, involving the fusion of two free-swimming cells, occurs as well. *Hydrurus foetidus* (Order: Chrysocapsales; Family: Hydruraceae) forms sessile gelatinous colonies up to 30 cm. in diameter on stones in cold mountain streams. Reproduction is generally by means of zoospores. In the order Chrysotrichales some species form branched or unbranched filaments.

An extremely isolated but fairly cohesive group is the class of diatoms (Bacillariophyceae). It contains close on 10,000 species, which are almost exclusively unicellular; at best the cells associate loosely into mucilaginous bands or more highly branched structures. In some species, special processes of the cell membrane play the part of 'coupling links' (e.g. *Syndetocystis barbadensis*).

Most diatoms have characteristic cell walls con-

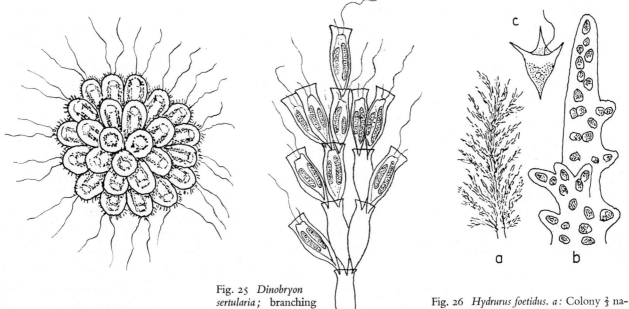

Fig. 24 *Synura uvella*; flagellate cell colony (highly magnified)

Fig. 25 *Dinobryon sertularia*; branching colony (highly magnified)

Fig. 26 *Hydrurus foetidus*. *a*: Colony ⅔ natural size; *b*: highly magnified; *c*: zoospore (highly magnified)

structed of pectin and highly silicified. Moreover, the walls consist of two parts which fit together like lid and jar. Few species have smooth 'shells'; each has distinct striae composed of sculptured dots and cavities, so tiny that they can be used to test the resolving power of microscopes. Some are exceedingly attractive. In general, each half of the shell is composed of a valve together with a connecting band, the latter forming the overlapping portion.

Diatoms are divided into two large orders, the Pennales, which have intercalary as well as connecting bands, and the Centrales, which lack intercalary bands. A simpler way of distinguishing the two is to think of the former as date boxes and of the latter as pill boxes. The Pennales have their striae arranged in segments with either a plain area in between or else a slit (raphe); the Centrales lack such structures and their striae are arranged radially. Moreover, cells of the Pennales usually have two large chromatophores while those of the Centrales have numerous disk-shaped chromatophores. The pigments – chlorophylls, carotenes and xanthophylls – are mixed in varying proportions to give the different species their characteristic appearance. *Navicula ostrearia* (Order: Pennales; Family: Naviculaceae) even develops a blue pigment when kept in oyster basins and apparently feeds on substances secreted by these animals; the oysters for their part devour these diatoms with the result that their gills and pulps turn bluish-green. French oyster lovers consider such gills a guarantee of quality.

Although diatoms frequently contain pyrenoids, they store a fatty oil and not starch as a food reserve, to which fact many diatoms owe their ability to float so well.

As in *Botrydium*, the protoplasm is confined to a peripheral zone, except for a central band containing the nucleus.

During cell division, the two shell-halves separate forming two daughter cells with one shell-half each only. However, while still under the protection of the mother cell, each daughter cell grows a new shell-half which fits closely into the older. As a result, the 'lid-daughter' is an exact replica of the mother cell, whereas the 'bottom-daughter' is two shell-thicknesses narrower. Since the cells can divide every four to five days the 'bottom' descendants

become smaller and smaller. Needless to say, this process does not continue indefinitely: below a certain minimum size the cells die off, unless they have previously compensated for the shrinkage by the formation of auxospores. During this process the silicified shell is cast off and the protoplast enlarges greatly and finally forms two new shell halves. Auxospores are, in any case, formed whenever there is a fusion of male and female gametes. In the Centrales, this fusion takes the form of oogamy: some cells become antheridia and form spermatozoa; others form a large ovum. Both types of gamete are liberated from the shell. In the Pennales, sexual reproduction usually takes the form of isogamy: the like cells come to lie side by side and their protoplasts, which have previously split, then leave the shells and fuse. Reduction division invariably occurs during the formation of the gametes – diatoms are therefore diplonts. Oddly enough, these sexual processes do not lead to multiplication, which invariably takes place by means of the cell divisions we have described. Diatoms do not produce motile zoospores. Their remarkable sensitivity to changes in illumination and other stimuli, together with their mobility, enables them to seek actively for the most favourable conditions; as a result plankton diatoms, for instand, tend to congregate at certain depths of the sea. Soil and mud diatoms, on the other hand, crawl away from intense radiation. Such reactions are, strangely enough, shown by sessile diatoms as well. Thus *Gomphonema* (Order: Pennales; Family: Gomphonemataceae), which lives in colonies attached by gelatinous stalks to water plants or stones in ponds and pools, can vary the length of the stalk depending on the water level.

In deciding the precise relationship between diatoms and other groups of algae, the spermatozoids of the Centrales serve as an important criterion. Their flagella are beset with cilia, which indicates a relationship to flagellate types (see Heterokontae), and also suggests that the Centrales are the original order and that the Pennales are derived from them. This view is supported by fossil finds going back to the Jurassic (200 million years), in which the Centrales represent the older strata. The structure of their shell (multiple segments), their pigmentation (lack of chlorophyll *b*) and the nature of their reserve materials (lack of starch) are some of the reasons why diatoms have been classified as Chrysophyta.

Because they are so tiny, diatoms are readily scattered, with the result that, like bacteria and other small organisms, they are almost ubiquitous. They occur in every type of water, on moist soil, on the bark of trees and even on the leaves of tropical evergreens. Occasionally, one comes across completely naked diatoms which move about like amoebae and even form plasmodia. As we saw (p. 30), a diatom was recently discovered to live in symbiosis with a turbellarian worm. Like blue-green algae, diatoms are found on ice and snow as well as in hot springs. Moreover, some species, e.g. *Navicula oblonga* or *Surirella striatula* (Order: Pennales; Family: Surirellaceae), are as much at home in cold mountain streams as they are in the Karlsbad springs (72.5° C.). Countless species are marine, many others inhabit brooks, rivers, ponds and lakes. Some species (especially among the Centrales) are typical plankton organisms with special floating devices; others keep to the bottom ooze, or live as epiphytes on water plants. Soil diatoms are able to crawl about, while many epiphytic species are able to cling to the substrate even in rushing rivers and in the swell of the waves; some species form colonies that mimic the shape of higher algae. Some of the epiphytes even look like insects,

for instance *Cocconeis*, the 'algal louse'. As we saw, diatoms may congregate in large masses in suitable sites; thus one litre of surface water in cooler oceans may contain some 20,000 organisms, of which diatoms constitute a considerable proportion. In warmer oceans, the number of organisms is considerably smaller – one count gave 2,300 per litre among which diatoms were once again strongly represented. Measurements suggest that a column of marine water with a surface area of one square metre contains up to twenty billion diatoms. Hence it is not at all surprising that their remains should have formed thick deposits in geological time, and that diatomite, i.e. rock composed almost entirely of silica and made up of the accumulated shells of diatoms, should be found all over the world. This substance, also known as diatom earth, is used as 'edible earth' in a number of underdeveloped countries; in industrial countries it goes into dynamite, toothpaste, packing materials, waterglass, fire-resisting materials, sealing wax, gutta-percha and various pharmaceutical preparations.

The two orders Centrales and Pennales comprise a total of 170 genera. The Centrales are divided into three sub-orders, the Coscinodiscineae, the Rhizosolenineae and the Biddulphineae. *Arachnoidiscus*, a marine genus with a perfectly circular, sculptured

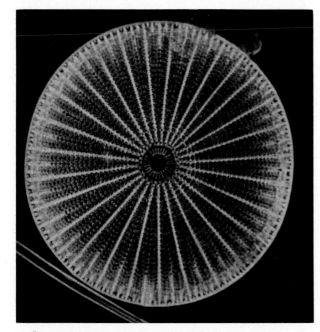

Fig. 27 *Arachnoidiscus* (highly magnified)

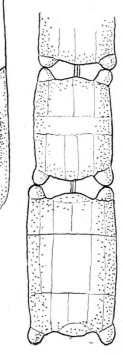

Fig. 28 *Rhizosolenia* (left) and *Biddulphia* (right), both highly magnified

39

shell, is a good example of central symmetry. While the connecting bands are relatively narrow in this genus, they are broad in *Biddulphia* which, like *Arachnoidiscus*, is predominantly marine, and in *Rhizosolenia* which occurs chiefly in marine plankton. In *Biddulphia*, the band bears horns at either side, and in *Rhizosolenia* it bears elongated 'ears'. The Coscinodiscaceae also include the many species of *Melosira* found in ponds either as plankton or as benthos, i.e. as members of the sedentary animal and plant life living on the bottom. Their cells are joined loosely into bands of varying length, and they appear in large masses during the spring. Sexual reproduction in Centrales is by oogamy.

The Pennales are subdivided into the four suborders Fragilarineae, Achnanthineae, Naviculineae and Surirellineae. Though most genera occur in fresh water, numerous species also live in the ocean. The crawling motion of many Pennales is a characteristic feature. The Fragilarineae include the genera *Tabellaria* and *Synedra* which have rectangular cells, and *Licmophora* which has wedge-shaped cells combined into colonies on gelatinous stalks. The Naviculineae include *Navicula cardinalis* (*Fig. 33*). The genus *Navicula* comprises more than 1000 species. Its cells usually live in isolation and have a true raphe (p. 38); they often move by strange jerks. Two

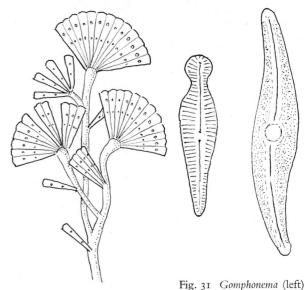

Fig. 30 *Licmophora* colony (highly magnified)

Fig. 31 *Gomphonema* (left) and *Pleurosigma* (right), highly magnified

further representatives of this sub-order are *Gomphonema* and *Pleurosigma* (*Pl. 4, p. 50*). *Surirella* (*Fig. 34*) has been included as a typical representative of the Surirellineae; it comprises some 200 species, all of which have conspicuous cross ribs. Another common genus in the same sub-order is *Nitzschia*, which comprises some 400 species. Here the cells may be elongated, sometimes tapering to fine hairs at either end. Other specimens have twisted shells. *Nitzschia*

Fig. 29 *Melosira arenaria*, colony of band-shaped cells (highly magnified)

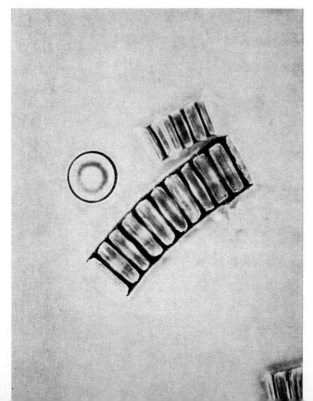

Fig. 32 *Tabellaria* (highly magnified)

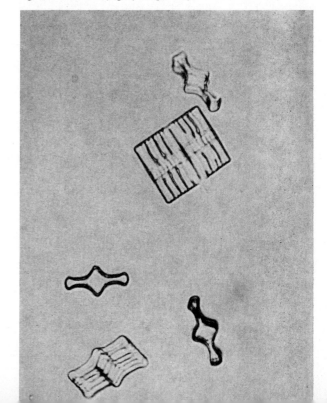

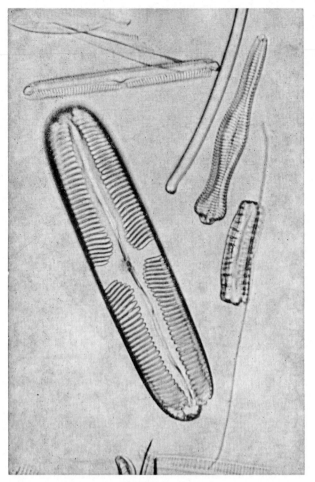

Fig. 33 *Navicula cardinalis* (highly magnified)

Fig. 34 *Surirella biseriata* (highly magnified)

differs from all other diatoms in that the connective bands do not run at right angles to the shell, so its cells look like rhombs in cross section.

CHLOROPHYTA

Green Algae

Most of the divisions we have been discussing consist of unicells – multicellular organisms are very exceptional among them. This position is reversed in the green algae. They, too, include many unicellular forms; but each of the 11 orders consists chiefly of multicellular forms large enough to be recognized with the naked eye. In fact, the Chlorophyta represent a turning point in plant evolution. Their very multiplicity of orders reflects a great variety in type. What they all have in common is the possession of normal leaf pigments, i.e. chlorophylls *a* and *b*, carotene, xanthophyll, and luteol. Their chloroplasts often include pyrenoids, and they all store starch, often in conjunction with fats. The cell walls are mainly built up of cellulose. Where zoospores occur, they are pear-shaped and provided with two or four equal flagella devoid of cilia. Most zoospores also have a red eyespot. It is impossible to prove the existence of tangible affinities to the other divisions; the green algae, like the preceding divisions, are quite independent. This in no way detracts from their importance as mediators between the simplest and the more highly developed divisions of the plant kingdom. In fact, the Chlorophyta comprise microscopically small unicells, colonial types, unbranched filaments, and extremely complicated structures resembling leaves, up to 3 feet long, and thus highly reminiscent of the higher plants. Among the lower Chlorophyta, unicellular organisms combine into colonies, but remain autonomous and are free to leave the association at any time. Such associations

41

are particularly common among the Volvocales. Even the more highly developed filamentous types, for instance *Spirogyra*, are capable of dissolving into their constituent cells, each of which is enclosed in a cellulose wall of its own. Their relative independence is also reflected by their lack of polarity – each *Spirogyra* cell is capable of developing into a separate thread. Other filamentous types are more highly developed, among them the shaggy-haired *Ulothrix*. Here, too, all the cells in the thread can divide independently and produce zoospores, though here each thread may be said to have a polar structure, with a distinct 'foot' and 'head'. Even more highly differentiated are the branched threads of *Cladophora*, in which only the apical cells are capable of growth. In the bristle algae (Chaetophoraceae) and the chandelier-shaped Charales, the thallus is divided into prostrate 'foot tissue' and erect assimilation tissue. Finally, in the tubular Chlorosiphonales, which, like *Vaucheria*, lack septa, the thallus is built up of a single cell and can be up to 3 feet in length. Yet many of these plants are so richly divided into 'branches', 'roots' and 'leaves' that they look suspiciously like higher plants.

By far the greatest number of Chlorophyta inhabit fresh water – green algae can be found in lakes, ponds, pools and puddles everywhere. Some groups are found chiefly on peat bogs, e.g. the decorative Desmidiaceae. Relatively few species occur in the sea; most of these belong to the order Chlorosiphonales. The division does, however, include a number of terrestrial forms, among them some unicellular Protococcaceae (Order: Ulotrichales); some filamentous Cladophorales and some Chaetophoraceae. While the orders Volvocales and Conjugales may be said to have 'repeated' the development from unicell to multicell, the Chaetophoraceae (sometimes treated as a separate order, the Chaetophorales) are remarkable in that they give us a hint of how the development from thallophyte into cormophyte might have occurred. One species in this family, *Stigeoclonium tenue*, has become adapted to terrestrial life, and has become differentiated into a prostrate 'sole' and an erect part. If we add that the sole contains regular 'foot' cells with special claws for clinging to the substrate; that other species in the family have an 'epidermis' consisting of corky and fatty materials; and

that there is a surprising degree of differentiation in the sexual organs – the fertilized egg cell developing into a kind of fruit ('zygote-fruit') – then it becomes clear that these algae have entered upon the path taken by the higher plants.

The same trend is also reflected in other characters, for instance in the form of the chloroplasts. The simplest green algae have a compact, basin-shaped chloroplast; in other genera, for instance in *Oedogonium*, the chloroplast takes the form of a loose network distributed through most of the cell; and in the still more advanced types, e.g. the Chlorosiphonales, the single chloroplast is replaced by numerous disk-shaped structures.

Evolutionary progress is further reflected by the nature of sexual relationships and the associated alternation of generations. The chain begins with the simplest of sexual processes, i.e. the fusion of similar flagellate gametes (isogametes) as in *Chlamydomonas* and *Ulothrix*. In the least complicated case the entire plant turns gamete, for instance in the colourless *Polytoma uvella*, in which any two individuals are apparently able to copulate with each other. Isogamy also occurs among the Desmidiaceae; here the protoplasts fuse into non-motile gametes. Other species, for instance *Chlamydomonas braunii*, represent the more advanced type of sexual union in which two unequal anisogametes combine into a zygote.

In anisogamy, the female gamete is always larger than the male. Occasionally, as in *Chlamydomonas suboogonium*, the female gamete loses the power to move its flagella and is therefore non-motile. We may consider this a transition to oogamy, which has been fully realized in the related *Chlorogonium oogamum*. In this species, the female gamete has completely lost its flagella – it has become an ovum and crawls out of its envelope like an amoeba. In yet another species, *Chlamydomonas coccifera*, the ovum is fertilized inside its envelope (oogoniogamy). This advanced form of oogamy also occurs in the filamentous *Oedogonium*. Here the male gametes (spermatozoids) slip into a special aperture in the oogonium and fuse with the egg inside. A further variation occurs in the Zygnematales (yoked algae). In the typical case, two cell threads come to lie next to each other, whereupon the walls between them dissolve and the contents of the one cell migrate into the other (gametangiogamy). This process is taken a step further in bristle algae of the genera *Coleochaete* and *Chaetophora*. Here the egg-containing cell (oogonium) becomes flask-shaped and the spermatozoid enters the flask at the tip of its neck. This type of fertilization foreshadows what happens in red algae and mosses. Most astonishing of all, fertilization in *Coleochaete* is followed by the development of cell filaments which eventually surround the fertilized cell, to form a primitive fruit ('zygote fruit' or sporocarp). Similar processes also occur in the order Charales; here the oogonium is 'wrapped up' from the very start. Later, the membranes of the ovum and the surrounding cells thicken, become lignified, and change colour. Sometimes the resulting 'fruit' becomes lime-encrusted, which enables it to withstand prolonged periods of cold or dryness.

In connection with these developments, we must also mention a phenomenon that bears directly on evolutionary trends and on specialization. We have stressed more than once that the fusion of two gametes leads to the duplication of the nuclear matter in the cell and hence of the number of chromosomes. Thus while the gametes have haploid sets of chromosomes, the product of their fusion, the zygote, is a diplont. Biologists call this process a change in nuclear phase. In the simplest cases, e.g. in most Volvocales, Tetrasporales, Chlorococcales and Ulotrichales, the diploid phase is confined to the zygote, which, after a resting phase, germinates to give rise to four swarmers (gonozoospores). Their formation goes hand in hand with meiosis, i.e. the type of nuclear division by which the chromosomes are reduced from the diploid to the haploid number. During this process the sex of the swarmers is often determined as well; in *Ulothrix*, for instance, the resulting two male and two female swarmers establish themselves as male and female *Ulothrix* plants, which can either form fresh gametes or else reproduce asexually. In many green algae, for instance *Cladophora*, the zygote does not produce swarmers: instead it develops into a diploid plant which is externally indistinguishable from the haploid. Here the diploid zygote gives rise to a diploid generation. Reduction division takes place when the latter produces haploid swarmers (gonospores) which, in their turn, produce haploid and sexually differentiated

Cladophora plants. In the case of *Cladophora*, therefore, we have a clear alternation of generations. Both generations can, moreover, reproduce asexually as well. While they are almost indistinguishable in *Cladophora*, the two generations differ considerably in other green algae, so much so that it took a long time to establish that they were distinct phases rather than distinct species. Cases in point are *Urospora-Codiolum* (Cladophoraceae) and *Halicystis-Derbesia* (Chlorosiphonales). In most Chlorosiphonales, however, there is no alternation of generation. The plants, e.g. *Acetabularia*, *Bryopsis* and *Caulerpa*, are diplonts capable of producing gametes. This is unusual since, among plants, it is generally the haploid generation that produces the haploid gametes. In the Charales, too, there is no alternation of generations, but the plants are haplonts.

The origin of alternations of generations is relatively easy to reconstruct. In a normally haploid cycle, i.e. one in which the zygote is diploid, meiosis may fail to occur for any number of external or internal reasons. In that case the zygote will develop into a diploid plant. When this plant produces spores, we have precisely the situation we have described for *Cladophora*. Diploid plants can also be obtained from haploid plants by experimental intervention – years ago Wettstein was able to grow diploid moss plants (they are normally haploid) from the tissue of the spore capsule. Now a diploid generation is clearly advantageous to the life and development of plants: diploid cells contain twice as many gene complexes as haploid cells and hence provide for the formation of twice as many characters. Sexual reproduction involving the combination of the genes of two distinct individuals increases the possible combinations even further.

We must emphasize yet another important point: in the course of the development from unicell to multicell, we first come face to face with the phenomenon of death. Unicells are immortal inasmuch as the mother cell splits up completely into living daughter cells, whereas such organisms as *Volvox* have become so highly differentiated that only a few of their cells have a reproductive function. When the daughter cells are released, the rest of *Volvox* dies off to produce what may be considered one of the most primitive 'corpses' in the plant kingdom.

As far as we can tell from fossil finds, green algae are a very old group; the remains of several orders, particularly of the Chlorosiphonales, go back to the Silurian, i.e. to at least 400 million years ago.

Order
CHLOROCHYTRIDIALES

Some taxonomists head the division Chlorophyta with the order Chlorochytridiales, whose unicellular representatives lack a cell wall and contain a single chloroplast. The cells are flagellate and move about like tadpoles. They occur in puddles and on moist ground, and are predominantly saprophytic.

Order
VOLVOCALES

Much more important is the order Volvocales. Here, too, the unicellular species (Family: Polyblepharidaceae) are naked. One of these is *Dunaliella salina*, which inhabits saline water, and owes its blood-red colour to the pigment haematochrome. The Chlamydomonadaceae are unicellular as well, but have a cellulose wall and a large, basin-shaped green plastid. The cell has an aperture and a prominent eyespot, and bears two long flagella at the anterior end. The bottom of the plastid contains a pyrenoid body (centre of starch formation). The nucleus is roughly in the centre of the cell, and there are two contractile vacuoles. The cells multiply by repeated longitudinal division to form 2 to 16 daughter cells, which are

released when the surrounding membrane splits open. An interesting variation is found in *Chlamydomonas seriata*: the first division is diagonal, whereupon the two daughter cells arrange themselves horizontally and divide again – this time at right angles to the maternal axis. In this way something like a cell filament arises and, in fact, *C. seriata* may be considered an illustration of how the filamentous type first arose.

Chlamydomonadaceae can also reproduce sexually, by progressively more complex techniques. An advanced case is the sexual reproduction of *Chlorogonium oogamum*: here a male cell produces numerous spermatozoids, and a female cell a single ovum. Once both types of gamete have been released from their respective mother cells, the spermatozoids (or antherozoids as they are sometimes called) are able to fertilize the ova. This, as we saw, is the case of oogamy. In other species, the female cell can be fertilized without first being transformed into a proper ovum (oogoniogamy). The resulting zygote forms a resting stage and later 'germinates'. Reduction division then gives rise to two male and two female swarmers.

The Chlamydomonadaceae, too, include many species containing haematochrome; these often turn puddles (*Haematococcus pluviatilis*) or snow (*Chlamydomonas nivalis*) red. The green forms are more common in rain butts and puddles, which they often cover with a bright green to yellow scum, particularly after thunderstorms. The colourless *Polytoma uvella* invariably appears in plant infusions. In many

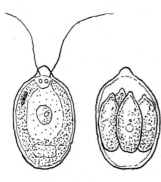 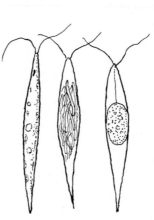 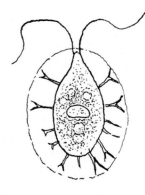

Fig. 35 *Chlamydomonas*. Left: vegetative cell; right: mother and 4 daughter cells.

Fig. 36 *Chlorogonium oogamum*. Left: vegetative cell; centre: male individual with spermatozoids; right: female individual with egg cell (highly magnified)

Fig. 37 *Sphaerella* (highly magnified)

species, the chloroplast lacks the typical basin shape. In *Sphaerella* (a genus that is sometimes treated as a separate family), the protoplast lies in the centre of the cell and is attached to the cell wall by thin cytoplasmic threads.

The family to which the whole order owes its name, i.e. the Volvocaceae, contains the richest variety of forms, including as it does every possible type from colonial species to true multicells. All colonial species are aggregates of individual cells resembling *Chlamydomonas*. *Oltsmannsiella* forms a band consisting of 4 cells, *Gonium* a flat plate of 4–16 cells, and *Pandorina morum* a 'morula' of 16 cells surrounded by a mucilaginous envelope. The 32 cells of *Eudorina* and the 128 cells of *Pleodorina* are combined into a hollow sphere. In all these colonies, the flagella of every cell beat synchronously; this suggests that the individual cells must be interconnected, probably by means of very fine plasma threads. *Eudorina* and *Pleodorina* colonies, moreover, show a degree of polarity and division of labour: the cells at one 'end' of the hollow sphere are small and have larger eyespots than those at the other end; the smaller cells produce spermatozoids and ova. In *Eudorina*, the development of plasma bridges and the division of labour have gone so far that the cells are no longer capable of leading an independent existence.

This is particularly obvious in the 13 species of *Volvox* (Pl. 7, p. 51), the colonies of which contain 5000 to 30,000 bright green cells arranged in a hollow sphere, connected by means of broad plasma-bridges (plasmodesmae); their thousands of pairs of flagella beat synchronously whenever the sphere is in motion. The sphere is clearly divided into two poles, and the eyespots increase in size as we pass from the front to the back. Hence *Volvox* may, in fact, be called a multicellular organism. Reproduction is both sexual (oogamy) and asexual. In the latter case, a number of scattered cells in the rear half of the sphere start to divide, producing cell plates that gradually develop into hollow spheres and are liberated into the maternal cavity, where they remain until the mother bursts open. This, as we said, was the most primitive 'corpse' in the plant kingdom – further proof that *Volvox* must be considered a true multicell.

Interesting experiments have **shown that** *Volvox*

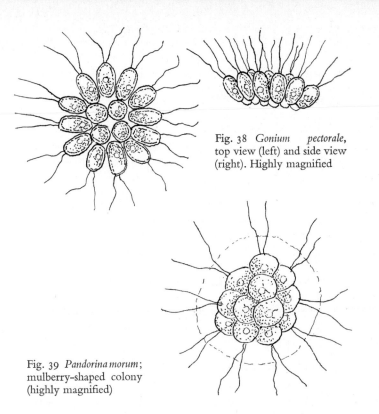

Fig. 38 *Gonium pectorale*, top view (left) and side view (right). Highly magnified

Fig. 39 *Pandorina morum*; mulberry-shaped colony (highly magnified)

reacts to light stimuli. Thus if *Volvox* colonies are fished out of a pond and placed in a bowl half covered with cardboard, they will move from the darker part to the lighter, or rather to the half-shadow at the edge of the cardboard, where they produce a clear green seam. In other words, the plants seek optimum light conditions. Nor is that all. Their 'light mood' varies with their stage of development, i.e. with age. Mature spheres 'desire' less light and migrate away from the 'bachelors' to congregate in the darker parts of the bowl.

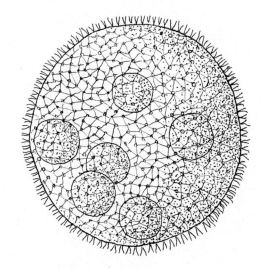

Fig. 40 *Volvox aureus*; adult colony including 6 daughter cells (highly magnified)

Order

TETRASPORALES

This order comprises a number of unicells and multi-cells, or rather of cell colonies. All are immobile, though some have strange processes resembling flagella. The cells are enclosed in a mucilaginous envelope. The order includes the families Palmellaceae and Tetrasporaceae.

Order

CHLOROCOCCALES

The Chlorococcales are a far more important order. Much as in the Volvocales, they range from unicells to cell associations, though the latter are never the kind of multicells with distinct tissues we found in *Volvox*. Nevertheless, some species are of very high botanical interest. None of them is self-propelled; motile stages occur only during the phase of vegeta-

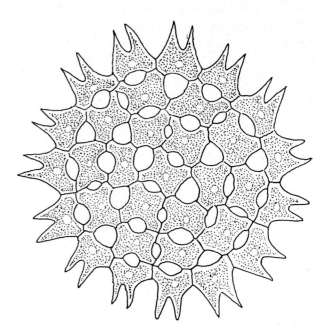

Fig. 42 *Pediastrum* (highly magnified)

tive (zoospores) or sexual reproduction (gametes). The zoospores are not, as in the Volvocales, produced by longitudinal cell division; instead the protoplasm of the mother cell becomes divided by numerous clefts. The zoospores first swim about freely in the common mucilaginous sheath and then combine into aggregates after shedding their flagella (e.g. in *Pediastrum* and *Hydrodictyon*). Occasionally, a daughter colony will arise within the body of the mother cell, not to be released until the maternal cell wall breaks down.

We shall now look at a complete life cycle, choosing the genus *Pediastrum* as a typical case. Here we can distinguish a minor and a major cycle. The minor cycle results from vegetative, asexual reproduction, during which individual cells are split up to produce 16 zoospores – just as many as the original plant has cells, each with its own nucleus. The multiplication of nuclei apparently takes place during the development of the original cell aggregate. The zoospores swarm about within the mother cell until the wall of the latter breaks down. The 'litter' is then released in a mucilaginous envelope, gradually stops swarming and comes to rest. Once their flagella have been shed, the 16 cylindrical zoospores combine into a plate which eventually turns into a cog-shaped disk. The combination of the zoospores into a new colony is ensured by the presence of fine cytoplasmic threads

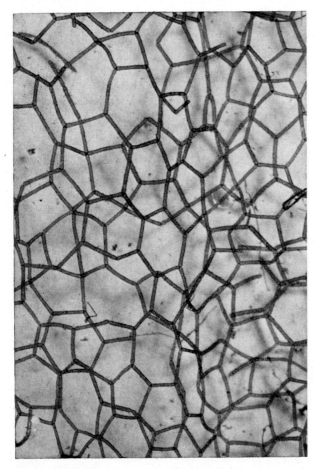

Fig. 41 *Hydrodictyon reticulatum* (magnified)

46

between them. The major, sexual, cycle begins with the formation of isogametes by the disk cells; these fuse in pairs to produce gametes which, in their turn, give rise to four swarmers each. The swarmers shed their flagella after a time, and grow until they look like so many polyhedra. Clearly, these polyhedra are equivalent to the disk cells for, like them, they eventually release a 'litter' of 16 zoospores which come to rest to produce a new disk. The latter then grows into a new *Pediastrum* colony.

Similar reproductive cycles occur in *Hydrodictyon*, except that they are even more clearly distinct – if only because *Hydrodictyon* colonies can be made up of many as 20,000 multinucleate cells each with a reticulate chloroplast. The result is a hollow, free-floating network closed at either end and up to 20 inches long. In this genus, the zoospores are combined into a daughter net within the mother cell, and released as a kind of net-embryo.

Of the remaining families and genera, we must make special mention of the unicellular, immobile and spherical forms of the *Chlorella* type (Family: Oocystaceae). Together with others they are frequently encountered on tree trunks, moist walls, ponds and puddles. However, they also occur in association with fungi (lichens), as endosymbionts of animals, e.g. *Paramecium*, various sponges and worms,

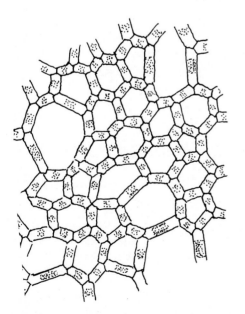

Fig. 43 *Hydrodictyon reticulatum*, part of young colony (highly magnified)

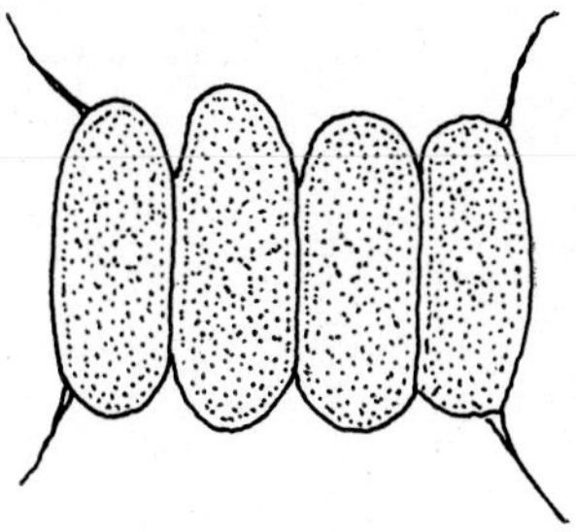

Fig. 44 *Scenedesmus* (highly magnified)

and *Hydra*, which benefit from the products of their assimilation, feed on their offspring, and absorb the oxygen they produce. Such associations have been termed 'animal lichens' by some biologists, but the term has not been generally adopted. The economic importance of *Chlorella* has been discussed on p. 31.

Individuals of the genus *Scenedesmus* (Greek = rope-fetter) consist of 4 or more cells (*Pl. 8, p. 51*). The two external cells of the 'rope' have strangely shaped processes in many species. The cells are attached to one another by mucilage bands. Oddly enough, they are not completely immobile: changes in light conditions may cause them to shift to and fro on the substrate.

Order

ULOTRICHALES

In brooks and springs, on the banks of rivers and also on the wave-lapped shores of lakes, we often find *Ulothrix zonata* (Family: Ulotrichaceae), a species whose unbranched filaments are attached to the substrate by means of a modified basal cell. The cells have a simple cylindrical shape, a nucleus, and a chloroplast which forms a characteristic circular band round most or all of the cell circumference. Every cell can form zoospores. These each have an eyespot and 4 flagella, and escape from a hole in their mother cell. *Ulothrix* more than any other organism bears out the truth of Thomas Huxley's dictum that a plant is an animal in a wooden box. The zoospores later lose their flagella, attach themselves sideways to the substrate and, splitting along their original axis, build up new *Ulothrix* threads. Sexual reproduction occurs as well: isogametes escape from the cells and copulate in pairs. Each zygote produces four swarmers of which two are of the plus and two of the minus strain. When these come to rest, they give rise to haploid plus and minus

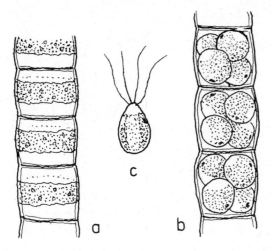

Fig. 45 *Ulothrix. a:* Part of vegetative filament; *b:* part of filament with zoospores; *c:* zoospore (highly magnified)

Fig. 46 *Ulva lactuca*, sea-lettuce (½ natural size)

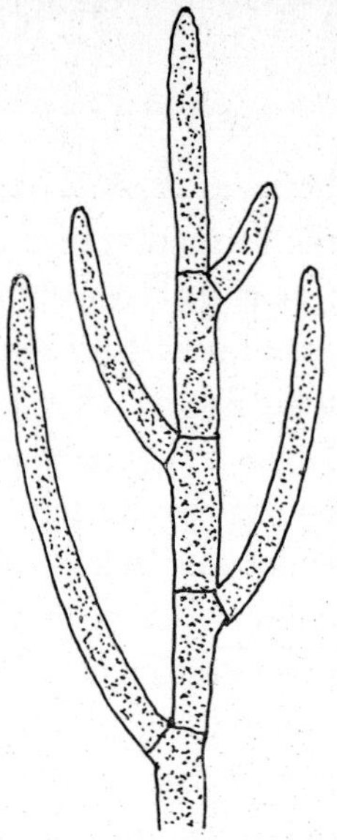

Fig. 47 *Cladophora*, tip of cell filament (highly magnified)

plants. Swarmer formation goes hand in hand with reduction division. Every cell in an *Ulothrix* filament can form either zoospores or gametes; after their formation, the mother plants often consist of only the wall substance and look pale and empty. Observations of *Ulothrix* cultures have shown that a particular filament does not produce both zoospores and gametes, but that zoospore- and gamete-forming threads alternate: hence there is a kind of alternation of generations, with the zoospore-forming plant representing the sporophyte, and the gamete-forming plant the gametophyte.

Ulva (sea-lettuce) and *Enteromorpha* (Pl. *9*, *p. 52*), two genera in the family Ulvaceae (sometimes treated as a special order) are common on temperate coasts. *Ulva* looks like a large, curly leaf, *Enteromorpha* like a belt-shaped hollow tube. (This results from horizontal and longitudinal cell division.)

In many Ulotrichales the two generations occur in two (dimorphous) forms, for instance in the genus *Monostrama*. This condition is more prevalent among brown and red algae, and indeed among all higher plants.

The Ulotrichales include two families that are treated as a separate order in some systems, namely the Chaetophoraceae and the Trentepohliaceae. *Chaetophora*, which often lives attached to other algae, is, as we saw, remarkable for the fact that it is divided into a prostrate basal section and an erect upper part. Both consist of branched filaments.

However, *Chaetophora* differs even more characteristically from the mass of other green algae in that it produces 'zygote fruits' (see p. 43). This, as we saw, is the most primitive fruit formation in the plant kingdom though, morphologically speaking, the term 'fruit' does not really apply. *Trentepohlia* (Pl. *6*, *p. 51*) has become completely adapted to terrestrial life. Its broad threads can often be seen covering stones and bark with a rust-coloured skin. These algae shed their zoosporangia and zoospores as one whole, and leave their dissemination to the water and more particularly to the wind – just as higher plants do with pollen.

The order also includes a group of highly reduced algae, the Protococcaceae (Pl. *14*, *p. 53*). These are the most common of all aerial algae, and are found throughout the world.

Order

CLADOPHORALES

The members of this order have characteristic branched threads, consisting of elongated multinucleate cells. Zoospores and gametes generally arise at the tip. Alternation of generations occurs much as in *Ulothrix*. A typical representative of this order, *Cladophora*, forms bright green two to four inch clumps in relatively unpolluted rivers, ponds, lakes and even in the sea. On lake shores, *Cladophora* may sometimes appear in the shape of balls, produced by

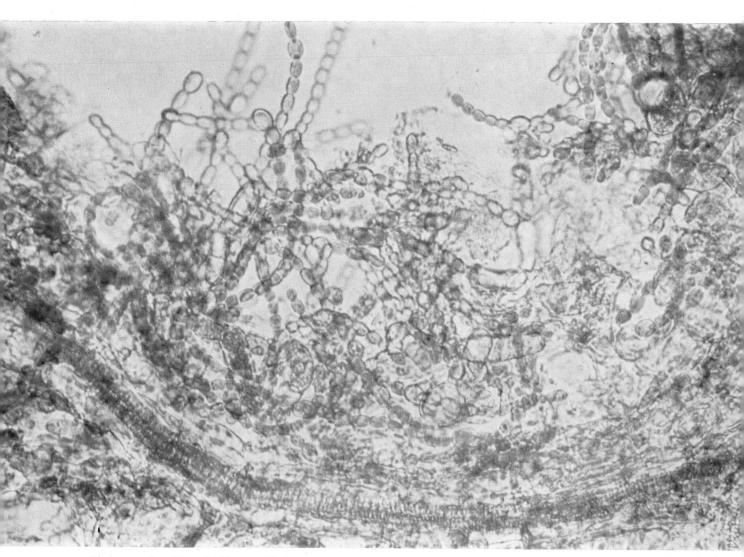

1 Blue-green alga, *Nostoc* (highly magnified)

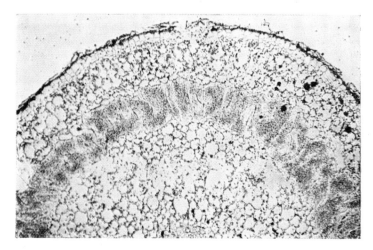

2 Blue-green alga, *Anabaena*, as symbiont in a
Cycas 'coral-root' (magnified)

3 Yellow alga, *Botrydium granulatum* (magnified)

4 Diatom, *Pleurosigma* (highly magnified)

5 Blue-green alga, *Gloeocapsa* (highly magnified)

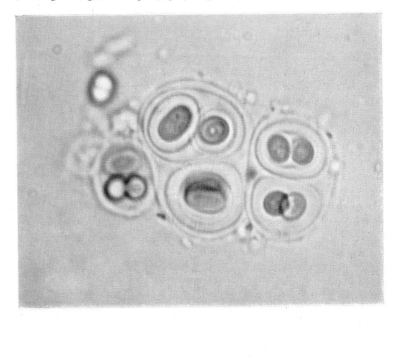

6 *Trentepohlia aurea* (Ulotrichales)

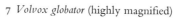
7 *Volvox globator* (highly magnified)

8 *Scenedesmus* (Chlorococcales; highly magnified)

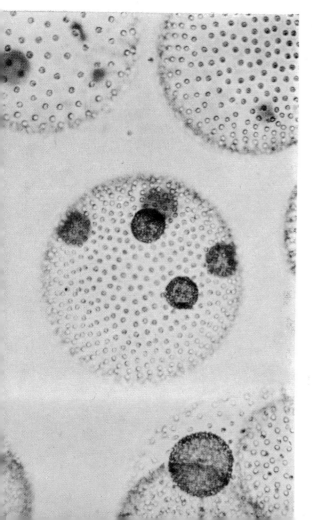

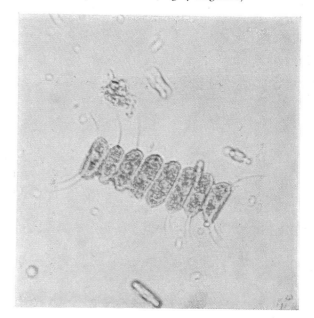

9 *Enteromorpha* (Ulotrichales)

11 *Spirogyra* (magnified)

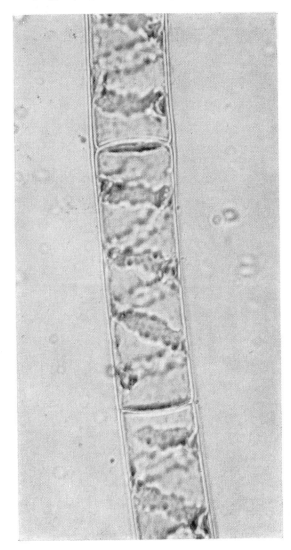

10 *Halimeda opuntia*

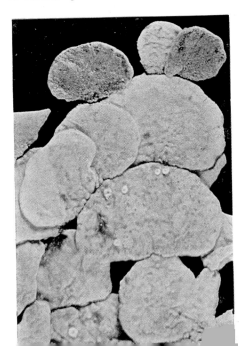

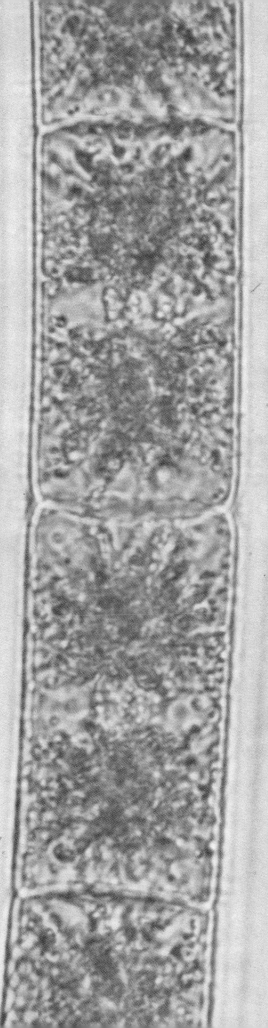

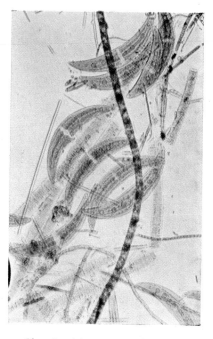

13 *Closterium* (nigny magnified)

14 *Protococcus* (Ulotrichales)

12 *Zygnema* (highly magnified)

15 *Padina pavonia*

16 Brown algae exposed at ebb tide

17 *Nitella*

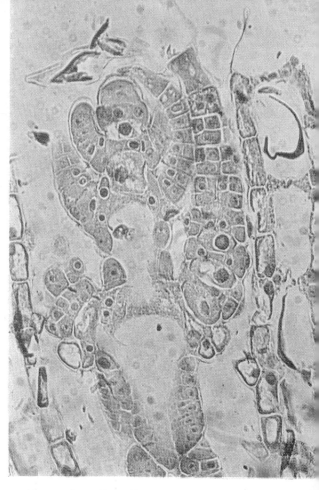

18 *Chara*; nodes and lateral branches
(highly magnified)

19 Brown alga (*Leathesia difformis*)

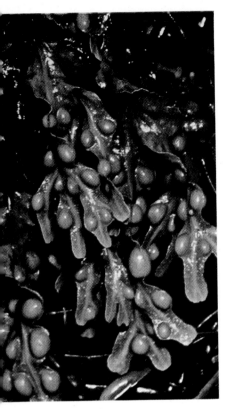

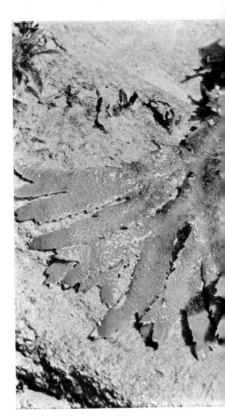

20 *Fucus vesiculosus*

21 *Fucus platycarpus*

22 *Fucus serratus*

23 *Himanthalia lorea*

24 *Chorda tomentosa*

25 *Saccorhiza bulbosa* (Laminariales)   26 *Alaria oblonga* (Laminariales)

27 *Ascophyllum nodosum*

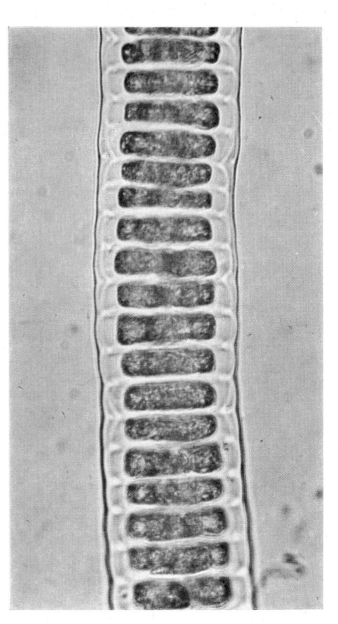

29 Red alga, *Bangia atropurpurea*

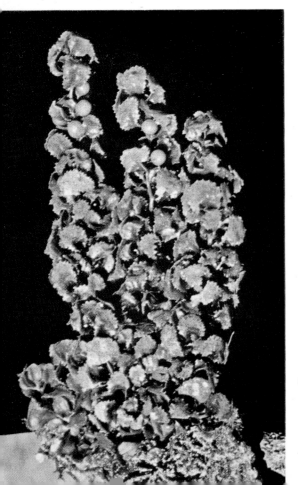

28 *Turbinaria* (Fucales)

30 Red alga, *Lithophyllum sociale*

31 Red alga, *Lithothamnion glaciale*

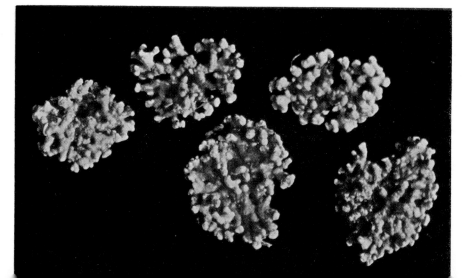

32 Red alga, *Phymatolithon*

33 Red alga, *Corallina officinalis*, growing
on another red alga *(Chondrus crispus)*

34 *Plocami*

35 Red alga, *Rhodymenia palmetta*

36 Red alga, *Chondrus crispus*

37 The tropical ascomycete *Engleromyces goetzi* (Sphaeriales)

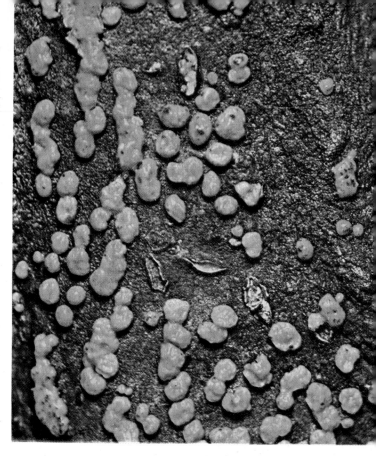

38 The ascomycete *Nectria cinnabarina* (Hypocreales)

39 The alga-like fungus *Phycomyces* (Mucorales)

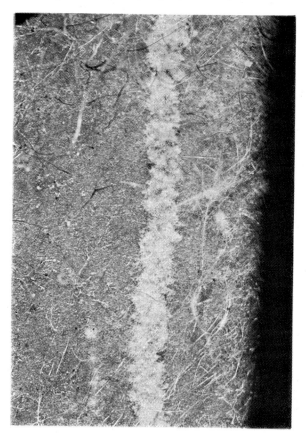

40 Red alga, *Delesseria sanguinea*

41 *Claviceps purpurea*, ergot

42 The ascomycete *Xylaria hypoxylon* (Xylariales)

a continual rolling motion of the threads under the influence of wave action.

Some taxonomists include the Sphaeropleaceae, a family of spherical thread-algae, in this order. They are easily identified by the presence of annular chloroplasts. Each plant consists of unbranched filaments and is oogamous; the ova are developed and fertilized inside the mother cell. After the formation of zygotes, these algae cover the ground with a rust-coloured web. This phenomenon, which used to be called 'meteor-paper', gave rise to a host of superstitious theories.

Order
OEDOGONIALES

The Oedogoniales have been called a strange mixture of animals and plants by von Flotow, one of the first biologists to study *Oedogonium*, the main representative of this order. Flotow made this remark after noticing that individual cells of this filamentous alga liberate oval zoospores surrounded by a ring of cilia, hence resembling unicellular ciliates. Egg cells and spermatozoids can be produced by one and the same or by two distinct threads – the algae are therefore monoecious-dioecious. The zygote hibernates, and in the spring releases four haploid cells which grow into new threads. This process is more compli-

cated in several species, where the spermatozoids do not fertilize the ova directly, but settle in the vicinity of the oogonium and grow into structures consisting of three cells. These are the so-called dwarf male plants, from whose top cell the active spermatozoids are later released. This phenomenon once again represents an alternation of generations, even though it is restricted to the male cycle only. *Oedogonium* is a common sight in ponds, and is easily identified under the microscope by the presence of a thickened transverse ring or cap near the upper end of the cell. This ring arises as a result of a special form of cell division during which part of the old cell wall breaks and a new, younger and thinner wall is drawn in between the old portions.

Order
CHLOROSIPHONALES

The tubular Siphonales, or rather Chlorosiphonales, are vaguely reminiscent of *Vaucheria*, which used to be counted among them. Every tubular alga is really a large aseptate cell – very large indeed, when we consider that its thallus may attain a height of several inches. The protoplasm contains numerous disk-shaped chloroplasts together with numerous nuclei. Despite their simple structure, the Chlorosiphonales include a host of different forms, whose

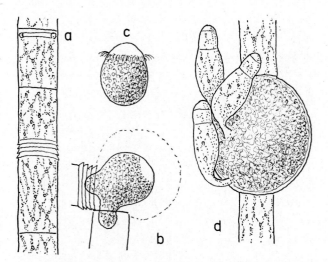

Fig. 48 *Oedogonium. a:* Part of vegetative filament; *b:* formation of zoospore; *c:* liberated zoospore; *d:* cell filament with oogonium bearing 3 dwarf male plants on its outer wall (highly magnified)

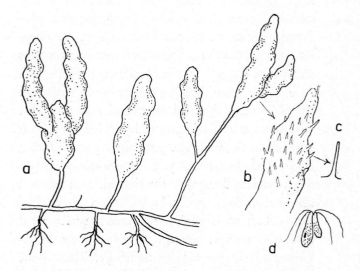

Fig. 49 *Caulerpa. a:* General habit; *b:* 'leaf'-section studded with papillae through which the reproductive cells are liberated; *c:* papilla; *d:* copulation of two reproductive cells (the female one is the larger of the two). Highly magnified

65

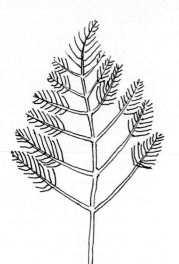

Fig. 50 *Bryopsis*, part of plant (natural size)

body may be divided into 'leaves', 'shoots' and 'rhizomes' (*Caulerpa*), or else may take the form of fine pinnules (*Bryopsis*). Other species look like cacti (*Halimeda; Pl. 10, p. 52*), and yet others 'imitate' the spongy tissue of higher fungi (*Codium*). Members of this order are found in all warm seas.

Order
SIPHONOCLADALES

The Siphonocladales, too, are mostly distributed in warm oceans and owe their name (= tube-branch) to the fact that their thalli have particularly prominent branches. In this order, the single-chambered cell becomes rounded off into one or more portions as it grows. Reproduction is almost exclusively sexual, generally by means of anisogametes produced by distinct male and female plants. *Acetabularia*, which grows to a height of several centimetres and occurs throughout the Mediterranean coast, has an elongate 'stem' bearing one or more whorls of lateral branches that make it resemble an umbrella. The stem has a rhizoid process by which the plant is attached to the substrate, generally a stone. During the longest phase of its cycle, *Acetabularia* has only a single nucleus, located in the rhizoid. This fact and also that various species have distinct 'umbrellas' makes *Acetabularia* particularly suited to grafting and regeneration experiments, designed to study the influence of the nucleus on the shape. Thus if the 'stem' of *A. mediterranea* is grafted on to a rhizoid of *A. wettsteinii*, a *wettsteinii* 'umbrella' is regenerated and vice versa. Research on this subject is still in

progress. The presence of the nucleus in the holdfast section is of extreme importance to the life of the plant – should the upper part be torn away by waves or animals, the rhizoid part is able to regenerate the lost top section. Once the umbrella is fully developed, the nucleus divides into numerous secondary nuclei, most of which migrate to the umbrella lobes, which now act as gametangia. These give rise to a number of cysts from which the gametes are released after a period of rest.

Acetabularia, like all other members of this order, is lime-encrusted, and is responsible for the presence of chalk deposits – hundreds of metres thick – going back to the Triassic and the Permian.

Order
ZYGNEMATALES

Most readers will be familiar with the threads known as water silk or mermaid's tresses which form in spring and summer at the edges of puddles, pools and lakes. If these threads are slimy they are almost certainly due to the presence of Zygnematales (zygo = yoked), particularly to the genus *Spirogyra*.

Spirogyra threads are easily identified under the microscope – each of their cells contains one or more chloroplasts with a smooth or serrated margin, arranged in a characteristic spiral band (whence the name of the genus). The band is capable of turning

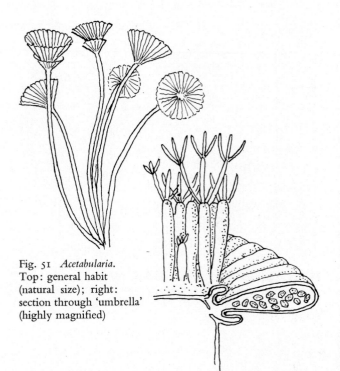

Fig. 51 *Acetabularia*. Top: general habit (natural size); right: section through 'umbrella' (highly magnified)

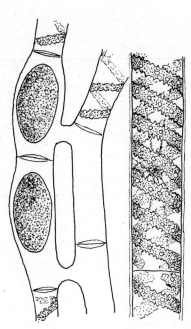

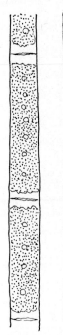

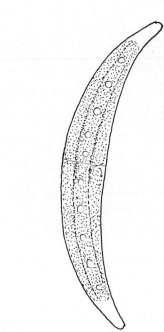

Fig. 52 *Spirogyra*. Right: part of cell filament with spiral chloroplast; left: copulating cell filaments (of a different species). Note the two zygotes in the left branch

Fig. 53 *Mougeotia*: part of a cell filament containing chloroplasts seen from the top (left) and from the side (right). Strongly magnified

Fig. 54 *Closterium* (strongly magnified)

towards sources of light and of altering its shape. The related genus *Mougeotia*, which has large, flat chloroplasts, can respond even more quickly to changes of light intensity. Early observers of these reactions found them rather puzzling; more recently it has become clear that polarization phenomena are involved. The light-sensitive elements, or photoreceptors, are thought to form spirals parallel to the walls of the cylindrical cells. Light which enters the cells at right angles to the axis is absorbed by receptors at the opposite side of the cell, but not by the receptors to the right and the left. As a result an energy gradient is established, and it is this gradient which causes the chloroplasts to alter their shape. Close observation shows, moreover, that the threads as a whole are able to move towards or away from light stimuli; they probably do so as a result of the partial gelatinization of the pectin membrane. *Spirogyra* is also unusual in that some of its threads can protrude vertically above the water surface – possibly in order to absorb more oxygen.

Many of the 90 species of *Spirogyra* live in running water. In them, the terminal cell is divided into numerous holdfast threads. Such formations can also occur in *Spirogyra* species inhabiting stagnant ponds – here the stimulus is surface tension.

As a final physiological peculiarity, we must mention that whereas *Spirogyra* – much like flagellates and *Volvox* – will produce maximum growth in running water rich in food, it will copulate to form resting stages in drying puddles and bright light, surrounding its zygotes with a tough brown wall and with large reserves of starch and oil.

During copulation, *Spirogyra* threads come together in pairs, send out papillae which fuse and form a canal through which the contents of one thread can pass into the other. In other species, the protoplasts of both cells pass into the canal and fuse in its centre. The zygote usually rests until the spring, when it germinates to produce four gonospores, three of which abort. The newly produced thread itself is haploid; meiosis therefore occurs during germination. During vegetative reproduction the thread simply splits apart.

The reader may have noticed the absence of a flagellate stage in the life cycle of *Spirogyra*. This is, in fact, a characteristic distinction between the Zygnematales and other green algae. A closer investigation of the structure of the cell wall shows, moreover, that every one of their cells is wrapped in a separate cellulose membrane, and that all cells share a common pectin sheath. Since all cells are physiologically

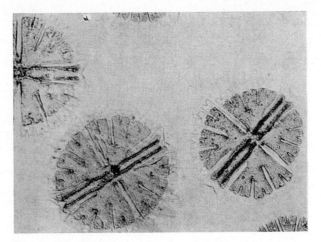

Fig. 55 *Micrasterias*

equivalent and since the threads can split up into a random number of pieces without suffering damage, the Zygnematales must be considered cell aggregates, i.e. colonies of unicells.

Spirogyra, *Mougeotia* and *Zygnema*, which latter has two star-shaped chromatophores to every cell (*Pl. 12, p. 53*), belong to the family Zygnemataceae. The second family, the Mesotaeniaceae, includes a few species forming filamentous colonies, and a far greater number of unicells. However, these, too (e.g. *Mesotaenium*, *Spirotaenia*, and *Cylindrocystis*), are highly reminiscent of *Spirogyra* cells, the more so as some of them have spiral chromatophores. The various species, which live chiefly in upland pools and peat bogs, are in fact a link between the Zygnemataceae and the next family, the Desmidiaceae, which are predominantly unicellular, or at most united into fragile filaments.

Their cells often have an extremely attractive shape, ranging from crescents (*Closterium: Pl. 13, p. 53*) to stars, wheels and cogs of all sorts and sizes. The chromatophores are correspondingly varied in shape as well. Some of the most beautiful forms are found in the genus *Micrasterias*, which includes the Maltese cross, *M. crux militensis*. All these species have a deep central invagination. In fact, their cells consist of two distinct halves, like those of diatoms. Copulation, too, is reminiscent of the auxospore formation in diatoms: two neighbouring cells become enclosed in a common mucilaginous envelope and split in two, whereupon their protoplasts combine into a zygote, often provided with a spinous membrane. Meiosis is

followed by germination, which gives rise to four daughter cells, two of which abort. Vegetative reproduction takes place much as in diatoms as well: after nuclear division, the two halves of the shell separate, and then complete the missing parts – the two halves are therefore of different ages. Unlike those of diatoms, however, the shells of Desmidiaceae consist of cellulose (inner layer) and pectin (outer layer). The outer layer is often iron-encrusted. A submicroscopically small system of pores in their membranes enables the cells to expel mucilage and thus to achieve a small degree of motility. This can be demonstrated by placing *Cosmarium* or *Closterium* into coloured water, when the expelled mucilage will form a lighter zone.

The inclusion of the Zygnematales among the green algae is justified by the presence of cellulose membrane, by the storing of starch and oil as the chief reserve materials, and by the characteristic distribution of pigments.

Order
CHARALES

For much the same reasons, the Charales, too, are treated as green algae, although they have few other affinities to the remaining orders. The Charales are, in fact, the most highly developed of all fresh-water algae. They vaguely resemble miniature horse-tails, grow to a height of four inches and more, and consist of a 'stem' with whorls of 'leaves' at the nodes. When the dark-green oogonia and the orange antheridia mature, they begin to look like flowers, and the resemblance becomes even greater. In reality, the stem sections between the whorls are gigantic cells which, in some species, may attain a length of 8–10 inches. In the genus *Nitella* (*Pl. 17, p. 55*), each internode consists of only one cell; in *Chara* a central cell is surrounded by narrower, peripheral cells. Inside the gigantic inner cell the original, single nucleus splits up into several nuclei. The nodes have a more complicated structure. They give rise to short lateral branches (*Pl. 18, p. 55*) which, in turn, are divided into nodes and internodes, but resemble leaves rather than twigs. Each node, moreover, gives rise to a long shoot resembling the main stem. The nodes of the short branches produce

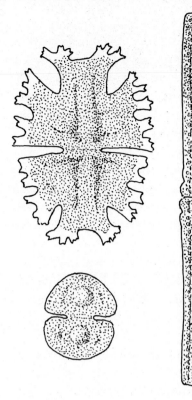

Fig. 56 Various Zygnematales. Top left: *Micrasterias*; bottom left: *Cosmarium*; right: *Pleurotaenium* (highly magnified)

on handle-shaped manubria attached by basal cells to the nodes. Here there also arise further spherical cells which develop into spermatogenous threads. These consist of a series of disks, each of which gives rise to a male germ cell with a strong resemblance to the spermatozoids of mosses and ferns. After fertilization, the oogonia lay down a rich supply of reserve materials and, like their enveloping cells, develop a tough membrane; the whole structure may be likened to a nut. The Characeae comprise monoecious as well as dioecious species, the former being protandrous – i.e. their spermatozoids escape before the ova mature.

Embryological development is remarkable as well. During two successive divisions of the zygote nucleus four nuclei are formed, three of which degenerate. In the older literature, we learn that the young plant develops from a protonemal stage, i.e. from a small plantlet produced by the embryo, of the kind normally found in mosses.

Characeae are also extremely active vegetatively. They can form 'roots' or small 'tubers', and produce a host of protonemal branches, which explains their massive presence at the bottom of shallow waters. Because their cell walls often become lime-encrusted, they play an important part in the formation of calcareous tuff.

oogonia and antheridia. The oogonia, which originally consist of a single large cell, later become surrounded by a spiral of protective cells, whose septate tips form a small crown. The antheridia are located inside spherical structures, each bounded by eight disk-shaped cells or shields. The shields are borne

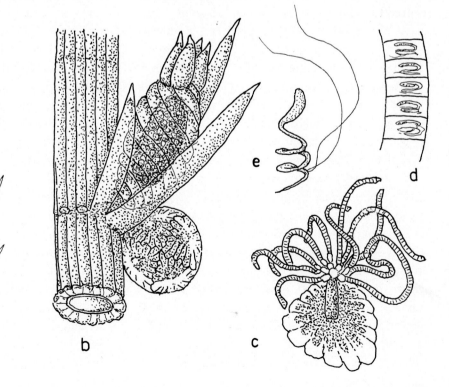

Fig. 57 *Chara*.
a: Part of a plant;
b: oogonium (top right) and spherical antheridium;
c: shield-shaped basal pad bearing spermatogenous filaments; d: part of a spermatogenous filament with spermatozoids (highly magnified);
e: spermatozoid (more highly magnified)

PHAEOPHYTA

Brown Algae

Brown algae are extremely widespread in salt water, particularly in the colder seas. Though they occur in a large variety of forms (*Pl. 16, p. 54*), all have one thing in common: their chlorophylls, carotenes and xanthophylls are masked by the brown pigment fucoxanthin. They lack chlorophyll *b* and have little chlorophyll *c* – most of their chlorophyll is of the *a* type. The Phaeophyta do not include unicellular organisms, but range from plants with branched and often interwoven threads consisting of simple cells (Ectocarpales), through more complicated forms composed of prostrate and erect parts (Tilopteridales, Chordariales), to highly segmented and tree-like types (Laminariales, Fucales). *Lessonia*, for instance, resembles palms, *Nereocystis* looks like a turnip with 6-inch leaves, *Cladostephus* resembles a moss, and *Alaria* (*Pl. 26, p. 57*) a fern. The pod-weed, *Halydris*, seems to bear oak leaves, and the gulf-weed, *Sargassum bacciferum*, resembles a berry-bearing shrub. Bladder-kelp (*Fucus*), knotted-wrack (*Ascophyllum* – *Pl. 27, p. 58*) and oarweed (*Laminaria*) are highly segmented, and the individual segments bear a strong resemblance to the leaves, stems and roots of higher plants. These parts are therefore commonly referred to as phylloids, cauloids and rhizoids. Some species can assume gigantic proportions – a number of *Laminaria* species grow to 16 feet and more. The antarctic *Lessonia* species easily attain a length of 50 feet; *Nereocystis* can grow to 100 feet; *Macrocystis pyrifera* is said to attain a length of 1000 feet and a diameter of more than one foot. These plants often occur in large concentrations, which are sometimes referred to as 'submarine forests', and usually take 'root' on rocky coasts, where the swell makes extraordinary demands upon them. They can only survive because they are extremely pliable and yet have so tough an internal structure (thanks to special walls and other reinforcing materials) that they are almost immune to injury. Moreover, they are so firmly attached to the rocks by special adhesive pads and 'claws' that the waves find it easier to smash the stone than tear the plants from them. In the South Pacific, for instance, rock fragments have been kept afloat for weeks by *Macrocystis* plants.

Most of these 'forests' grow at depths of 15 to 90 feet. Only the smaller species live at higher levels, sometimes even above the high-water mark. The problems these species have to overcome have been discussed on p. 29: they include dilution by rain-water or concentration of salt content by evaporation. As a result, the higher up in the littoral zone a plant normally grows, the better adapted it is to withstanding sudden environmental changes. Thus species of *Fucus* in the supralittoral are able to increase their photosynthetic activity whenever the tide recedes.

Despite marked differences in form and physiological adaptability, brown algae have a relatively simple internal structure. Nevertheless, it is in this group that the transformation of web 'tissue', consisting of independent threads, into true vegetative tissue in which growth is delegated to an apical cell takes place. The apical cell produces new cells in one or several directions, and these divide in turn to give rise to an entire zone of growing and dividing tissue – the meristem. The plant developing in this way can be divided into an inner medullary zone (storage tissue) and an outer cortical zone (assimilation tissue). The cell walls are pitted and, in the most highly developed brown algae, there are rows of tubular cells with regular sieve plates in their cross walls. It seems likely that these structures help to transport organic matter (assimilation products) to the growing tissues. The plants are apparently capable of absorbing nutrient salts through their entire surface.

Brown algae never produce starch; instead the end product of assimilation is mannitol (a sugar alcohol), oil and particularly laminarin, a polysaccharide which is used industrially. Also of industrial importance is algin, a calcium salt obtained from the pectin which, together with cellulose, makes up the cell wall. Another important assimilation product of brown algae is fucoidin.

In addition, brown algae have long been used as rich sources of sodium and more recently of iodine. The weed is burnt in kilns and the iodine extracted by leaching of the ashes. Off the coasts of France, Ireland, Scotland, Norway and Japan this so-called kelp-industry (kelp originally referred to the ash of brown seaweeds) is based on various species of

Macrocystis, *Nereocystis*, *Pelagophycus* and *Alaria*. Of great industrial importance also are the alginic acids. In *Laminaria* they account for from 20 per cent to 60 per cent of the dry weight. They have exceptional colloidal properties and are used in the dressing of fabrics, as binders in the paper and cardboard industries, and incidentally in the manufacture of marbled paper. They are also used in the manufacture of briquettes, and in the preparation of waterproof materials, linoleum, artificial leather and vulcanized fibres. We meet alginic acids in paints, in the film industry, in surgical sutures and in styptic pencils, as calorie-free fillers in various dietetic preparations and particularly in ice creams, where their colloidal properties prevent the formation of large ice crystals. Edible sausage skins are made from alginates, and alginic acid also goes into face creams, soap, and shaving soap – the Romans were among the first to manufacture rouge from *Fucus* plants.

Laminarin and mannitol are extremely useful products of brown algae. The mannitol yielded by *Laminaria saccharina* accounts for 12 per cent to 16 per cent of the plant's dry weight, and makes a welcome addition to the world's sugar supplies. Because of their vitamins (A, B, and C), brown algae can also be used as vegetables and fodder – they constitute the 'kobu' of East Asia, but are also consumed in North America.

Since olden times, sea-shore farmers have been using washed-up algae as fertilizers; more recently such algae have become the basis of a large industry. All the algae concerned are now 'harvested' in the tidal zone, often with complex machinery. Attempts to grow algae as major crops are still in their infancy; in Japan, the plants are provided with artificial substrates to speed their development.

Very few species of brown algae occur naturally on sandy or muddy beaches. One that does is *Chorda filum* or sea-lace. *Sargassum natans* is unusual in that it can float freely in water. It occurs as large masses of seaweed on the coast of the Gulf of Mexico, from where the waves carry plant fragments to the so-called Sargasso Sea, part of the N. Atlantic Ocean, between 40° and 70° W. longitude and 20° and 35° N. latitude. The Sargasso Sea covers an area of some $4\frac{1}{2}$ million square miles, and the weeds used to present a serious obstacle to navigation.

Some brown algae live as epiphytes on other algae, for instance *Elachista fucicola* which lives on *Fucus*. A few are even endophytic or endozoic.

However, by far the greatest number of brown algae are marine. Only a very few genera (e.g. *Thorea*, *Lithoderma* and *Pleurocladia*) occur in rivers and streams.

Altogether the Phaeophyta comprise some 1500 species in about 240 genera. Just as their vegetative structure shows a development from simpler, filamentous structures to true thalli, so also do their reproductive organs show an advance from isogamy to oogamy. With few exceptions, alternation of generations is the rule, so much so that variations in it can be used to distinguish three classes: the Isogeneratae in which the two generations have more or less the same shape; the Heterogeneratae in which the two generations are clearly distinct; and the Cyclosporae which *appear* to do without alternation of generations. As we go up from class to class, the haploid generation is increasingly dominated by the diploid. The haploid generation, as we know, is always the sexual, gamete-producing generation. Reduction division occurs during spore formation.

Class

ISOGENERATAE

The Isogeneratae include five orders, of which the first, the Ectocarpales, contains the most typical representative of the whole class, i.e. *Ectocarpus siliculosus*. This plant has profusely branched filaments and resembles *Cladophora* in shape. Each of the cells in its filaments is capable of growth and division, though not of producing zoospores or gametes. This function is restricted to specialized cells at the tip of the threads, where numerous zoospores are produced in bladder-like, single-chambered containers (sporangia); reduction division occurs during their formation, the spore-bearing plant being diploid. The zoospores often develop into gametophytes, bearing gametangia at the tips of their branches. These are not single-chambered like the sporangia but subdivided into a number of disk-shaped cells, each of which gives rise to an isogamete. Once the cross walls of the gametangia dissolve, the isogametes begin to fuse in pairs. The

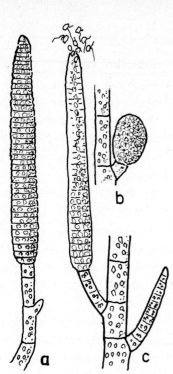

Fig. 58 *Ectocarpus*.
a: Plurilocular gamet-
angium; *b*: unicellular
sporangium; *c*: pluri-
locular gametangium
releasing gametes
(highly magnified)

zygote develops into a sporophyte directly, i.e. with-out first forming a resting stage. That stage is, incidentally, absent in all marine algae.

Some genera do not follow the above general rule. These produce isogametes which, though of the same appearance, can be physiologically distinguished into a plus or a minus type. In some epiphytic brown algae, alternation of generations goes hand in hand with a change of host. Thus while the sporophyte generation of *Pylaiella* lives on *Fucus*, the gameto-phyte lives on *Ascophyllum*.

The order Sphacelariales is remarkable in that its thallus grows by means of a large apical cell. (In the Ectocarpales every cell is capable of independent growth and division.) Moreover, horizontal and longitudinal cell divisions lead to the formation of true tissue. Vegetative reproduction is by means of modified branches or propagules. These algae, which may attain a height of several centimetres, are found in all seas.

In the Tilopteridales, again, the thallus consists of a basal disk and erect filaments, multiseriate in the lower section. These plants, which can attain a height of 4 inches, differ from the Ectocarpales chiefly in that their spores are non-motile, and that they are produced singly (monospores) by each sporangium.

In the Cutleriales, the two generations are of distinct shape. Moreover, these algae are decidedly

anisogamous. *Cutleria multifida* is a 4-inch plant inhabiting the warmer seas of Europe. Male and female plants can be clearly distinguished: the female gametangia have fewer and larger cells than the male; the gametes, too, are of different size. The zygote develops into a small diploid disk that used to be taken for a species of *Aglaozonia*. It produces single-chambered sporangia which give rise to flagellate, haploid and unisexual zoospores; these develop into male and female plants. In *Cutleria*, the sporophyte generation is smaller than the game-tophyte.

Dictyota dichotoma, fork-weed, is a typical repre-sentative of the order Dictyotales, and is usually cited as a classic case of isomorphous alternation of generations, i.e. of the uniformity of the diploid and haploid forms. And indeed both male and female gametophytes look indistinguishable from the sporo-phyte. The single-chambered female gametangia each release a single, immobile ovum which is able to float in the water. The single-chambered sporangia produce four immobile spores, the so-called tetra-spores. These are haploid and sexually differentiated, and give rise to male and female plants. Another

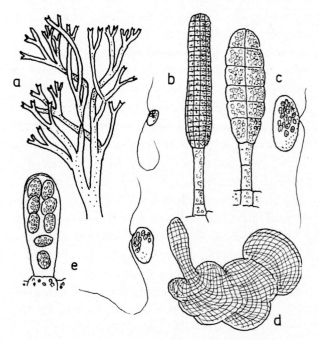

Fig. 59 *Cutleria multifida*. *a*: Partial view of gametophyte ($\frac{1}{2}$ natural size); *b*: male gametangium and male gamete; *c*: female gametangium and female gamete; *d*: young sporophyte; *e*: sporangium and zoospore (at right). (Highly magnified)

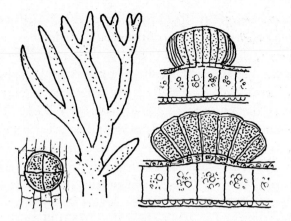

Fig. 60 *Dictyota dichotoma*, fork-weed. Left: sporangium with 4 spores (highly magnified); centre: part of sporophyte (natural size); right: longitudinal section through a group of oogonia (highly magnified)

noteworthy fact is that the thallus of *D. dichotoma* is divided into central storing tissue and peripheral assimilation tissue. This 4-inch plant is called fork-weed because median septation in the apical cell gives rise to a continued series of bifurcate branches. The order also includes *Padina pavonia*, peacock's tail (*Pl. 15, p. 54*), which is common on the south coast of Britain. Its 4-inch fan-shaped fronds are marked with concentric growth rings. The plant is vaguely reminiscent of fungi in the *Polyporus* group.

Class

HETEROGENERATAE

The second class of brown algae is headed by several uncommon orders. The basic construction in this order is the cable type, in which one or more parallel strands arise from a prostrate basal thallus, and are often enclosed in a mucous matrix. The thallus is generally differentiated into a central medulla and peripheral assimilatory filaments. Isogamy is the rule in all the eight families constituting this order. *Leathesia* (*Pl. 19, p. 55*) has an irregular, spherical shape, a diameter of about 3 inches and is dark brown in colour; it occurs in all seas.

The Sporochnales are filamentous and have short lateral branches. At its tip, each lateral branch bears a cluster of assimilatory hairs. Sexual reproduction is by oogamy. The antheridia are strongly reduced. There is only one family, the Sporochnaceae.

The Desmarestiales produce a single gamete in

each of their antheridia and oogonia. Sexual reproduction is by oogamy. The relatively high degree of development of this order is also reflected in the production of sporophytes up to 16 feet in length. The thalli of the sporophyte generation exhibit regular pinnate branching which is continued into the terminal pinnules. The branches are generally built up of loose rows of cells, surrounded by an external coat, the 'cortex'. It is here that the sporangia originate. The male and female gametophytes are small filamentous structures, and hence differ markedly from the sporophytes. Many Desmarestiaceae store large quantities of acid and are therefore unsuitable as fodder.

The order Punctariales is treated by some taxonomists as a family in the next order. These algae, whose thalli are of various shapes and sizes, are found in all northern seas. Many have their entire surface covered with hairs. The sporangia frequently arise in clusters and the sexual generation is microscopically small. Two common genera are *Punctaria* and *Soranthera*.

The Dictyosiphonales, too, are an extremely varied group, combining a host of 'advanced' and 'primitive' characters. Thus while their sporophytes are built up of true tissue, sexual reproduction is by

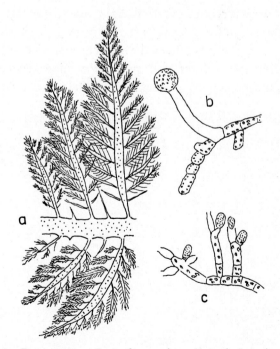

Fig. 61 *Desmarestia*. *a*: Part of sporophyte (natural size); *b*: female gametophyte; *c*: male gametophyte

73

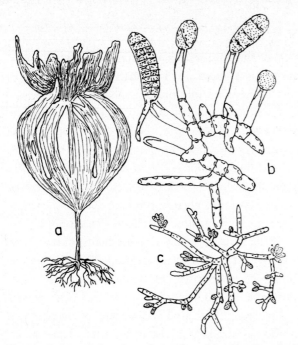

Fig. 62 *Laminaria clustoni. a:* Sporophyte (greatly reduced); *b:* female gametophyte; *c:* male gametophyte (both magnified to scale)

isogamy, and sometimes even by parthenogenesis. The order includes several families. A fairly well-known genus is *Dictyosiphon*, in which growth occurs from an apical cell.

This brings us to our tenth order, the Laminariales, a group with distinctly advanced characters. Representatives of this order inhabit the lower littoral zone in temperate and cold seas. They include the largest brown algae of all, e.g. *Laminaria* (16 ft.), *Lessonia* (50 ft.), *Alaria* (60 ft.; *Pl. 26, p. 57*) and *Macrocystis* (over 300 ft. and weighing several hundredweight). All of them exhibit a high degree of morphological differentiation. Most live attached

to stones by claw-like organs (rhizoids); *Saccorhiza bulbosa* (*Pl. 25, p. 57*), an Atlantic and Mediterranean species, clings to rocks not only by means of a round sucker but also with the help of numerous threads. A 'stem' (cauloid), which may be several yards long, bears the leafy part of the thallus (phylloid). In *Macrocystis*, the upper part of the plant floats on the water surface, buoyed up by the basal bladders of the long leaves. The leaves of *Laminaria saccharina* are band-shaped, those of *L. digitata* finger-shaped or fronds. *Chorda filum*, sea-lace, and its relatives (*Pl. 24, p. 57*), lack a cauloid and branches; their whip-like thalli may grow to a length of up to 25 feet. The anatomical differences in this group are as marked as the structural. The thick cauloids exhibit a kind of secondary thickening – something that does not recur in the plant kingdom until we reach the Gymnosperms and Angiosperms. Between the cauloid and the leaves, Laminariales often develop a kind of growing tissue which can give rise to a new phylloid. Since the latter generally pushes the old phylloid to the outside, where it drops off, we are in the presence of what may be called a primitive deciduous plant. In addition, this group is also characterized by the presence of such specialized cells as sieve tubes with highly developed sieve plates, collenchyma cells, mucilage ducts, etc.

All this goes hand in hand with a highly advanced type of alternation of generations. All the Laminariales we have been describing are sporophytes – the gametophytes are microscopically small, filamentous structures. The male forms bear unicellular (uni-

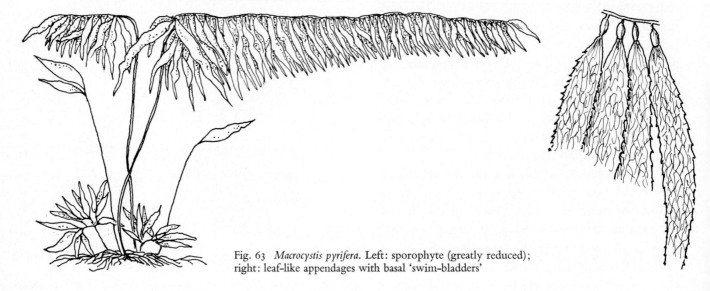

Fig. 63 *Macrocystis pyrifera*. Left: sporophyte (greatly reduced); right: leaf-like appendages with basal 'swim-bladders'

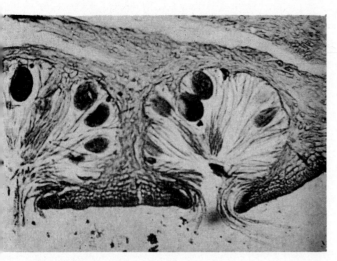

Fig. 64 *Fucus vesiculosus*, bladder wrack, showing conceptacles and sexual organs embedded in them

locular) antheridia at the tips of their threads, each antheridium producing one male gamete only. (This is considered another 'advanced' character.) The female forms produce their oogonia in the same place; their non-motile ova develop into sporophytes after fertilization. Each sporophyte produces masses of unilocular sporangia between sterile hairs; spore formation is accompanied by reduction division.

Class
CYCLOSPOREAE

Although the Cyclosporeae, which include only one order, the Fucales, are in no way descended from the Laminariales, they must be considered the final link in the evolutionary chain constituting the brown algae. In particular, they no longer produce separate gametophytes; instead, spermatozoids and ova are borne on the sporophyte. In the more common species of *Fucus*, for instance in *F. vesiculosus*, bladder wrack, sac-like pits (conceptacles) are formed on several thallus tips; in them unilocular antheridia or oogonia are surrounded with sterile hairs. The antheridia produce 64 spermatozoids each; the oogonia 8 non-motile ova. When they are released, the ova are still held inside a multi-layered wall, which bursts some time later. This is interpreted as meaning that the zoospores (microzoospores and macrozoospores) remain inside the sporangia, and that the cycle spore → gametophyte → gamete has become greatly reduced and accelerated. It is during

this exceedingly quick development that reduction division takes place. This method of sexual reproduction, incidentally, is highly reminiscent of what happens in higher plants – here, too, the development of gametophyte and gametes is telescoped into microspores (pollen grains) and macrospores (embryo sacs). The male gametes or spermatozoids of Cyclosporeae are tiny pear-shaped structures bearing two unequal flagella, the shorter of which is covered with cilia and points forward – a characteristic distinct from all other brown algae. Those ova which are not swept out to sea before they can become fertilized develop into diploid sporophytes.

The Fucales are divided into 7 families, including the Fucaceae. The genus *Fucus* itself includes some 30 species, 3 of which – all belt-shaped, up to 3 feet long and 1 foot wide – are common throughout the northern hemisphere. Of these *F. serratus*, saw wrack, (*Pl. 22, p. 56*) has a serrated edge; *F. vesiculosus*, bladder wrack, (*Pl. 20, p. 56*) is studded with bladders the size of a bean, and *F. platycarpus* has a smooth edge and no bladders (*Pl. 21, p. 56*). These plants generally grow in distinct zones of the littoral: *F. platycarpus* on top, followed by *F. vesiculosus* and

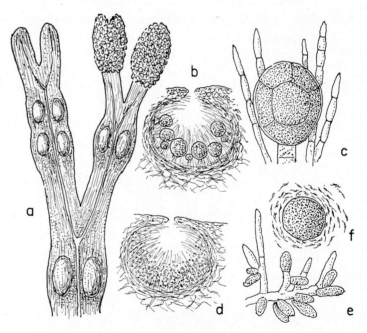

Fig. 65 *Fucus vesiculosus*, bladder wrack. *a*: Tip of branch with swim bladders and conceptacles (natural size); *b*: conceptacle with oogonia; *c*: oogonium surrounded by paraphyses; *d*: conceptacle with antheridia; *e*: cell filament studded with antheridia; *f*: egg cell surrounded by spermatozoids (highly magnified)

F. serratus. F. vesiculosus is dioecious; the male plants are readily identified by the red colour of their thallus tips; these bear the conceptacles and, in them, spermatozoids with red eyespots. During fertilization, the spermatozoids begin to swarm about the egg cells in large numbers, until a gelatinous envelope suddenly develops round the egg: a spermatozoid has entered, and fertilization is complete.

Other Fucales include *Ascophyllum nodosum*, knotted wrack (*Pl. 27, p. 58*), which bears conspicuous air bladders on its main branches, and *Himanthalia*, thong weed (*Pl. 23, p. 56*), which has whip-like thalli with multiple branches. The 'whips' rise from a distinct, and often funnel-shaped, basal part of the thallus. *Hormosira*, a brown alga from Australia and New Zealand, has a forked and bead-shaped thallus. Our illustration of *Sargassum* shows the tip of a branch bearing phylloids, each with a distinct 'midrib' while the sporangia arise on berry-shaped 'short shoots'. *Turbinaria* (*Pl. 28, p. 58*) has shield- or funnel-shaped side branches, and shorter, but more highly branched fruiting shoots. It inhabits the South Pacific.

The brown algae probably go back to the Silurian period, i.e. they are more than 450 million years old. They have a certain affinity to the Chrysophyta – their flagellate gametes, pigments, and assimilation products are similar. However, Phaeophyta cannot be considered the direct descendants of the Chryso-

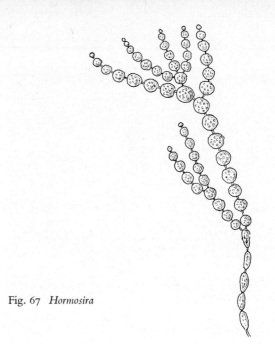

Fig. 67 *Hormosira*

phyta; the two probably developed from a common ancestor along distinct lines.

RHODOPHYTA
Red Algae

Interspersed with the brown seaweeds of the tidal zone we often find a host of small to medium-sized algae with a reddish colour. These include many species common off the coasts of Britain, for instance *Ceramium rubrum* (hornweed), *Plocamium coccineum* (combweed), *Polyides rotundus* (scissorweed) and, at greater depths, *Delesseria sanguinea* (red-leaf; *Pl. 40, p. 63*), the forked *Furcellaria fastigiata*, the lime-encrusted *Corallina officinalis* (*Pl. 33, p. 60*), and the thin and glistening *Lithothamnion polymorphum* (*Pl. 31, p. 59*), concentrations of which look like so many red spots. The red algae include not only a great variety of extremely beautiful forms (for instance *Ceramium rubrum*) but also a large range of colours – from pink through red to mauve, violet and brown. The group includes near-black plants (*Porphyra*) as well as near colourless ones (*Bangia*; *Pl. 29, p. 58*). The red algae are found chiefly in the sea where, like the brown algae, they live anchored to stone and wood. Many species, however, live on plants, including other red algae; some have turned into colourless parasites and, in some, the diploid sporophyte is parasitic on the haploid gametophyte, which greatly complicates their study.

Fig. 66 *Sargassum*, showing spherical swim-bladders (reduced)

We have said that red algae live side by side with brown algae of the tidal zone (e.g. *Ceramium* and *Plocamium*; *Pl. 34, p. 61*); but some also occur above the high-water line (e.g. *Bangia* and *Porphyra*). In general, the number of individuals and species increases with depth – red alga can be found down to 200 feet and sometimes even as deep as 600 feet. Their red pigment enables them to utilize the blue-green and blue radiations that alone penetrate to these depths. Their main pigment is phycoerythrin, a water-soluble, highly fluorescent form of phycobilin which masks the presence of chorophyll *a*, carotenoids and xanthophylls. Many species owe their colourful appearance to the additional presence of the blue pigment phycocyanin in different proportions. The pigments are stored in highly differentiated plastids, generally star- or disk-shaped and never basin-shaped as they are in so many green algae. The reserve materials, too, differ from those present in earlier groups: in addition to fatty oils, red algae chiefly store floridean starch, a substance related to, but chemically distinct from, ordinary starch. The chemical composition of the cell wall, on the other hand, is similar to that found in many green and brown algae: an inner layer of cellulose and an outer layer of partly gelatinized pectins.

Despite their wealth of forms – the group ranges from unicells through filaments to forms resembling leaf-bearing plants – red algae do not attain the degree of organization found in brown algae. Quite apart from the absence of giant individuals, they never develop any kind of true tissue. Instead, their thallus is composed of individual threads that may be interwoven to resemble the plectenchymatous tissue of the higher fungi, and that, more rarely, has undergone secondary fusion. Two main types of organization can be distinguished as (*a*) the fountain type, in which a mass of parallel filaments leads out like a spray to the surface, with the central filaments either occupying the centre of the thallus or else forming a ring round a central hollow; and (*b*) the central filament type, in which there is a central corticated or uncorticated main axis bearing the branches.

As a sign of more advanced organization, however, the cell walls of red algae often bear prominent spots. Reproduction is highly specialized. There are no motile forms whatsoever – not even the male cells are provided with flagella; they are known as spermatia, to distinguish them from the motile spermatozoids of the previous groups.

The reproductive processes and life cycle of red algae will be illustrated by means of the most typical cases, but it must be stressed that the processes are vastly more complicated in a number of species. In the simplest case, for instance in *Bangia* (Class: Bangioideae) the spermatia are produced by repeated divisions inside the filamentous mother cell. The ovum, too, develops within a filamentous cell, but one that usually develops a swelling, known as the carpogonium. The fertilized ovum (zygote) gives rise to carpospores by reduction division; they are released as naked cells and grow into new plants. In the Class Florideae there is a clear trend from simple to more complicated life cycles.

As an example of a simple cycle we shall consider that of *Batrachospermum moniliforme*, which forms a muddy brown 'frog spawn' in brooks. The plant consists of a central bundle of threads that branch out in whorls from the so-called nodes. The whole structure is embedded in gelatine. The antheridia occur at the apices of lateral branches, generally in pairs. They liberate a naked and perfectly spherical cell, the spermatium. Since the latter is non-motile, it has to be carried to the oogonium (carpogonium) by the current or by animals. As in *Coleochaete* (green algae), the carpogonium bears a flask- or hair-shaped process (trichogyne) which, in the case of *B. moniliforme*, arises from a special, originally independent cell with a nucleus of its own, whereas that of *Coleochaete* is part and parcel of the oogonium. When a spermatium adheres to the trichogyne, a hole is formed in the cell wall through which the contents of the male cell can enter. The fertilized ovum gives rise to filaments (sporogenous threads) whose apical cells release haploid, naked and non-motile carpospores. The spores develop into haploid plants which pass through a simple juvenile stage. This stage can reproduce itself asexually, and used to be mistaken for a special genus – *Chantransia*.

In other species, which we may designate as more 'advanced', the sexual process is much more complicated. Thus *Polysiphonia* produces distinct male and female plants. In the latter, the carpogonium is firmly surrounded by vegetative cells from its inception. The sporogenous filaments and the carpospores are both diploid. The latter give rise to diploid plants producing haploid tetraspores in so-called tetrasporangia. The diploid plants are externally indistinguishable from the haploid; hence the alternation of generations is highly reminiscent of that found in such brown algae as *Dictyota*. This is perhaps the place to point out that red algae, too, exhibit a tendency to pass from haploidy to diploidy. A further complication in the development of the *Polysiphonia* is the fusion of the fertilized egg cell with a neighbouring vegetative cell, the so-called auxiliary cell. Their nuclei do not, however, become fused; hence the process is not one of secondary fertilization, but rather a means of providing the zygote with extra food reserves.

Numerous auxiliary cells are present in *Dudresnaya*, an alga found in the Mediterranean and the North Atlantic. Here the auxiliary cells arise in special filaments, while the carpogenous filaments proliferate in the thallus like so many fungal hyphae. The apical cells of the carpogenous filaments fuse with the auxiliary cells to produce a host of carpospores. As in *Polysiphonia*, the latter give rise to a diploid tetrasporophyte, and the haploid tetraspores once again produce male and female gametophytes.

In principle, therefore, we can distinguish two types of reproductive cycles in the Florideae: the *Batrachospermum* type in which two haploid generations are combined in a single plant and in which the zygote is diploid, and the *Polysiphonia* type with distinct haploid and diploid generations; the diploid

generation lives partly attached to the gametophyte (carpogenous filaments) and partly as an independent plant (tetrasporophyte).

Most of the 500 genera of red algae (with nearly 4000 species) are marine; only some 200 species live in fresh water. Their classification is based primarily on the structure of their reproductive apparatus and on differences in their life cycles. Using these criteria, taxonomists distinguish two classes: the Bangioideae and the Florideae.

Class
BANGIOIDEAE

The Bangioideae include a small number of unicellular genera inhabiting saline soils, e.g. *Porphyridium*. One species, *Rhodospora sordida*, occurs in moist alpine sites, another, *Vanhoeffenia antarctica*, in fresh water on the Kerguelen Islands. All the species we have mentioned belong to the first of the five orders in this class, namely the order Porphyridales. A typical representative of the order Bangiales (*Pl. 29, p. 58*) is the genus *Bangia* which includes *B. atropurpurea*, a supralittoral species common in Heligoland. The genus *Porphyra* (laver), in the same order, is universally distributed, and includes *P. atropurpurea*, another supralittoral species. These plants, whose colour ranges from purple to violet, look like leaves and are built up of parallel filaments. Several species of *Porphyra* are consumed as sea-lettuce (amanori or askusanori) in Japan, where they are cultivated on a vast scale. They are generally grown on bamboo poles placed in the shallow waters of bays and river mouths. Laverbread, which is *Porphyra* made into cakes with oatmeal and fried with bacon, is considered a great delicacy in South Wales.

Class
FLORIDEAE

Among the Florideae, we have already met the genera *Batrachospermum* and *Polysiphonia*. *Batrachospermum* belongs to the first and simplest order of the Florideae, the Nemalionales. This order also includes the olive green to purple *Lemanea*, which occurs chiefly in cool mountain streams; this genus is less branched than *Batrachospermum* and hence of even

Fig. 68 *Bangia atropurpurea*

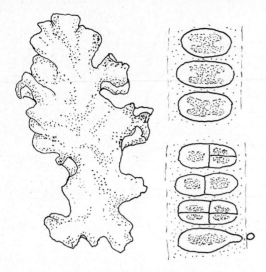

Fig. 69 *Porphyra*. Left: thallus (reduced); top right: section of vegetative part of thallus; bottom right: section of fertile part of thallus, showing carpogonium and carpospore formation (highly magnified)

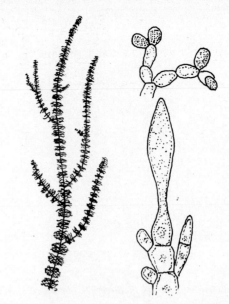

Fig. 70 *Batrachospermum moniliforme*. Left: part of thallus; top right: branch bearing antheridia; bottom right: carpogonium

simpler structure. The genus *Nemalion* is particularly widespread; here the central filaments are unpigmented, while the cortical region is filled with plastids and covered with colourless hairs. Off European coasts we often find *Scinaia furcellata*, an erect species with forked branches. Its thallus, too, is divided into colourless and pigmented zones *Nemalion* and *Scinaea*, incidentally, are constructed on the fountain-type pattern.

By contrast, the internal architecture of the next order, the Gelidiales, is based on the central filament type. The Gelidiales, which are particularly widespread in warmer oceans, generally exhibit pinnate branching. They produce two separate, but similar, generations, and distinct male and female gametophytes. The genus *Gelidium*, which includes 40 species, is one of the chief sources of agar-agar.

The order Cryptonemiales includes species with highly complex auxiliary cells, for instance *Dudresnaya coccinea* and *Dumontia incrassata*. It also includes the striking red coral algae, or Corallinaceae, in which the cell wall is lime-encrusted. As the plants die and the lime accumulates, they build up whole mountains of limestone; this happened particularly during the Jurassic and Cretaceous periods, and to a lesser extent during the Tertiary. Thus the magnificent buildings of Old Vienna are chiefly constructed of the lime of red algae from the Leitha mountains. In tropical regions, coral algae are responsible for the formation of coral reefs. The genus *Lithothamnion*

(*Pl. 31, p. 59*) includes some 120 species in all oceans. The plants are as hard as stone and have knobbly branches. *Phymatolithon* (*Pl. 32, p. 60*) is similar in appearance. The Atlantic *Lithothamnium calcareum* is a source of coral sand, a valuable lime fertilizer. *Lithophyllum* (*Pl. 30, p. 59*), which includes some 100 species, is chiefly found in warmer seas; the plants are as thin as leaves, irregularly corrugated and lobed, and only partially attached to the substrate. Far more widely distributed are the 25 species of *Corallina* (*Pl. 33, p. 60*). Here the thallus rises erect

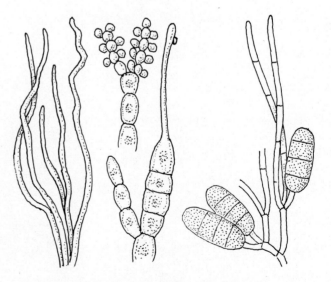

Fig. 71 *Nemalion lubricum*. Left: general appearance (natural size); top centre: branch with antheridia; bottom centre: carpogonium with spermatium attached to trichogyne (highly magnified); right: branch with tetrasporangia (highly magnified)

79

Fig. 72 *Gelidium cartilagineum*

Fig. 75 *Furcellaria fastigiata*

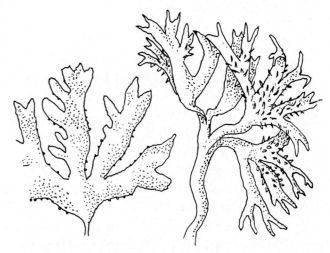

Fig. 76 *Rhodophyllis* (left) and *Gigartina*

Fig. 77 *Plocamium coccineum*

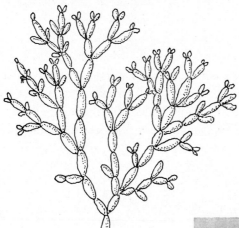

Fig. 73 *Lomentaria articulata*

Fig. 74 *Chrysymenia*

above a flat holdfast disk, shows various forms of branching, and is not encrusted at the 'joints' of its segments. The Corallinaceae also include such parasitic species as *Choreonema thureti* which lives on *Corallina*, and *Schmitziella endophora* which lives in the cell walls of *Cladophora*. Closely related to the coral algae is the genus *Hildenbrandtia*, which includes *H. prototypus*, a large, irregularly shaped and thin plant which covers stones on the North Sea coast with a blood-red 'skin'. *H. rivularis* lives in mountain streams.

The Grateloupiaceae, all built on the fountain plan, are almost exclusively confined to the warmer seas of the southern hemisphere; the genus *Grateloupia* itself, however, is also found in the Mediterranean and the North Atlantic. These leaf-like, flat, and often branched plants are some eight inches in length, gelatinous, fleshy, and purple in colour.

In establishing the order Gigartinales, taxonomists have had to rely on such criteria as the relationship between the auxiliary cells and the carpogenous filaments, and the origin and development of the carpospores. The Gigartinales are of great economic importance – many Asiatic species of *Gracilaria*, together with *Eucheuma*, *Phyllophora* and *Gigartina*, yield agaragar. In addition, *Phyllophora* has an iodine content of 1.3 per cent and is used as a source of iodine, particularly in the Soviet Union. One of the most widespread algae in the North Atlantic is *Chondrus crispus* which, with *Gigartina*, constitutes Carragheen or Irish moss, used in making soups, jellies and other gelatinous preparations for treating coughs, dressing textiles, clarifying liquids, adding body to paints, the manufacture of paste and cosmetics, and a host of other purposes.

Iridophycin, which is yielded by the antarctic *Iridaea cordata*, has similar properties. It, too, consists of highly viscous membranous substances whose main constituent is an ethereal sulphate. Iridophycin also serves as an anti-coagulant during blood-transfusions, etc.

Well-known red algae off the coast of North Europe include the genus *Plocamium* (*Pl. 34, p. 61*), most of whose species are raspberry-coloured and finely-branched. Another common genus is *Furcellaria* (Family: Furcellariaceae); here the branches are conspicuously forked and rust-coloured. *Rhodophyllis*, finally, is a common genus with branched lobes.

In the order Rhodymeniales, the auxiliary cells do not appear until after the fertilization of the carpogonium. The family Rhodymeniaceae is represented in our latitudes by *Rhodymenia palmetta* (*Pl. 35, p. 62*); its finger-shaped, flat-lobed thallus is muddy red in colour, stiff and thin-skinned. *Chrysymenia* is very similar in shape and is common in the Adriatic. European coastal species among the Lomentariaceae include *Lomentaria articulata*, a two to six inch carmine plant whose branches are 3 mm. thick, cylindrical and so irregularly segmented that they look like miniature glassworts (*Salicornia*).

The Ceramiales are the most highly developed order of red algae. Their life cycle has already been described by the example of *Polysiphonia*, a member of the Rhodomelaceae. These reddish-brown to red plants have thin, highly ramified branches up to one foot in length. The plants are generally soft and flabby, though some may be stiff and bristly. The spermatangia and carpogon bodies (cystocarps) are borne on the branches of male and female plants, each branch consisting of a central axis and four or

Fig. 78 *Polysiphonia cystocarpus*; thallus and carpogonia

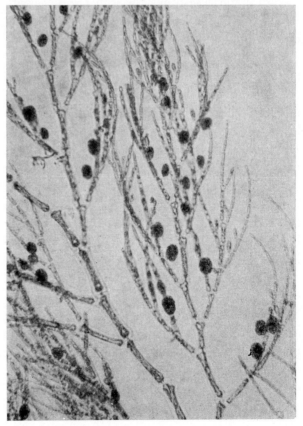

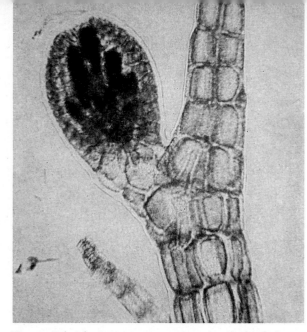

Fig. 79 *Polysiphonia cystocarpus;* carpogonium (magnified)

more layers of 'cortical' cells. The genus includes some 150 species, many of which are found in the Adriatic, though some are common in the North and Baltic Seas as well. The same family also includes the erect genus of *Rhodomela*, the more knobbly genus of *Laurencia*, and the finely branched, knobbly and fleshy genus of *Chondria*. The Rhodomelaceae are probably the most 'advanced' family in the group.

The Ceramiaceae include the genus *Ceramium* with some hundred species; of these *C. rubrum* is found in our latitudes. Also found is the beautiful *Plumaria elegans*, which has pinnate branches; similar branching is shown by various species of *Callithamnion*.

The large, thin and ribbed fronds of members of the family Delessariaceae look deceptively like the leaves of higher plants. The best-known species, *Delesseria sanguinea* (*Pl. 40, p. 63*), lives several yards under water. In the autumn, the 'leaves' often decay down the conspicuous 'mid-rib', which produces new 'leaves' in the spring. The genus *Nitophyllum* forms thin red to yellow-coloured thalli that may be narrow and belt-shaped but can also resemble leaves.

Red algae, which are clearly very ancient plants since red alga-like remains have been found in Silurian deposits, constitute a closed group, lacking clear affinities with the other algae. The idea that they are directly related to the green algae has had to be abandoned long ago; the resemblance between the carpogon of red algae and the oogonium of *Coleochaete* seems to be no more than chance external

correspondence. Moreover, red, unlike green, algae are completely lacking in chlorophyll *b*.

More recently, botanists have looked at the possible descent of red algae from blue-green algae. One argument in support of this thesis is that both groups are devoid of flagella. Moreover, both show strong affinities in their pigment complement (phycoerythrin and especially phycocyanin). However, while blue-green algae are akaryobionts, red algae are typical karyobionts. Even though the discovery of nuclear equivalents in blue-green algae has lessened the gulf between the two divisions, the differences remain considerable. Now the formation of flagella is intimately connected with the presence of a nucleus. Many biologists therefore argue that red algae must have lost their flagella in the course of evolution – they support this view by pointing to the Zygnemataceae among the green algae. If they are right, the red algae may well be related to red-coloured flagellates and particularly to the Cryptophyceae in the division Pyrrophyta.

A somewhat sensational view has recently been put forward by those who argue that the red algae are not, in fact, simple organisms, but symbiotic

Fig. 80 *Polysiphonia urceolata*

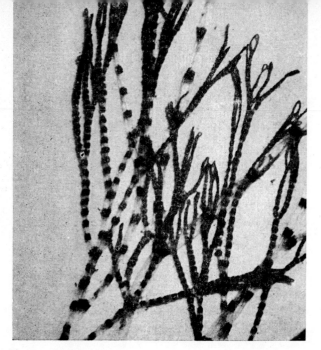

Fig. 81 *Ceramium*

Fig. 83 *Delesseria*

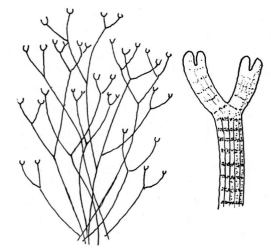

Fig. 82 *Ceramium rubrum*; tip of branching thallus

Fig. 84 *Plumaria*, part of pinnate thallus. Left: highly magnified

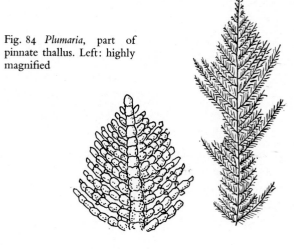

Fig. 85 *a: Delesseria sanguinea; b: Polysiphonia:* branch with antheridia; *c:* cystocarp (highly magnified); *d: Chondria,* natural habit; *e:* branch segment with sporangia

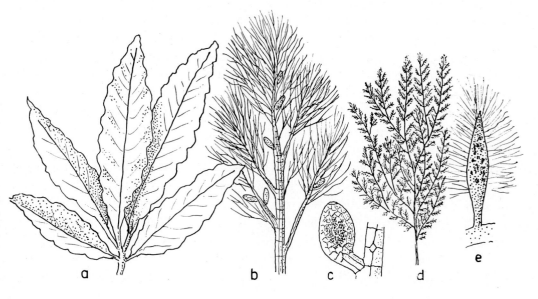

entities originating from the combination of colour-less and probably fungus-like host organisms with blue-green algae. In support of their contention, they refer to the symbiotic association between the *Geosiphon*, a fungus, and *Nostoc*, a blue-green alga; here the alga acts as a chromatophore. By analogy, the chromoplasts of all higher plants (and also their mitochondria) are said to be mere symbionts. In that case, the plastids of red algae would be transformed blue-green unicells, and the plastids of green algae,

mosses, ferns and higher plants transformed green unicells. The supporters of this view claim that investigations with the electron microscope have shown that plastids are, in fact, independent entities, clearly differentiated from other domains of the cell. This is not the place to pronounce for or against this thesis; suffice it to say that what relationship there may be between red algae and any other group of plants must go back to common ancestors in the very distant past.

4 MYXOPHYTA and ACRASIOPHYTA
Slime moulds

During wet weather, the forest floor often sprouts slimy or creamy masses measuring two inches and more in diameter, sometimes as large as twenty square feet, covering moss, leaf litter and decaying wood. The slime may be yolk-coloured, pink, car-mine, or a variety of other colours and, in fact, re-presents the plasmodia of 'slime fungi'. Such plas-modia may be made up of hundreds to tens of thousands of amoeboid organisms, each with a nucleus and a pulsating vacuole but without a cell wall, plastids or pigment. The resulting multi-nucleate mass crawls about by means of the amoe-boid movements of arm-like portions of the naked protoplasm, termed pseudopodia (false feet), con-suming rotten organic substances, bacteria and other small organisms as it creeps along. Some plasmodia secrete enzymes with which they 'prepare' their food before ingesting it; others simply absorb the sub-stances as they find them. Often a plasmodium will look like a loose, open network, thickened at the front, i.e. in the direction of its motion. As the plas-modium grows, so its diploid nuclei keep dividing. Slime moulds lay down reserves of glycogen, an animal carbohydrate which is, however, also found in true fungi. They generally make for dark, moist and moderately warm spots. However, when about to produce spores, they creep out of their dark and moist hiding places and begin to look for dry spots

on tree stumps or leaves, where they convert their substance into sporangia containing asexual spores. The sporangia, which are visible to the naked eye, generally have a supporting stalk, a firm wall, and an interior lacy framework – the capillitium, which persists after the spores have been scattered. The wall (peridium) and capillitium do not consist of chitin as they do in fungi, but of keratin, an insoluble scleroprotein; cellulose constituents have been re-ported as well. The fruiting structures, like the spores themselves, are generally brightly coloured – violet, red and yellow tints predominate in them. The spores of terrestrial species – some slime moulds are aquatic – are surrounded by a membrane; all are diploid. During moist weather they release highly motile and haploid swarm cells, each with one or two flagella. These swim about freely for a time, living saprophytically; then they shed their flagella and turn into amoeboid bodies. Flagellates and amoebae divide repeatedly by fission, before fusing in pairs. The nuclei, too, become fused and finally all the amoebae (and sometimes even the flagellates) creep together to form a new plasmodium.

The best-known slime mould is *Fuligo varians*, flower of tan, which forms its bright yellow, one foot plasmodia on tanner's (oak) bark and in wood-land, where its fruiting bodies form large, cake-shaped masses of brown. The colour of other plasmodia may be white (*Stemonitis*) or red (*Lycogala*); the sporangia of the latter are a muddy grey. *Tubifera ferruginosa* has a red, strawberry-like plasmodium and brown sporangia; *Acryria nutans* forms yellow plasmodia and red sporangia; *Comatrycha typhoides* produces dark brown sporangia; *Mucilago spongiata* looks like cuckoo-spit and develops ash-coloured sporangia. *Reticularia lycoperdon* forms flat, dark brown fruiting bodies. In *Cribraria rufa*, which lives on decaying pine wood, the fruiting bodies are orange. In fact, the tiny fruiting bodies of slime moulds can assume a variety of shapes as well as of colours. Thus they are rounded and unstalked in *Lycogala*, *Trichia* and *Ophiothea*; rounded and stalked in *Cribraria*, *Physarum* and *Lamproderma*; and cylindrical and stalked in *Comatricha*, *Acryria* and *Stemonitis*. Moreover, the shape of the fruiting body may vary within one and the same genus.

All the species we have been discussing are Endosporae: their spores are formed inside sporangia. By contrast, the slime mould *Ceratiomyxa fruticulosa*, which lives on decaying conifers, is placed in a separate group, the Exosporae – its spores arise as external swellings on the white fruiting bodies.

The slime moulds comprise altogether some 500 species in 60 genera, and are occasionally described as fungi. That is the reason why we have mentioned them in this particular section, though it must be emphasized that with present knowledge it is impossible to determine their precise taxonomic position – the Myxophyta are an independent group, unrelated to any other. Their amoeboid stages resemble animal rhizopods. Slime fungi may truly be said to feed like animals and the presence of keratin in their skeletal substance is also highly reminiscent of the animal kingdom. The nuclear phases, life cycle and spore formation of slime moulds, however, are all typical of plants. All in all, therefore, slime fungi must still be treated as a kind of vague half-way house between the animal and plant kingdoms. The old name of Mycetozoa ('fungus animals') reflects this state of affairs very well. There is no doubt that the Myxomycetes are a very ancient and original group. For that reason, many taxonomists place them immediately after the blue-green algae. More recently, however, attention has again returned to their zoological characters, with the result that Myxomycetes are completely absent from quite a few systems of botanical classification.

No less doubtful is the position of the cellular slime moulds (Acrasiophyta) which, though often combined into one group with the true slime moulds (Myxophyta), probably lack any relationship to them. If anything, they have even more pronounced zoological traits. Their life cycle, which in many respects is reminiscent of that of Myxomycetes, does not include a flagellate stage. The spores germinate directly into amoebae, which aggregate to form pseudoplasmodia, in which the components never fuse (the name Acrasiophyta is derived from the Greek *acrasis* meaning non-mixing and *phyton* meaning plant). Because of this phase in their life cycle, the Acrasiophyta are also referred to as communal slime moulds. Under the microscope, it is easy and fascinating to watch the establishment of new centres of aggregation, towards which the amoebae stream from all sides to form an ever higher pile. Finally, a 'stalk' is sent out from beneath the pile, and the whole structure turns into a stalked head. Each of the amoebae now adopts a social task, and begins to act as a specific stalk cell or a head cell capable of producing spores. Cellulose fibres rise up between individual spores, helping to support them.

Since the time that Arndt (1937) first captured the whole process on film, many investigators have confirmed that the amoebae in the pseudoplasmodia eat, grow and reproduce as individuals. If different strains of amoebae, suitably stained, are introduced into one and the same aggregate, they will separate out just before it comes to the formation of fruiting bodies. Their 'social behaviour' is thought to be due to the presence of the chemical substance called acrasin, which attracts other cells within a certain radius towards the aggregation centre. The same substance is probably responsible for the formation of the fruiting bodies, though J. Bonner and co-workers were recently able to show that gases exuded by the amoebae also play an important role in this process. These gases (which are thought to consist at least in part of carbon dioxide) accelerate the streaming of the amoebae into the fruiting body, and also keep different fruiting bodies at a certain distance from one another, with the result that the number of such bodies per unit area is kept down. (If two fruiting bodies are placed too close to each other in the laboratory, they begin to separate at once.) Again, if the gases expelled by a culture of Acrasiophyta in a closed vessel are absorbed by activated charcoal or oil, the number of fruiting bodies increases perceptibly. A vertical gas gradient, finally, is thought to control the differential organization of cells in the various parts of the fruiting body.

5 MYCOPHYTA
True Fungi

Though this group includes the familiar mushrooms, toadstools and puff-balls, most species are, in fact, very much less conspicuous, and many cannot be seen with the naked eye.

Like the algae, fungi are thallophytes: their vegetative body is not divided into what could be described as true stems, roots or leaves – it is a simple thallus. In many other ways, too, especially in respect of their great variety, fungi are rather similar to algae. Thus they may be unicellular, filamentous or massive; and there is further agreement in the structure of the cell nucleus. Unlike algae, however, fungi are mainly terrestrial – only the lowest among them, in the Class Phycomycetes (alga-like fungi), occur as aquatic forms.

The most important characteristic of fungi, which not only distinguishes them from most algae but makes them unique in the entire plant kingdom, is the complete absence of chlorophyll. True, a few mushrooms and toadstools have a green colour – for instance many relatives of *Russula emetica*, the sickener – but their colour is not due to the presence of chlorophyll. Since chlorophyll is an essential component in all photosynthetic processes, it follows that fungi lack the means of building up organic materials by their own metabolic activity. In other words, they are unable to live autotrophically, i.e. as self-feeders, but have to rely for their food on the plants or animals on which they live as saprophytes or parasites.

The saprophytes among them feed on dead organic remains, dissolving carbon and nitrogen compounds by means of ferments. Being particularly rich in organic remains, the forest soil is the favourite haunt of fungi which, together with soil bacteria, play an important part in transforming plant debris into humus. However, saprophytic fungi are not restricted to the soil alone, and may be found in quite different habitats. Thus a number of Zygomycetes are able to live on sugar in raw or cooked fruits, in jams, syrups and similar substances. Cellulose and wood, too, serve many fungi as sources of food; the ability to break down cellulose makes *Mucor hiemalis* and *Rhizopus nigricans* (both in the order Mucorales) two important aids to the textile industry. Wood-inhabiting fungi also include *Serpula lacrymans*, cause of dry rot (Class: Basidiomycetes), which is greatly feared for the havoc it causes among roof beams and floorboards.

A few very undemanding fungi, including a number of yeasts, are able to live in the clear, food-deficient water of lakes.

So much for the saprophytes. Parasitic fungi, which feed on living hosts, do not differ from saprophytes in many other respects, the more so as a large number of them can live on decaying matter as well. One of these is *Armillariella mellea*, the honey or bootlace fungus (Order: Agaricales), a common, yellow, edible mushroom which is parasitic on the roots of trees, causing them to decay. As soon as the host is destroyed, the honey fungus alters its parasitic way of life and continues to live on the host's remains as a saprophyte.

In addition to such regular transitions from the parasitic to the saprophytic mode of life, fungi also include many facultative, i.e. occasional, parasites. Thus *Candida albicans*, a small Deuteromycete (imperfect fungus) which normally lives unnoticed as a saprophyte in the human buccal cavity, may occasionally turn parasitic and pathogenic to cause candidiasis, a disease of the mucous membranes, which may also affect the skin and the lungs.

Parasitic fungi attacking man are fortunately few and far between, whereas practically every group of fungi includes plant parasites. Some of these are limited to a single host, for instance *Puccinia adoxae*, a rust that lives exclusively on the common woodland plant *Adoxa moschellina*, moschatel. Most parasitic fungi, however, can live on more than one host. In the case of *Claviceps purpurea*, ergot (*Pl. 41, p. 64*) all hosts belong to a single family: the grasses. Other parasitic fungi attack plants of quite unrelated families; thus *Erysiphe polygoni* (Ascomycetes) attacks Ranunculaceae, Leguminosae, Polygonaceae, Compositae, etc.

Some rusts (Order: Uredinales) are remarkable for a change of host in the course of their development; thus *Puccinia graminis*, wheat rust, spends the winter on the barberry, and the summer on wheat.

Various plant parasites exhibit marked differences in the intensity of their parasitic activity, due chiefly to differences in the extent to which parasitic and host tissue have become fused.

Ustilago maydis (Order: Ustilaginales), the cause of smut in maize, lives parasitically on all parts of the maize plant. Other parasites are limited to certain of the host's organs only; thus ergot will only develop in the ovaries of wheat flowers. Often the parasitic fungus sends special suckers into the host's epidermis. Thus *Plasmopara viticola*, an alga-like fungus in the order Peronosporales, which causes downy mildew in grapes, dissolves the pectin in the host's cell walls and penetrates into the intercellular spaces. An extreme case is represented by those forms which infest the protoplasm of the host cell, e.g. by *Olpidium* (Order: Chytridiales), a very small simple fungus which inhabits pollen grains.

Parasitic fungi usually cause marked pathogenic changes in the host, generally involving individual organs, but sometimes the entire plant. A fungal infection that does not actually kill the host, but completely alters its appearance, is that caused by the pea rust, *Uromyces pisi* (Order: Uredinales), whose alternate host is the spurge, *Euphorbia cyparissias*. When this fungus attacks young spurge shoots, it not only renders them sterile, but also inhibits branching and leads to the formation of relatively broad, fleshy leaves.

Of the countless parasitic fungi that attack animals and man, many can cause fatal diseases, particularly in tropical countries. Hygienic measures such as the sterilization and protection of open wounds, and a certain degree of care in dealing with animals subject to fungal attack (for instance pigeons, in which fungi can produce a lung condition that may be transferred to man), can go a long way towards preventing fungal attack. Some parasitic fungi are, moreover, useful to man, among them the Entomophthoraceae, which live on insects and can thus be put to work as a natural 'insecticide'.

In addition to saprophytes and parasites, fungi also include many types that enter into symbiotic associations with their host. In a particular case, such associations have led to the emergence of a new type of composite plant: the lichens, which consist of an alga and a fungus in intimate union (see p. ooo ff.).

Here we shall consider the more typical symbiotic associations between fungi and the roots of higher plants, known as mycorrhizae (Greek *mykes* meaning mushroom and *rhizo* meaning root). Mycorrhizae may be ectotrophic or endotrophic. In the former, the symbiotic fungus establishes itself on the root surface and feeds chiefly on organic detritus it finds in the soil. The fungal partner of endotrophic mycorrhizae, too, is capable of living as a saprophyte, but once it has entered into symbiotic association with a root, it obtains all its food from the latter's cortical cells.

Ectotrophic mycorrhizae are particularly common in woods; the fungal partners are chiefly mushrooms, and most of these prefer specific hosts, so much so that mushroom collectors know just where to look for them. The precise contribution of the fungus to the tree has not yet been fully established, but it is believed that by breaking down complex organic nitrogen compounds in the soil into ammonia and nitrates, the fungus makes them available to the root in the only form in which they can be assimilated.

While ectotrophic mycorrhizae are, by and large, restricted to trees, endotrophic mycorrhizae are extremely widespread. There is barely a species of plant that does not form such associations, at least for a time – in most cases the endophytic fungus is eventually absorbed by the host's cells. Durable endotrophic mycorrhizae are known in only two families of plants: the Orchidaceae and the Ericaceae.

The mycorrhizae of orchids have been known for a long time, though their importance to the host plant was only discovered when attempts were first made to cultivate the flowers from seed in hothouses. If the seeds are grown under sterile conditions they never germinate; germination depends on the presence of a mycorrhizal fungus and one, moreover, that is tolerated as an endosymbiont. Clearly the fungus helps to provide the seed, which lacks any kind of food reserves, with the nutriment essential to its successful germination. Experiments in which orchid seeds were provided with concentrated food media instead of mycorrhizal fungi have shown that seeds treated in that way do germinate, but produce sterile plants. All in all, therefore, the association with a fungus is of vital importance to these plants.

The Ericaceae, too, depend on the presence of a symbiotic and endophytic fungus. In their case, however, it is not restricted to the root, but spreads throughout the entire plant, and is present in the peripheral tissue of the seed from the very beginning of its development. If the seeds are polished to remove the fungus, they will still germinate, but the seedlings will not take root, and die soon afterwards. Beyond that, the endophytic fungi of Ericaceae are believed to have the ability to fix atmospheric nitrogen, and to supply it to their partners, thus enabling them to survive on poor soils.

Two interesting cases of symbiosis between animals and fungi have not yet been fully investigated. The first involves termites, which fill the chambers of their runs with a mass of chewed-up wood and clay; it is here that the queen lays her eggs, and that certain fungi, chiefly of the genus *Termitomyces*, which flourish in a warm, moist, oxygen-poor atmosphere, establish themselves. It used to be thought that the larvae of the termites fed on the fungi but, in fact, the association is rather one in which each partner helps to provide a better living environment for the other. The second, far more interesting, case involves the association of scale insects and fungi in the family Septobasidiaceae. This

is not really a case of symbiosis but rather a sort of half-way house between symbiosis and parasitism. The female insects, which are unable to fly, live on the bark, leaves and fruits of various trees, feeding on their sap. They become completely encrusted with fungi, which protect them not only from desiccation but also from attack by birds. At the same time, the fungi feed on the insect larvae, which they partly suck dry. This part symbiotic and part parasitic community behaves as a pure parasite towards the tree it infests – the louse directly and the fungus indirectly.

Fungi play an important role not only in the life of plants and animals, but also in that of man, particularly by attacking his crops and by causing diseases. However, a very large number of fungi are useful to man – we have only to think of edible mushrooms. Far more important still, from even a purely dietary point of view, are the many fungi that go into the production of various foods and of alcoholic beverages. Certain saprophytic fungi, which we commonly describe as moulds, live on milk and other dairy products; it is to them that many cheeses owe their distinctive flavour. Thus the taste and appearance of Camembert and Roquefort are due to the presence of *Penicillium*.

No alcoholic drinks could be prepared in the absence of fungi, in this particular case, of yeasts, which are able to transform sugar into alcohol by fermentation. The precise processes involved were first explained by Louis Pasteur. Among the various species of yeast, *Saccharomyces ellipsoideus*, wine yeast, and *S. cerevisiae*, brewer's yeast, are probably the best-known. Wine yeast transforms the glucose in grape juice into alcohol, while brewer's yeast helps to ferment maltose, the sugar produced from starch during the germination of cereal grains. Yeast is also an essential ingredient in the baking of bread, helping to transform the sugar in the flour into alcohol, which evaporates during the baking process, releasing large numbers of carbon dioxide bubbles, and thus causing the dough to rise. Finally, yeasts are actively involved in the transformation of fresh into fermented milk, particularly into yoghurt.

Fungi also play an increasingly important role in medicine. One fungus in which poisonous and curative effects go very closely hand in hand is ergot; this fungus, which, as we saw, lives as a parasite on cereals, causes ergotism, a condition that leads to muscular and vascular cramps and often proves fatal. In the past, ergotism frequently assumed epidemic proportions, but today when there are adequate ways of cleaning the infested grains, the disease has ceased to be a serious threat. Instead, the spasm-inducing properties of ergot have been put to good effect in gynaecology and obstetrics, where ergot is now administered on a wide scale. These beneficial effects were known to the ancient Chinese and have been utilized in Europe since the sixteenth century. More recently, it has been possible to isolate the beneficial from the poisonous components, and thus to eliminate the dangerous side-effects.

Yeasts have also long been used as curative agents, particularly in the treatment of such deficiency diseases as rickets and various skin eruptions. Their beneficial effects are due to the presence of concentrated vitamins, particularly of vitamins in the B group. In popular medicine *Fomes fomentarius*, tinder fungus, which lives on deciduous trees on the Continent but is rare in Britain, used to serve as a coagulant and a balm for wounds, and was also used as tinder. Also prized as a coagulant, a purgative and an antisudorific was *Polyporus officinalis*, or purging agaric.

It is not generally known that what is today the best-known medicinal fungus, namely *Penicillium*, was used long ago in popular medicine: peasants in various parts of Europe used to treat suppurating wounds and boils with this fungus. In 1928, the Scottish microbiologist Alexander Fleming discovered that *Penicillium* had an anti-bacterial and antibiotic effect: a colony of *P. notatum* had accidentally invaded a culture of staphylococci and had created a bacterium-free zone in its neighbourhood. Fleming then established that a certain substance released by the fungus (which he later called penicillin) inhibits the development of the bacteria and finally causes them to die. Penicillin, which is produced in particularly large quantities by both *P. notatum* and also *P. chrysogenum*, was later obtained in a relatively pure state by H. W. Florey and E. B. Chain, who shared the 1945 Nobel Prize with Fleming. Since the Second World War, various types of penicillin, now produced on an industrial scale, have been used in the treatment of abscesses and such infections as pneu-

monia and meningitis; penicillin is also used to good effect in the treatment of puerperal fever, tetanus, and venereal diseases. Unfortunately, many bacteria have developed strains resistant to penicillin, so that other antibiotics have had to be introduced. Most of these are derived from moulds, particularly from *Streptomyces griseus*.

Antibiotics are also yielded by the large funnel caps of the genus *Clitocybe*. They produce clitocybin, a substance that promises to play an important part in the treatment of tuberculosis. Its antibiotic properties can occasionally be observed in nature: funnel caps often grow in circular colonies, and though the grass inside the ring may be dead, there are no signs of putrefaction – bactericidal substances produced by the fungi see to that.

In our discussion of the useful and harmful effects of fungi, we cannot but mention the many poisonous mushrooms or toadstools which, year after year, claim new victims. Their poisons are not usually eliminated by cooking, and perhaps the worst thing about them is that the poisons often do not act for several hours or even days. As a result, the main symptoms of mushroom poisoning – intestinal cramps, vascular failure, breathlessness, and giddiness – are often misdiagnosed or not identified until it is too late. Among the most noxious of all these mushrooms are *Amanita phalloides*, death cap (*Pl. 63, p. 137*), and *A. virosa*, destroying angel; both contain the powerful liver-poison, amanitin. Of the two, *A. virosa* is, if anything, the more dangerous, because it grows side by side, and is easily confused, with the edible *Agaricus arvensis*, horse mushroom (*Pl. 66, p. 138*). Many other poisonous mushrooms also resemble edible species, to which they can, moreover, be closely related. Hence it is absolutely essential to collect only such mushrooms as can be identified with complete certainty.

All our remarks so far will have shown that although fungi share many common characters, they are a surprisingly many-sided group. This is reflected first of all in the way in which they compensate for their inability to fend for themselves. In addition, they include an astonishing variety of forms – both vegetative and reproductive.

By the structure of their vegetative body, fungi can be divided into three distinct groups. The first comprises microscopically small, unicellular plants, mostly bladder-shaped in appearance. The second includes fungi whose thalli are built up of variously branched and tubular filaments, generally lacking in septa. The fungi in the third and largest group all have a highly branched thallus known as a mycelium, whose constituent filaments or hyphae are invariably divided into cells by septa. Such hyphae are characteristics of all higher fungi – they may be combined loosely or may become intertwined into densely packed strands, the so-called rhizomorphs (e.g. in honey fungi). In many species, the hyphae form sclerotia, hard, resting bodies resistant to unfavourable conditions and often disseminated by animals. The sclerotium of ergot is shown in *Fig. 137*; it forms a kind of horn on the host plant.

Not only the mycelia, but also the so-called fruiting bodies of fungi are built up of hyphae. In the formation of these bodies the hyphae become intensely intertwined, often fusing into dense masses resembling the parenchymatous tissue of higher plants. The stalks and heads of mushrooms are built up of this type of 'tissue'.

In parasitic and symbiotic fungi, the hyphae are frequently transformed into sucking organs or haustoria, which enter the host's cells and often form branches inside.

The vegetative bodies of fungi are surrounded by a relatively tough membrane which in most species contains a substance that bears a strong chemical resemblance to the chitinous armour of insects. In a few alga-like fungi, however, the membrane is built up of cellulose.

In contrast to the majority of other plants, most fungi have multi-nucleate cells – only the lowest order among the alga-like fungi, the Chytridiales, make do with a single nucleus. Among the cell inclusions of fungi, reserve materials play a most important part. These are chiefly glycogen – in droplet form – and fats; fungi never store starch, the main reserve material of green plants. Pigments, too, are extremely rare and almost exclusively confined to the fruiting bodies of the most highly developed fungi.

The great diversity of fungi finds its highest expression in the reproductive sphere. Fungi multiply by means of spores differing radically both in origin and form. The chiefly aquatic alga-like fungi produce motile spores known as swarmers or, because of their resemblance to flagellates, as zoospores. They consist of a naked, more or less spherical cell bearing one or two flagella. All other fungi are terrestrial and produce non-motile spores enclosed in a firm wall and known as aplanospores. Botanists distinguish between endogenous spores that arise in sporangia within the fungus and exogenous spores that arise on the tips or sides of the hyphae. Endogenous and exogenous spores are of two distinct types each, and differ in a number of important respects. This is best illustrated by means of actual examples.

The first of the two types of endogenous spore is common among the alga-like fungi (Phycomycetes), where they are produced in large numbers inside sporangia. In the most primitive family, the Olpidiaceae and some of its near relatives (Order: Chytridiales), the entire vegetative body is transformed into a sporangium; in more highly developed groups, whose thalli are built up of hyphae, some of the hyphae swell into sporangia at the tip, and lay down a septum. Each sporangium contains numerous cell nuclei which gradually become surrounded by a plasmatic envelope and develop into zoospores or aplanospores, depending on whether they are aquatic or terrestrial types.

The second type of endogenous spore is confined to the Ascomycetes (sac fungi). Here, too, the spores are formed inside sporangia, but these no longer arise inside the thallus but result from sexual processess. They are known as asci (Gr. *ascos* = sac), and usually look like elongated tubes. Young asci contain a diploid nucleus produced by the fusion of two haploid nuclei. From it, three (and more rarely two) reduction divisions produce 8 (or 4) haploid nuclei, which become enveloped in part of the protoplasm inside the ascus and develop into tough-walled structures, the so-called ascospores.

Exogenous spores, too, arise partly from the vegetative body and partly as the result of a sexual process. Vegetatively produced exogenous spores are known as conidia. Among Phycomycetes, this type of spore-formation is the exception, but among higher fungi it is extremely widespread. Conidia are usually produced on separate, often erect, hyphae, the so-called conidiophores. Some arise individually from special branches, others arise in conspicuous chains (e.g. in *Penicillium* and in *Aspergillus niger* – Order: Moniliales; Class: Deuteromycetes). In the former, the chains look like rows of bristles, in the latter they form rays. Conidia often combine into heads that rise like crowns over the tip and branches of the conidiophores; such crowns are found for instance in *Botrytis*, a genus related to *Penicillium*. Conidia are usually unicellular and of spherical or oval shape; quite a few are multicellular and club-shaped. In *Helicoma* (Order: Moniliales; Class: Deuteromycetes) the multicellular conidia are crook-shaped, while in *Asterosporium* (Order: Melanconiales; Class: Deuteromycetes) they are star-shaped.

Exogenous spores derived from sexual processes also arise on the outside of a specialized spore-producing body, the basidium. Basidiospores are usually unicellular and haploid, and like ascospores, are generally produced at the rate of four to the basidium. The simple club-shaped basidium of the higher Basidiomycetes (*Fig. 171*) may be considered as characteristic. It originates as a terminal cell of a binucleate hypha from which it is separated by a septum. The basidium gradually enlarges and four slender processes, the sterigmata, push out at the top, swell up and form the so-called basidiospore initials. The four haploid nuclei, produced by fusion of the two nuclei within the young basidium and by subsequent reduction division, now squeeze through the stigmata into the young basidiospores. Though the spores are formed inside the sterigma tips, they completely fuse with them, so that we are fully entitled to call them exogenous.

Conidiophores, asci and basidia are usually combined into fruiting bodies, hollow or solid structures of various shapes, built up of hyphae. Such fruiting bodies first appear among the most highly developed of the Phycomycetes; they have become the general rule among the higher fungi. Their origin, structure and form will be discussed when we deal with the various groups of fungi in detail.

In addition to true spores, produced sexually or asexually, many fungi also produce thallospores, i.e. fragments of the thallus resulting from the decomposition of hyphae into individual cells or oidia. This type of spore formation is characteristic of a whole series of fungi, among them the ink caps (Genus: *Coprinus*; Class: Basidiomycetes) and *Candida albicans* which, as we saw, lives saprophytically in the human mouth. Thallospores can, however, also be produced by budding; in yeasts (especially of the genus *Saccharomyces*; Class: Ascomycetes) this is, in fact, the sole method of growth, leading to the formation of a rudimentary mycelium built up from chains of oval cells. The chains usually break up into individual cells which act as thallospores to form the starting point of new mycelium, but occasionally become transformed into sexual cells.

The great variety of shapes in which the spores of fungi occur, and the great variety of processes leading to their formation, suggest strongly that the general development of fungi did not follow a unified pattern.

Like the life history of most living organisms, that of fungi, too, involves the alternation of haploid and diploid nuclear phases. Generally, the haploid phase is the dominant one in fungi, while the diploid phase is only of short duration. However, the position can also be reversed, as it is, for instance, in yeasts.

Unlike most other plants, fungi interpose a third phase between the haploid and diploid, namely the dikaryotic (binucleate) phase. Thus whereas karyogamy (nuclear fusion) is immediately preceded by plasmogamy (union of protoplasts) in the majority of living organisms, these two processes are separated in time and space in many fungi, especially in the most highly developed of the Basidiomycetes – the mushrooms.

The lowest fungi, the Phycomycetes, reproduce by means of unicellular swarmers. In the most primitive forms, i.e. in the Olpidiaceae and related families (Order: Chytridiales), the swarmers are produced inside the bladder-shaped cells constituting the vegetative body. After they have been released into the water, the swarmers either behave like zoospores and as such look for a host in whose cells they can develop into new fungi, or else they behave like gametes and copulate in pairs. The fusion product is a zygote resembling the gametes in external appearance but having two nuclei instead of only one. When the zygote finds a host, it becomes transformed into a resting stage during which the dikaryotic (binucleate) condition is maintained. Nuclear fusion only occurs at the beginning of the next vegetative period; it is followed soon afterwards by reduction division leading to the formation of numerous zoospores. What is important to remember here is that sexual reproduction involves the activity of gametes which, though similar in appearance (isogametes), are of distinct sexuality and motile (planogametes; from Gr. *planetes* = wanderer, and *gametes* = husband).

While the swarmers of Olpidiaceae are produced inside the vegetative body, they arise in separate sporangia and gametangia in the Blastocladiales (another order of Phycomycetes). In *Allomyces*, the best-known representative of the order, the gametangia exhibit clear differences in sizes. The smaller ones liberate small male planogametes; the larger give rise to large female planogametes. The two copulate in the water and fuse into zygotes. Soon after nuclear fusion has occurred, the zygotes shed their flagella, settle down, and germinate into diploid thalli bearing sporangia and hence called sporothalli. Each sporothallus gives rise to two types of sporangia, the first thin-walled and containing diploid spores; the second thick-walled and containing haploid spores. While the diploid spores develop into new sporothalli, the haploid spores give rise to plants that only produce gametangia. Sporothalli and gametangium-bearing thalli represent the sporophyte and gametophyte generations respectively. In the Blastocladiales, we thus have a true alternation of generations, which does not occur among other Phycomycetes.

Sexual reproduction in the Monoblepharidales (Class: Phycomycetes) is of a far more advanced type. Here only the male gametes (spermatozoids) are motile. They are produced in narrow elongated antheridia borne on the larger oogonia. The protoplast of the oogonium becomes rounded into an oosphere, i.e. a single spherical and non-motile gamete. A single sperm enters the oogonium through a papilla in the oogonial wall, penetrates the oosphere and fuses with it. The fertilized egg then emerges from the oogonium, and while still attached to its outer wall, changes into a thick-walled oospore. The oospore germinates after some time by producing a thallus; meiosis probably takes place during this process. The fusion of a motile with a non-motile, sessile gamete, as it occurs in Monoblepharidales, is called oogamy. It represents a higher stage of sexual development than the fusion of two gametes of equal shape (isogamy).

In many fungi, sexual processes take place in the absence of gametes. Instead, gametangia may become fused as such (gametangial copulation or gametangiogamy). Just as in the copulation of two gametes, gametangiogamy is associated with the presence of organs of copulation that vary from the near-identical to the most highly differentiated. Again, the two types of gametangium may be found either on a single (homothallic) individual, or else on two distinct (heterothallic) individuals.

Among the Phycomycetes, the Mucorales have gone over to gametangiogamy. In *Mucor mucedo*, downy mildew, gametangiogamy is based on the copulation of two similar gametangia produced by distinct (heterothallic) mycelia. When brought into close proximity, they send out pairs of club-shaped branches that grow towards one another. As soon as they touch, a septum is laid down across the tip of each, cutting off a multinucleate cell inside. These cells, which are identical in form, represent the gametangia. They fuse into a thick-walled zygote, which gradually turns a darker colour and becomes densely covered with wart-shaped processes. The zygote then enters a resting stage, during which the gametangial nuclei fuse in pairs. Later the zygote sends out a germinal tube with a haploid nucleus. Its tip develops into a sporangium, which eventually releases countless spores. These germinate into male and female mycelia.

Gametangiogamy is the general rule among ascus-bearing fungi, i.e. among Ascomycetes. Here we shall illustrate it by looking at a yeast (*Saccharomyces*; Order: Endomycetales) and at *Pyronema* (Order: Pezizales), a small, soil-inhabiting fungus that likes to settle on burned ground.

Individual yeast cells usually form new mycelia by budding. They can, however, act as sexual organs as well; this happens when cells from mycelia of different sexes come together. The copulating cells, which are identical in appearance, are generally treated as uninucleate gametangia. They fuse into a zygote whose nuclei usually combine at once. (A more durable binucleate phase occurs in only a small number of species.) The zygote develops into a sac-shaped sporangium, the ascus. Its diploid nucleus undergoes meiosis, and produces 4 or 8 nuclei which grow into the so-called ascospores.

In *Pyronema*, as in the majority of Ascomycetes, the copulating gametangia arise side by side from one and the same hypha and can be clearly distinguished into male and female. The male organs or antheridia are built up of club-shaped cells with numerous nuclei. The female organs, which are also multi-nucleate, consist of a swollen basal cell, the so-called ascogonium, and a small crescent-shaped apical cell known as the trichogyne. When the sexual organs are ready for copulation, the trichogyne bends over to touch the antheridium and opens at the point of contact. The nuclei of the antheridium then migrate into the trichogyne and thence into the ascogonium with whose nuclei they fuse in pairs. Soon afterwards, the ascogonium produces a number of papillae, the ascogenous hyphae, and the nuclei move into these. The ascogenous hyphae, whose apical cells produce the asci, represent the gametophyte generation of *Pyronema* and of all other Ascomycetes whose development corresponds to that of *Pyronema*. Their sporophyte generation is unusual in that it is binucleate (dikaryotic) and not diploid. The ascogenous hyphae branch out and divide into septate cells, each with a male and a female nucleus. In a large number of Ascomycetes, one of the binucleate cells elongates and bends over to form a hook. The two nuclei in the hook now divide, and two daughter nuclei – one male and one female – move to the bend of the hook, while one of the two remaining nuclei migrates to the tip of the hook and the other to the basal septum of the hook. Two septa are laid down, dividing the hook into three cells. The tip and basal cells are uninucleate, one containing an antheridial and the other an ascogonial nucleus; the crook cell is binucleate. The binucleate crook is destined to become the diploid ascus and is called the ascus mother cell. As the ascus develops, its nucleus undergoes meiosis to produce 8 haploid nuclei by three successive divisions. The haploid nuclei develop into ascospores, each surrounded by a wall of cytoplasm, derived from the ascus. In many Ascomycetes, each ascogenous hypha branches and rebranches to give rise to a cluster of asci. This generally happens when the crook cell elongates into a new hook instead of developing into

an ascus, with the tip and basal hook cells fusing to form another hook by the side of the first. This process may be repeated several times, leading to the formation of a cluster of hooks, the crook cells of which finally give rise to asci.

The most 'advanced' type of sexuality is characteristically found in the most highly developed group, i.e. in the basidium-forming fungi. Basidiomycetes usually produce two types of mycelium which, in the absence of sexual organs, are distinguished as being of plus and minus type respectively. If two compatible mycelia come into contact with each other, any two of their vegetative cells may act as copulatory organs, and fuse with each other. This type of sexual reproduction is known as somatogamy. Since the cells in question are uninucleate, the fusion cell will contain a single pair of nuclei. In the Basidiomycetes, the resulting binucleate or dikaryotic phase dominates over the haploid and diploid phases. The fusion cell produces a conspicuous binucleate mycelium whose growth is regulated by characteristic division mechanisms.

The separation of a new cell begins with the growth of a hook-shaped 'clamp' connection, roughly at the level of the nuclei; the clamp eventually bends over to touch the cell wall. One of the two nuclei in the cell now migrates into the clamp and divides into two daughter nuclei; one of these remains in the clamp but the other moves on to the tip of the cell. The second mother nucleus meanwhile undergoes division as well; of its two daughters, one migrates to the tip of the cell where it forms a nuclear pair with the one from the clamp; the other migrates to the base of the cell. Next the cell itself divides by laying down a septum just beneath the clamp connection. A second septum arises obliquely and divides the clamp from the upper of the two daughter cells. Where the clamp makes contact with the basal cell, there now appears an aperture through which the clamp nucleus migrates back into the cell, which again becomes binucleate. As the apical cell grows, it divides by means of a new clamp connection. This type of cell division is repeated throughout the development of the binucleate mycelium, which is therefore called a clamp mycelium.

As the clamp mycelium keeps branching out, it creeps across ever wider areas of the substrate. At a given point, however, it begins to form compact and erect fruiting bodies. These bear the basidia, i.e. the organs in which true sexual union (the fusion of two sexual nuclei) takes place; it leads to the formation of reproductive cells, the so-called basidiospores.

Our short survey of sexuality in fungi has shown that it includes every possible mode of sexual reproduction known in the plant kingdom: from the copulation of planogametes, through oogamy, i.e. the fertilization of sessile female gametes by motile male gametes, and gametangiogamy in which the part of the gametes is played by the organs that normally produce the gametes, to somatogamy in which no reproductive organs are involved. If we compare these various methods of reproduction, we find that they represent a process of gradual reduction. Far from being a primitive trend, such reduction is a sign of biological progress, as are a host of other features that go hand in hand with it.

In their attemps to classify fungi, taxonomists rely greatly on differences in sexual behaviour. To begin with, they distinguish two major groups: the lower fungi with motile reproductive cells, and the higher fungi with non-motile ones. The first group includes the Phycomycetes or alga-like fungi; the second group includes all the rest, most of which can be fitted into two classes: Ascomycetes or sac fungi, and Basidiomycetes or basidium-forming fungi.

Class
PHYCOMYCETES
Alga-like Fungi

Though the Phycomycetes are the most varied group of fungi, all its members have very simple vegetative bodies of relatively small dimensions. There is considerable agreement in their habit as well: most Phycomycetes are parasitic on plants or animals. In all other respects, however, Phycomycetes differ considerably from one another, for instance in their choice of environment: while most are aquatic, quite a few have become adapted to terrestrial life.

They also differ markedly in shape. As we saw, Phycomycetes have a simply constructed vegetative body which, in the most primitive forms, consists of a microscopically small spherical cell, and in the most highly developed a filamentous thallus made

up of relatively few cells. While the primitive types transform their entire bodies into sporangia, the filamentous types reserve certain portions of their thalli for that purpose. Again, while the spores of aquatic forms are flagellate swarmers, those of terrestrial Phycomycetes are non-motile with few exceptions.

The greatest differences, however, occur in the sphere of sexual reproduction. Among the various methods employed, the copulation of motile gametes and oogamy deserve special mention, since they do not occur in any other group of fungi. In addition, gametangiogamy is very widespread among Phycomycetes.

The lowest Phycomycetes are microscopically small, simple organisms. The majority are found in the order Chytridiales.

Order
CHYTRIDIALES

The best-known representatives of this order are the Olpidiaceae, a family of fresh-water fungi, parasitic on algae, higher plants and aquatic animals. Some of them, for instance *Olpidium pendulinum*, parasitize pollen grains blown into the water by the wind, especially those of conifers. Within the host cell, Olpidiaceae become attached to the host nucleus, secrete a membrane round themselves, and grow into sporangia while their nuclei divide repeatedly. The zoospores escape through an exit tube, and swim about in the water until they find a new host. When

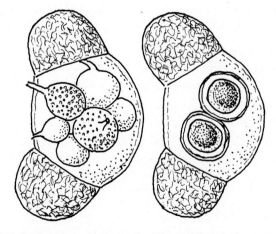

Fig. 86 *Olpidium pendulum*. Left: sporangia in a pollen grain of *Pinus*; right: resting spore (highly magnified)

94

they do, they shed their flagella and encyst themselves on the host's surface. Infection takes place through a minute pore dissolved in the host cell wall, through which the protoplast of the parasite can enter.

The zoospores also play a part in sexual reproduction, for they can behave as planogametes, and fuse to give rise to a biflagellate zygote. The zygote swims about in the water for a time, then settles on a host, enters one of its cells, develops a thick wall, and turns into a resting spore which later germinates to produce zoospores. The resting spore has the same function as a normal sporangium, from which its only external difference is the presence of the thick wall.

While the Chytridiales agree widely in the nature of their development, they vary considerably in external appearance. In the Olpidiaceae, one and the same cell acts as vegetative body and sporangium; things are similar in the Synchytriaceae, the only family in the order to have left the water completely and became parasitic on terrestrial plants. This family includes the notorious *Synchytrium endobioticum* which causes black wart disease in potato tubers.

In most Chytridiales, however, the thallus is divided into a filamentous vegetative part and vesicular sporangia, cut off from the rest by a special wall. The filaments look very much like the hyphae of higher fungi, but are built up of widely-branching multinucleate tubes instead of cells. The simplest type of filamentous vegetative body is that of the Phlyctidiaceae, tiny fungi whose appearance and

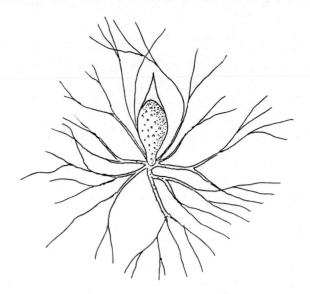

Fig. 88 *Obelidium mucronatum* (highly magnified)

choice of host are highly reminiscent of those of Olpidiaceae. These fungi form root-like threads through which they feed on their host; in *Rhizophydium* the threads penetrate into the host cell, while the spherical sporangia and resting spores develop on the host's external wall.

In the Rhizidiaceae, whose sole representative, *Obelidium mucronatum*, lives chiefly as a saprophyte on dead aquatic insects, the filaments are much more profusely developed, enabling the fungus to spread over a much wider area of the substrate. This development is even more pronounced in the Chytridiaceae (e.g. *Chytridium*), which live on fresh-water algae, and the Megachytriaceae, which live on dead plants. The latter, represented by the genus *Nowakowskiella*, send an extensive and richly-branched

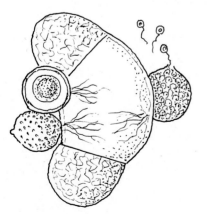

Fig. 87 *Rhizophydium pollinis-pini*; sporangia and resting spore on a pollen grain of *Pinus* (highly magnified)

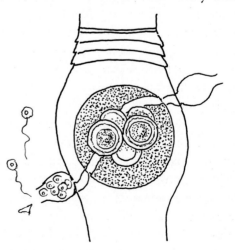

Fig. 89 *Chytridium olla*: resting spores, some of them germinating in the egg cell of *Oedogonium*

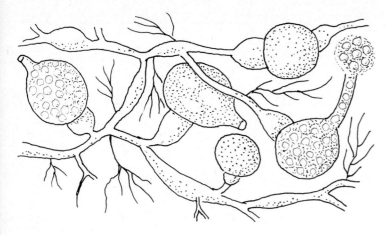

Fig. 90 *Nowakowskiella macrospora*; part of thallus (highly magnified). The tips of the hyphae bear sporangia, one of which (right) can be seen releasing its zoospores.

system of filaments into the host; the filaments eventually form spindle-shaped terminal swellings, which give rise to sporangia or resting spores from which numerous zoospores are eventually released.

Order
BLASTOCLADIALES

The Blastocladiales have a well-formed thallus with branched rhizoids, by means of which they attach themselves to their substrate – plants, animals or organic detritus. The reproductive organs arise on special filaments, and in this order we meet our first fungi with distinct sexual and asexual organs, i.e. with distinct sporangia and gametangia; in some species these organs are borne by separate individuals, which therefore represent the sexual and asexual generations. The asexual thalli invariably produce two types of sporangia, one thin-walled and elongated, the other oval, thick-walled, pitted and resistant. Spores originating from thin-walled sporangia develop into asexual thalli which produce sporangia in their turn; those derived from resistant sporangia produce sexual individuals. The gametangia of the more primitive species are completely indistinguishable; the more highly developed Blastocladiales, however, produce smaller 'male' and larger 'female' organs that release small male and large female gametes respectively. Spores and gametes alike are motile, each with a posterior flagellum.

Of the three families constituting this order, two – the Catenariaceae and the Coelomomycetaceae – are predominantly parasitic; the Blastocladiaceae, on

the other hand, are saprophytic on plant and animal remains.

The Catenariaceae live chiefly on microscopically small aquatic animals and their eggs. *Catenaria anguilullae* has a marked predilection for rotifers. This fungus penetrates the host's body to grow a filamentous vegetative body studded with bladder-shaped sporangia. Occasionally it also produces gametangia which give rise to isogametes, but frequently there is no sexual phase at all. The Coelomomycetaceae, which consist of only one genus, *Coelomomyces*, are obligate parasites on mosquito larvae and adults. *C. dodgei* lives on the larvae of *Anopheles crucians*, one of the malaria-carrying species.

The Blastocladiaceae differ from all other Phycomycetes in which sexual reproduction occurs in that they produce two distinct types of gamete. These are developed in small male and larger female gametangia, spherical organs attached to special tubular hyphae of the highly ramified thallus. In *Blastocladiella*, the gametangia are shared out among distinct male and female thalli, whereas in *Allomyces* they grow in pairs on one and the same individual. Sporangia develop on separate hyphae or thalli. *Blastocladia* has a characteristic stem-like vegetative body anchored to the substrate by means of thin tubular hyphae and topped by a thick tuft of sporangia and sterile hyphae. No cases of sexual reproduction have been observed in this genus.

Order
MONOBLEPHARIDALES

The Monoblepharidales represent a clear advance on all the Phycomycetes we have been discussing, both in the structure of their vegetative body and also in

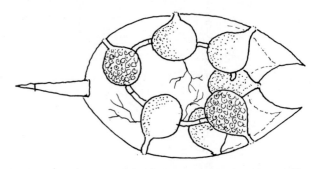

Fig. 91 *Catenaria anguillulae* living as a parasite on a rotifer (highly magnified)

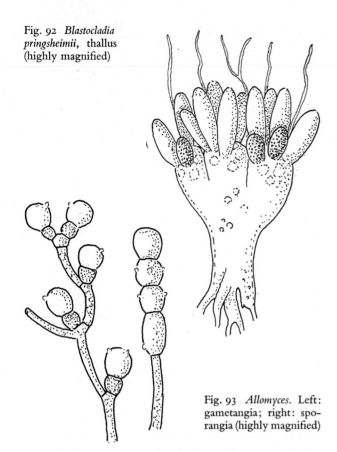

Fig. 92 *Blastocladia pringsheimii*, thallus (highly magnified)

Fig. 93 *Allomyces*. Left: gametangia; right: sporangia (highly magnified)

their method of sexual reproduction. *Monoblepharis* (Family: Monoblepharidaceae) has well developed branches and tubular hyphae; its thallus looks deceptively like the mycelium of higher fungi. More important still is the advanced method of sexual reproduction: oogamy makes its entry with this group, i.e. the Monoblepharidaceae present us with our first example of true fertilization, with a male gamete – here a spermatozoid produced in an antheridium – searching for and fertilizing an egg cell developed inside an oogonium. Antheridia and oogonia are borne on short lateral hyphae cut off from the rest of the thallus by septa. On maturing, the relatively small antheridia liberate a small number of uniflagellate spermatozoids which differ from the asexual reproductive cells, i.e. the zoospores, in size only. The spermatozoids swim towards the oogonia, pass through a pore in their wall and fertilize the egg cell. The resulting zygote slips out of the oogonium, settles on its outside and surrounds itself with a thick wall.

Monoblepharis is common on branches of plants that dip into rivers and lakes.

Order
SAPROLEGNIALES

The Saprolegniales are a partly parasitic and partly saprophytic order. They are common in aquatic media and in moist soils, and use a more advanced form of oogamy than the Monoblepharidales: the antheridia do not produce spermatozoids but drive short tubes into the oogonia. The antheridial nuclei then travel through these tubes, enter the oogonia, and generally succeed in fertilizing the great majority of the egg cells in them.

The motile stage of Saprolegniales is limited to the zoospores, each of which bears two flagella. On leaving their sporangia, the zoospores are pear-shaped and have anterior flagella. After some time, however, they surround themselves with a wall and enter a resting stage, during which their shape is radically transformed: they emerge as kidney-shaped structures with the two flagella inserted laterally.

The vegetative body of Saprolegniales is a richly developed and ramified tubular mycelium. The walls of the hyphae are built up exclusively of cellulose.

The Saprolegniales consist of only one family, the

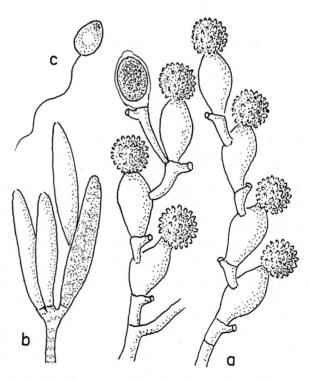

Fig. 94 *Monoblepharis*. *a*: Oogonia with escaping zygotes; *b*: sporangia; *c*: zoospore (highly magnified)

97

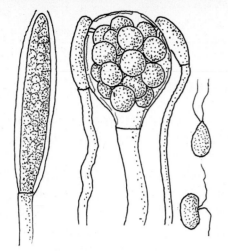

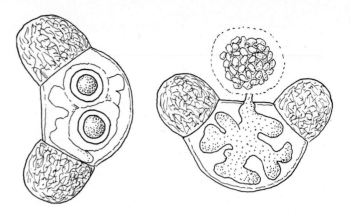

Fig. 95 *Saprolegnia*. Left: sporangium; centre: oogonium with antheridia; right: zoospores, motile stage (top) and resting stage (bottom). Highly magnified

Fig. 96 *Lagenidium pygmaeum*. Left: pollen grain of *Pinus* with resting spores; right: pollen grain with sporangia (highly magnified)

Saprolegniaceae; its best-known genera are *Saprolegnia* and *Achyla*. While the former lives chiefly as a saprophyte in fresh water and on moist soils, the latter is a dangerous parasite – it attacks fish and is greatly feared by aquarists.

Order

LAGENIDIALES

The Lagenidiales differ from other more highly developed Phycomycetes in having a relatively simple and often microscopically small thallus. They are parasitic on fresh-water algae, on other Phycomycetes and on small aquatic animals. *Lagenidium* develops its lobular vegetative body inside floating pollen grains, from which only the sporangia protrude above the water surface.

Order

PERONOSPORALES

With the Peronosporales we reach the group of Phycomycetes that have completely emerged from the water; only in the family Pythiaceae, which is the most primitive of all, do we still find a few aquatic species, all members of the genus *Pythium*. Most Peronosporales are parasitic on higher terrestrial plants. Their transition from aquatic to terrestrial life went hand in hand with certain other modifications. Thus while most Peronosporales still form sporangia, these are borne on special sporangiophores, are deciduous, and depend upon the wind for dissemination. Hence the whole sporangium

acts as a spore and in the highest form germinates by a germ tube instead of producing zoospores. Sexual reproduction is invariably oogamous – the antheridium transfers its nuclei – or frequently its single nucleus – through the so-called fertilization tube into the (usually unicellular) oogonium. The sexual organs are borne on the same or on different hyphae embedded in the tissue of the host plant. Hence sexual reproduction takes place within the host.

The vegetative body of Peronosporales is built up of cylindrical and usually hollow hyphae. Parasitic types spread their mycelia in the intercellular spaces of the host tissue and send special haustoria into the cytoplasm of the host cell.

The order is divided into three families: the Pythiaceae, the Peronosporaceae and the Albuginaceae. With few exceptions, all of them are dangerous parasites, causing great damage particularly to cultivated plants.

Among the Pythiaceae, the genus *Pythium* includes a number of aquatic fungi. The terrestrial species are chiefly parasitic on seedlings, causing the disease known as damping-off. *Pythium* sporangia germinate by sending out a long germ tube which swells into a thin-walled vesicle at the tip. The cytoplasm of the sporangium is then transferred through the tube into the vesicle, where a large number of kidney-shaped zoospores, each with two flagella, are formed. The spores are liberated by the bursting of the vesicular wall.

In the genus *Phytophthora*, the zoospores develop inside the sporangium itself, and leave it through a pore at the top, which opens by means of a papilliform 'lid'. The genus is tropical, but one species, *P. infestans*, is now common in temperate zones as well. Introduced into Europe with the potato, it causes late potato blight, a disease dreaded by farmers. In the past, the fungus often caused the complete destruction of potato crops over large areas, and the Irish famine of 1845 with all its dire consequences can be traced directly to it.

The Peronosporaceae include the genera *Plasmopara* and *Peronospora*. In these fungi, the mycelium spreads within the host tissue and sends out a crop of sporangiophores, each of whose numerous branches is crowned with a sporangium. The colourless sporangia cover the attacked plants with a dense layer of 'flour', to produce the diseases known as downy mildews. The most devastating of these used to be the downy mildew of the grape caused by *Plasmopara viticola*. This parasitic native of America has ceased to be a grave threat in the U.S.A., where vines have become resistant to it; all the more serious were its effects when, during the last century, American grapes were introduced into France, and with them the noxious parasites. Since then, vineyards have been regularly sprayed with Bordeaux mixture, a mixture of copper sulphate and lime, and the threat has been largely banished. Species of *Peronospora* also attack hops, beet and various other edible plants. During the past few years, several European countries have been plagued with *P. tabacina*, which causes 'blue mildew' in tobacco.

The Albuginaceae differ from other Peronosporales in a number of respects, particularly in the structure of their sporangiophores. These are cuboid or polyhedral and gradually cut off whole chains of sporangia at their tips; the chains develop inside the host plant, just beneath the epidermis, which they subsequently explode. The most common species, *Albugo candida*, attacks all crucifers, causing white rust (*Fig. 99*).

Order
MUCORALES

As typical land-dwellers, the Mucorales do not produce motile stages; with the exception of a small group of parasitic species, they live as saprobes on decaying plant remains, on horse manure and on

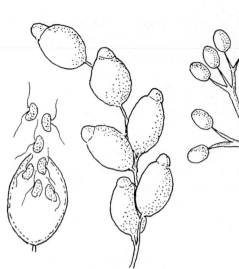

Fig. 97 *Phytophthora.* Right: sporangia; left: sporangium releasing zoospores (highly magnified)

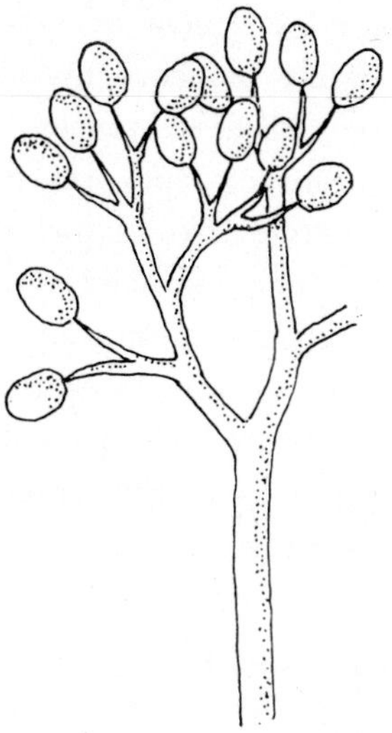

Fig. 98 *Peronospora*: part of sporangiophore (highly magnified)

Fig. 99 *Capsella bursa-pastoris*, Shepherd's purse, attacked and deformed by *Albugo candida*

the excrement of various other herbivores. Their highly branched mycelium which, at an advanced stage of development, becomes divided into cells by means of septa, remains partly embedded in the substrate, from which it sucks up nourishment with the help of haustoria. Occasionally, parts of the hyphae become transformed into thick-walled organs capable of storing large quantities of food. These are known as chlamydospores, and enable the fungi to survive unfavourable periods. Above the prostrate mycelium, a number of more or less rigid hyphae rise up bearing the sexual organs. The upright sporangiophores cut off a number of sporangia at their tips; these take the form of globose swellings in which a central columella becomes separated from the outer sporiferous region.

The Mucorales present us with our first example of gametangiogamy, involving the copulation of two gametangia which, in the main, are similar in structure, and are derived from clearly differentiated thalli, said to be of the plus or minus type.

The most typical of the Mucorales are found in the family Mucoraceae, which includes the widespread genera *Mucor* (white mould), *Rhizopus* and *Phycomyces*. *Mucor*, which prefers horse dung as its substrate, occasionally settles on moist bread which it then covers with a white to greyish mycelium. *Rhizopus* has a characteristic vegetative structure – instead of a branched mycelium, its hyphae take the form of runners (stolons) between groups of rhizoids anchored in the substrate. Above the anchoring organs, the sporangiophores arise in tufts and, as in *Mucor*, terminate in a single spherical sporangium. Species of *Rhizopus*, which live on all sorts of plant remains, on fruit and on bread, are sources of lactic and citric acids. *R. stolonifer*, bread mould, yields fumaric acid. Another species, *R. oryzae*, is able to produce alcohol in considerable quantities. Members of the genus *Phycomyces* grow to an unusually large size; the sporangiophores of these relatively rare fungi can attain a height of up to 10 ins. Some species of *Phycomyces* have a characteristic liking for substrates rich in oils; thus *P. nitens* is occasionally found on oily rags.

While the sexual processes of most Mucorales are similar, asexual reproduction may differ in a number of important respects.

In the small family Pilobolaceae, which consists of only the genus *Pilobolus*, the sporangia are disseminated in a most unusual manner. They are produced singly on elongated, erect sporangiophores, whose tips bear large bladders, each with a thick-walled

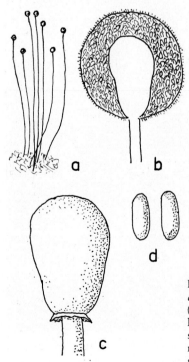

Fig. 100 *Mucor mucedo. a:* Sporangiophores (slightly magnified); *b:* longitudinal section of sporangium (highly magnified); *c:* columella; *d:* spores

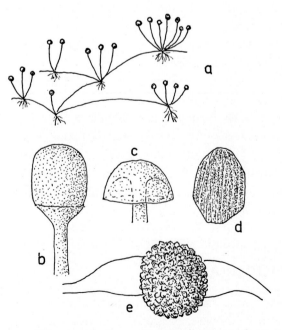

Fig. 101 *Rhizopus stolonifer. a:* Groups of sporangiophores on hyphal stolons (slightly magnified); *b:* columella; *c:* inverted columella; *d:* spore; *e:* zygote (highly magnified)

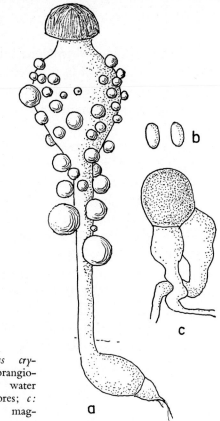

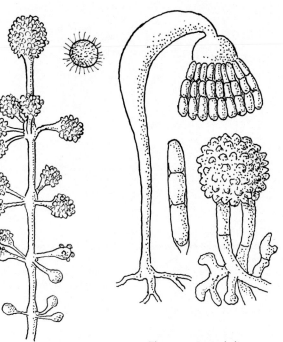

Fig. 102 *Pilobolus crystallinus*. *a*: Sporangiophores exuding water droplets; *b*: spores; *c*: zygote (highly magnified)

Fig. 103 *Cunninghamella bainierii*; conidiophore and conidium (highly magnified)

Fig. 104 *Syncephalis cornu*; left: sporangiophore; centre: part of sporangium; right: zygote (highly magnified)

sporangium. As the pressure mounts inside the bladder, it first exudes countless water droplets, and finally bursts just beneath the sporangium with such force that the sporangium is sent flying over a distance of up to six feet; oddly enough it is invariably flung in the direction of a source of light. *Pilobolus* is saprophytic on the excrement of herbivores. Its sporangia, which stick to grasses and herbs, are swallowed by plant-eating animals and later liberated in their excrement. The sporangia germinate into non-motile spores.

The family Thamnidiaceae forms two types of sporangia: typical large sporangia and atypically small ones known as sporangiola; the Cunninghamellaceae, whose only genus *Cunninghamella* is universally distributed, makes do without sporangia altogether; here asexual reproduction is by means of conidia. These are developed on special conidiophores which rise up vertically above the prostrate mycelium. They consist of a main axis and numerous whorls of lateral branches; the axis and branches are swollen at the tips, and the swellings are covered with a host of tiny conidia.

The Piptocephalidaceae, which include the genera *Piptocephalis* and *Syncephalis*, are the only parasites among the Mucorales; they live exclusively on other species of their own order.

Order
ENDOGONALES

The Endogonales are unusual in that their organs of reproduction develop within tuberous organs constructed of a dense web of hyphae – there is good reason for describing these structures as fruiting bodies. Hollow in some species and solid in others, they can attain a diameter of several centimetres. In the genus *Endogone* (family: Endogonaceae) the web thickens at the periphery into a kind of cortex which additionally protects the fruiting organ.

Order
ENTOMOPHTHORALES

The fungi constituting this order all have characteristically reduced vegetative bodies and reproductive organs and are highly specialized in habit. With the exception of the Basidiobolaceae, which live as saprophytes on the excrement of frogs and lizards, all are parasitic on lower animals and insects.

101

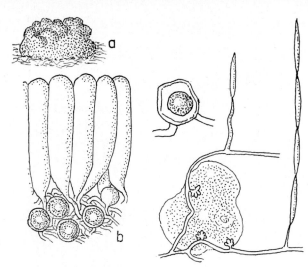

Fig. 105 *Endogone tjibodensis. a:* Fruiting body (slightly magnified); *b:* section through edge of fruiting body, showing part of the hyphal web and chlamydospores (highly magnified)

Fig. 106 *Zoopage.* Below: conidia-bearing mycelium penetrating amoeba by means of haustoria; top: zygote (highly magnified)

The parasitic species fall into two families: the Zoopagaceae and the Entomophthoraceae. The former, relatively simple and microscopically small fungi, live on amoebae and small worms. As the host comes into contact with the prostrate mycelium, the latter sends haustoria into the animal. While forms attacking amoebae, species of *Zoopage* among them, rely more or less on chance meetings with their hosts, species living on rotifers, infusoria and nematode worms develop regular traps – sticky vesicles,

coiled hyphae, close-meshed hyphal nets – with which they can catch and hold their unwilling benefactors. While the Zoopagaceae are relatively unfamiliar fungi, the Entomophthoraceae are well-known insect-killers. In contrast to the Zoopagaceae they develop their mycelia inside the host; the hyphae split up into individual cells, each of which can give rise to a new hypha, with the result that the fungal growth spreads rapidly through the entire insect body. Entomophthorales reproduce asexually by means of conidia formed at the club-shaped tips of conidiophores which eventually burst as inside pressure builds up. While the mycelium itself is embedded inside the insect's body, the conidiophores break out of it in large numbers. Thus dead houseflies are often surrounded by a dense white halo, consisting of innumerable conidia shot out from the conidiophores of *Entomophthora muscae.*

Class

ASCOMYCETES

Sac Fungi

With the Ascomycetes we come to the 'higher fungi', i.e. fungi whose life cycle does not involve motile stages, whose multi-cellular mycelia produce fruiting bodies, and in which sexual predominates over asexual reproduction.

One of the chief characteristics of sac fungi is the presence of an ascus – a club-shaped unicellular

Fig. 107 *Entomophthora muscae;* flies enmeshed in mycelium

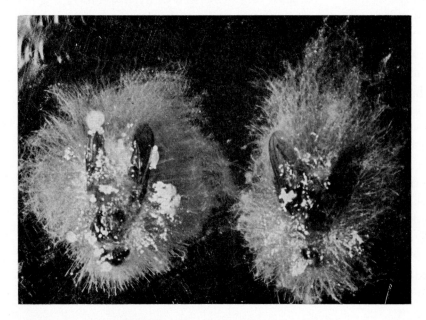

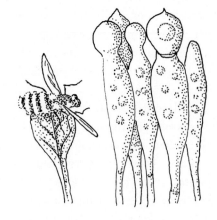

Fig. 108 *Entomophthora muscae.* Right: conidiophore (highly magnified); left: captured fly with conidiophores protruding from abdomen

102

sporangium in which a precise number of spores – usually 8 – is formed. The production of asci invariably involves sexual processes. In the lower Ascomycetes, the asci generally arise directly from the fusion product of the sexual organs; in the more highly developed forms they originate from a binucleate mycelium that grows out of the female organ after copulation. In most sac fungi, the asci are combined into erect fruiting bodies built up of densely interwoven or fused hyphae.

Sexual reproduction in Ascomycetes is exclusively by gametangiogamy. The copulating gametangia may be identical in shape; more often, however, they are clearly differentiated into male antheridia and female ascogonia. These are characteristically reduced in many Ascomycetes.

Asexual reproduction, which is so predominant in Phycomycetes, plays a subsidiary role in most Ascomycetes. It generally involves the presence of conidia, formed on special conidiophores and cut off from them by construction. Occasionally conidiophores, like asci, are combined into fruiting bodies.

The classification of Ascomycetes, a class comprising some 20,000 species all over the world, poses a number of special problems. However, differences in the structure of the asci and the presence or absence of fruiting bodies make it possible to fit all of them into one or the other of two sub-classes.

Sub-Class

PROTASCOMYCETIDAE

The Protascomycetidae have a characteristically simple vegetative structure: their mycelia are rudimentary, and the hyphae often consist of individual cells, each capable of producing a new mycelium by budding. The hyphae arise singly and show no inclination to combine or to become intertwined. As a result, no fruiting bodies can be formed, and their absence is, in fact, a typical feature of the Protascomycetidae.

These simple vegetative characteristics go hand in hand with special reproductive features: the haploid ascospore germinates into a haploid mycelium, certain cells of which act as isogametangia and copulate. Their fusion leads to the formation of a zygote, in which the nuclei lie side by side in pairs; they usually combine after a relatively short interval whereupon the zygote is transformed into a diploid ascus. From it, four haploid nuclei, or multiples of four haploid nuclei, are produced by reduction division. They surround themselves with cytoplasm and a cell wall and develop into ascospores, which later leave through the softened wall of the ascus and germinate into a new, haploid mycelium. What is important in this development is the fact that the ascus originates directly from a zygote. This type of development is characteristic of the great majority of Protascomycetidae; in a small number of species lacking sexual organs the fusion product of the copulating cells develops into a rudimentary binucleate mycelium, which later produces asci.

Protascomycetidae can also reproduce asexually. This they do by means of conidia borne on separate conidiophores or by mycelial fragments known as oidia.

The Protascomycetidae include the orders Protomycetales, Endomycetales and Taphrinales.

The Protomycetales are the most primitive Protascomycetidae; they produce a well-developed mycelium but no typical asci. They are parasites without exception, and their best-known family, the Ascosphaeraceae, attack beehives. They chiefly feed on the pollen stored in the combs, but also on the larvae.

The Endomycetales are the largest order in this sub-class; they have a characteristic tendency to dissolve their mycelia; beyond that they are distinguished by living on sugar-containing substrates. Various Endomycetales, such as the Dipodascaceae, live exclusively on the oozing of wounded trees. The Spermophthoraceae are fruit parasites; they are introduced into the ovaries of fruit trees by pollinating insects and cause severe damage to crops. The best-known genus, *Eremothecium*, causes the fruit disease known as stigmatomycosis. *Spermophthora gossypii* infests and destroys the capsules of the cotton plant.

The most important family in the Endomycetales are the yeasts (Saccharomycetaceae); their mycelia are built up of chains of oval cells which can break free from their loose association at any time, and multiply by budding. In this process, bud-like outgrowths are cut off by constriction, and finally split

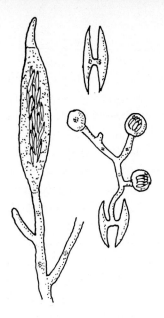

Fig. 109 *Spermophthora gossypii*. Left: gametangium; top right: copulating gametes; bottom right: zygote sending up mycelium with asci (highly magnified)

off by the formation of cell walls, after a daughter nucleus has first migrated into each 'bud'. This type of propagation is particularly characteristic of the genus *Saccharomyces*, to which all the fungi we normally designate as 'yeasts' belong. Occasionally yeasts also form asci by the copulation of two cells; the asci themselves can multiply by budding. Each ascus contains 4 ascospores. The genus *Saccharomyces* owes its great economic importance to its ability to change sugar into alcohol by fermentation. The best-known species are *S. cerevisiae*, brewer's yeast, and *S. ellipsoideus*, wine yeast. In nature, yeasts are found in fruits and in the soil; they are, however, easily grown

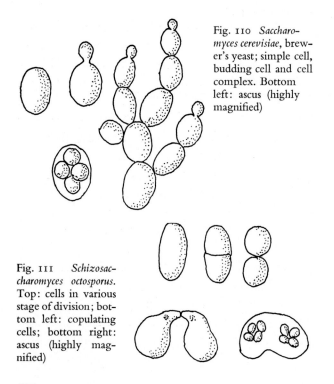

Fig. 110 *Saccharomyces cerevisiae*, brewer's yeast; simple cell, budding cell and cell complex. Bottom left: ascus (highly magnified)

Fig. 111 *Schizosaccharomyces octosporus*. Top: cells in various stage of division; bottom left: copulating cells; bottom right: ascus (highly magnified)

on suitable culturing media, so that brewers and bakers do not have to rely on natural sources.

Closely related to *Saccharomyces* is the genus *Schizosaccharomyces*, which has more elongated cells and usually produces 8 ascospores per ascus. This yeast is, however, of small economic importance and so are the genera *Saccharomycodes* and *Nadsonia*, both of which live on the oozing sap of trees.

Order
TAPHRINALES

The Taphrinales occupy a special position among the Protascomycetidae in that their ascus is not produced directly from a zygote cell resulting from the copulation of two cells but rather from a special, binucleate hypha derived from the mycelium.

The Taphrinales, whose sole genus is *Taphrina*, are all parasitic on vascular plants, particularly on deciduous trees, causing profuse growth and hence malformations of the host tissue. Thus *T. betulina*, which attacks birch trees, causes witches' broom; *T. deformans* causes peach leaf curl; *T. pruni* causes plum pockets; and *T. populina* causes spherical leaf on poplars.

Sub-Class
EUASCOMYCETIDAE

The Euascomycetidae are characterized by the production of fruiting bodies (ascocarps) of four types, all of which originate in the vegetative mycelium and are built up of densely intertwined and often fused hyphae.

The life cycle begins with an ascospore, which germinates into a haploid mycelium. From it, fruiting bodies arise in due course. Certain hyphae in the mycelium develop into organs of copulation which, in the typical case, are sexually differentiated gametangia. While the male organs, representing the antheridia, are unicellular and relatively small, the female gametangia are larger, divided into a swollen cell, the ascogonium, and a long hypha, the trichogyne, which receives the male nucleus. During copulation, pairs of gametangia come to lie side by side, whereupon the nuclei of the antheridium enter the ascogonium and combine with its nuclei to form

104

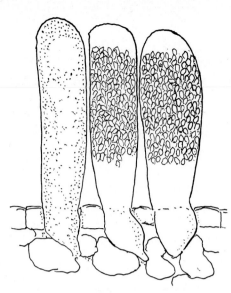

Fig. 112 *Taphrina populina* (highly magnified)

nuclear pairs. The ascogonium then sends up a host of 'ascogenous' hyphae, each of which receives one pair of nuclei. Cell division of the hyphae and conjugate division of the nuclear pair then lead to the formation of a binucleate mycelium. The terminal cells of its hyphae produce one or more asci in the manner that has already been described; in them the fusion of sexual nuclei and reduction division leads to formation of 4 or 8 ascospores. During asexual reproduction, which usually plays no more than a subsidiary role in this sub-class, the mycelia produce conidiophores from which conidia are cut off in due course.

The life cycle of Euascomycetidae involves the regular alternation of gametophyte and sporophyte generations: the gametophyte is represented by a haploid mycelium which produces the gametangia, and also gives rise to the fruiting bodies. The sporophyte is represented by the ascogenous hyphae and ends its development with the union of the sexual nuclei in the young ascus; it is therefore binucleate and hence differs radically from the diploid sporophyte of all other plants.

Asci are invariably formed and developed within the fruiting body, which generally arises simultaneously with the ascogenous hyphae. However, occasionally the fruiting bodies may be laid down before the gametangia. The temporal relationship between the formation of ascocarps and asci affects the form of the fruiting body which, as we saw, occurs in four types. The most primitive fruiting bodies are thought to be those which appear before the gametangia. They are built up of compact hyphal tissue, and some of the hyphae within them give rise to gametangia. After copulation, the ascogonium sends up binucleate ascogenous hyphae, with the result that cavities appear in the fruiting body in which the asci are eventually produced. Such fruiting bodies are known as pseudothecia, and they release the mature ascospores through a pore at their tip. The remaining three types of fruiting body are formed almost simultaneously with the ascogenous hyphae, but differ markedly from one another both in structure and in shape. Fruiting bodies of the second type are more or less spherical and completely closed; they consist of a loose mass of hyphae in which the asci are embedded and a tough envelope, the peridium. Such fruiting bodies are known as cleistothecia and decompose once the ascospores mature, or burst open under the pressure of the swelling asci. The so-called perithecia are bottle-shaped, and like pseudothecia, release their ascospores through an aperture at the tip. However, in their case the aperture does not result from a break in the wall but is laid down from the very beginning, as is the cavity within. From its base, narrow, club-shaped asci rise up to form a definite layer known as the hymenium (Gr. *hymen* = membrane); in it the asci are interspersed with sterile, elongated hairs, the so-called paraphyses. The fourth type of fruiting body also contains asci and paraphyses; however, it is no longer closed or half-closed but takes the form of a beak or disk-shaped structure (apothecium) with a vague resemblance to the cap of mushrooms. Apothecia are characteristic of Discomycetes, the most highly developed of all Euascomycetidae.

The resemblance between mature pseudothecia and perithecia suggests that fungi with such fruiting bodies are related; this assumption is supported by a further characteristic shared by all pseudothecial and perithecial fungi: their fruiting bodies are combined into a compact and often tough hyphal structure, the soma, which provides them with additional protection.

The structure of their fruiting bodies helps to divide the Euascomycetidae into four distinct series and is therefore of crucial taxonomic importance.

The first series produces pseudothecial fruiting

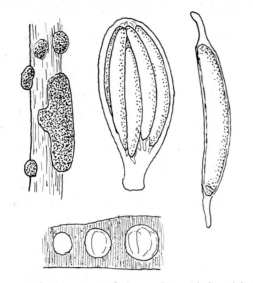

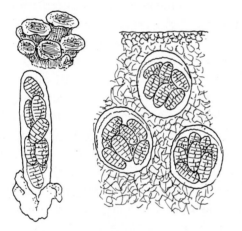

bodies and consists chiefly of tropical fungi. Its most important orders are the **M**yriangiales, Dothideales Pleosporales and Microthyriales. Most are parasitic on higher plants, though some, e.g. the Myriangiaceae and Piedraiaceae (Order: Myriangiales) attack different hosts as well. The Piedraiaceae, which include only the genus *Piedraia*, occur in South America and in tropical Asia. They are parasitic on human hair, causing black piedra. These fungi form their stromata around the hairs, where they feel like so many little grains. The Myriangiaceae, which are widely distributed, are partly parasitic on scale insects, e.g. on *Myriangium duriaei*. The order Dothideales includes such saprophytic genera as *Mycosphaerella* which feed on leaf litter, together with a host of parasitic forms. *Capnodium* (Family: Capnodiaceae) attacks edible plants in the tropics and subtropics; it feeds on the sugary excretions of plant lice and shield lice, and is not therefore a plant parasite in the true sense of the word; however, it covers the leaves infested by these insects with dense mycelia, known as sooty moulds, which eventually kill the plants, the more so as Capnodiaceae multiply rapidly by asexual reproduction. The mycelia produce oval fruiting bodies, together with a large number of flask-shaped conidia-bearing organs – the pycnidia. The order Pleosporales includes the family Venturiaceae which are parasitic on fruit; *Venturia inaequalis* is the cause of apple scab and *V. pirina* the cause of pear scab. The fungi enter the peripheral tissue of the fruit and develop fruiting bodies; their tips, surrounded by a wreath of bristly brown hyphae, eventually break out of the epidermis of the diseased fruit.

While all the orders we have been discussing produce more or less spherical pseudothecia, the Microthyriales have characteristically flat and shield-shaped fruiting bodies which open by pores or by star-shaped slits. All Microthyriales are parasitic on the leaves of higher plants. Most species spread their mycelia on the leaf surface, and send haustoria into the leaf tissue; the haustoria arise from unicellular outgrowths of the hyphae, the so-called hyphopodia. One family, the Trichothyriaceae (which includes only the one genus *Trichothyrium*), lives on other parasitic leaf fungi, and covers their hyphae with a membranous mycelium.

Fig. 113 *Piedraia javanica*. Left: human hair with fungal fruiting bodies (magnified); bottom left: longitudinal section through a fruiting body (magnified); centre: ascus (highly magnified); top right: ascospore

Fig. 114 *Myriangium duriaei*. Top left: fruiting body (slightly magnified); right: longitudinal section through fruiting body (magnified); bottom left: ascus after breaking out of its sheath

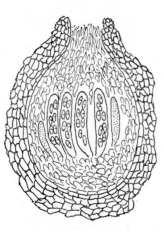

Fig. 115 *Mycosphaerella;* longitudinal section through a fruiting body whose central tissue has been partly displaced by the asci (highly magnified) ———

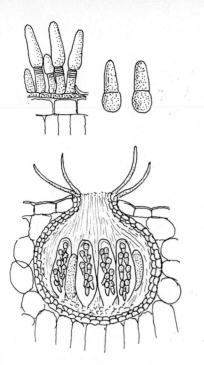

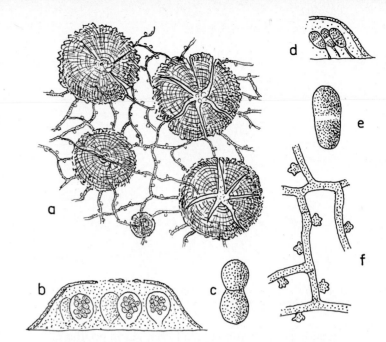

Fig. 116 *Venturia inaequalis*. Below: longitudinal section through fruiting body; top left: ascospores; top right: conidial stage (*Spilocaea*; highly magnified)

Fig. 117 *Asterina lawsoniae*. *a*: Part of colony viewed from the top (slightly magnified); *b*: longitudinal section through fruiting body with asci; *c*: ascospore (highly magnified); *d*: longitudinal section through conidial fruiting body; *e*: conidium (highly magnified); *f*: hyphae with hyphopodia (highly magnified)

The Myriangiales, Dothideales, Pleosporales and Microthyriales all open their asci in the same way. The asci are enclosed in a double wall with a thin and relatively brittle outer layer; as they mature the thick, elastic inner layer breaks out and opens by a pore, through which the ascospores are expelled one at a time.

All these orders, as we saw, have the same type of fruiting bodies, i.e. pseudothecia. In the more primitive forms, the pseudothecia are divided into numerous chambers or locules, each of which houses an ascus. In the more highly developed types, on the other hand, the pseudothecia are single-chambered and produce numerous asci, usually in association with sterile hyphae. Setting aside the fact that they are formed before and not after organs of copulation, the fruiting bodies of advanced pseudothecial fungi are highly reminiscent, both in structure and form, of perithecia, in which the central cavity and pore are present from the start. This similarity points to a

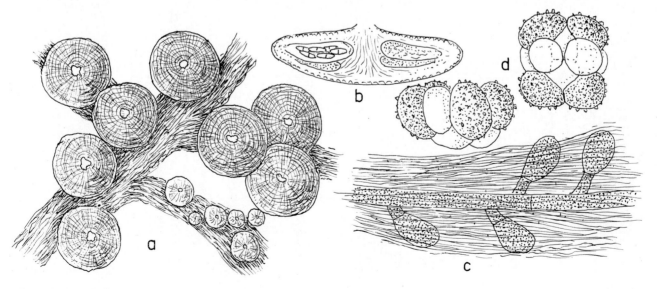

Fig. 118 *Trichothyrium asterophorum*. *a*: Fruiting body; *b*: fruiting body in longitudinal section (magnified); *c*: mycelium proliferating on a *Meliola* hypha; *d*: conidia viewed from the top and from the side (highly magnified)

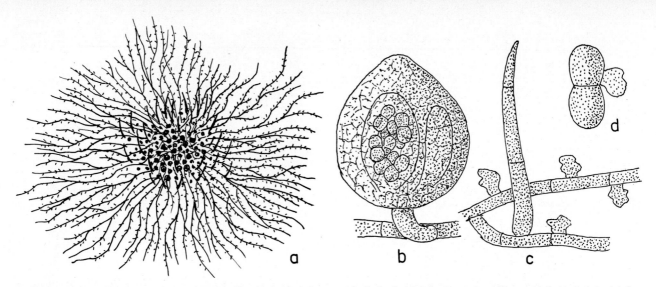

Fig. 119 *Balladyna velutina*. *a*: Top view of small colony (slightly magnified); *b*: fruiting body; *c*: mycelium with hair; *d*: germinating spore (highly magnified)

certain affinity between pseudothecial and perithecial fungi, though we have no evidence that they are directly related. More probably, both are related to the cleistothecial fungi whose fruiting bodies are produced after copulation has occurred, i.e. in the same way as perithecia, from which, however, they differ in external appearance, and also in being completely closed until the very end of their development – much like pseudothecia.

Cleistothecial fungi do not constitute a homogeneous group – the various orders have but few common characteristics. The mainly tropical Meliolales are parasitic on higher plants, and send haustoria into their leaf tissue. As in the Microthyriales, the haustoria arise from hyphopodia which, moreover,

help to anchor the mycelial hyphae. The fruiting bodies are mostly spherical in shape and often covered with hairy outgrowths. In a number of genera, e.g. in *Balladyna* (Family: Englerulaceae) and *Meliola* (Family: Meliolaceae), long, bristly hyphae rise up between the fruiting bodies. In the Coronophorales, which live on the bark of dead trees, the fruiting bodies are arranged in a circle and embedded in a stroma.

The cleistothecial group also includes one small order whose precise position among the Ascomycetes is still disputed. This is the order Laboulbeniales, whose vegetative bodies have a most unusual structure and development. These fungi produce a rudimentary mycelium which may be reduced to a

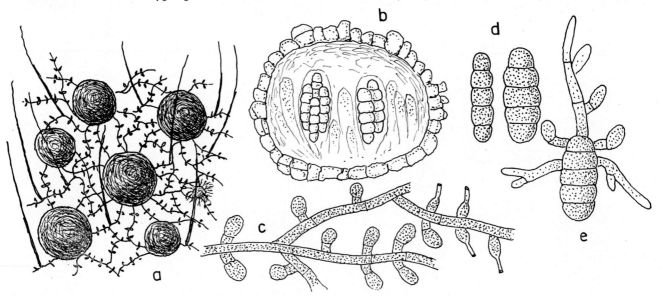

Fig. 120 *Meliola*. *a*: Top view of colony (slightly magnified); *b*: fruiting body in longitudinal section; *c*: mycelium with filamentous and tapering hyphopodia; *d*: side and top view of spore; *e*: germinating spore (highly magnified)

single hypha or may take the form of a multi-cellular, more or less compact mycelium. Special branches at its side or tip bear the sexual organs, which are usually combined in one and the same individual. The female organs, which are enclosed in a sac-shaped envelope, consist of three superposed cells; while the lowermost represents the ascogonium, the apical cell, which thins out into a fine thread, represents the trichogyne. It protrudes from the envelope, which later develops into a fruiting body. The male organs, flask-shaped antheridia, are attached to thin hyphae near the ascogonium. They give rise to non-motile gametes known as spermatia.

When a spermatium comes into contact with a trichogyne, it adheres to it and transfers its contents through a pore in the trichogyne to the ascogonium, with whose protoplasm it combines. The now binucleate ascogonium becomes transformed into an ascogenous cell which cuts off asci in all directions. Each ascus gives rise to 4 or 8 ascospores which escape into the fruiting body when the ascus wall dissolves. Since the ascogenous cell keeps producing new asci, the thin-walled fruiting body becomes filled with a large number of ascospores and swells up; its wall finally tears, and the spores are liberated. All Laboulbeniales are parasitic on insects and mites. Most of them are ectoparasites and, being very small, do not impede their hosts' motion to any appreciable extent. The Ceratomycetaceae, which include the genus *Zodiomyces*, live on water beetles. The Laboulbeniaceae and the Peyritschiellaceae (which include the genus *Stichomyces*) are predominantly tropical and attack every conceivable kind of insect. *Stigmatomyces baeri* (Laboulbeniaceae) is a widespread parasite of the house fly.

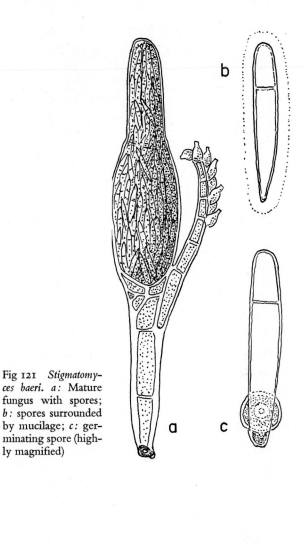

Fig 121 *Stigmatomyces baeri. a:* Mature fungus with spores; *b:* spores surrounded by mucilage; *c:* germinating spore (highly magnified)

Order
ERYSIPHALES

The Erysiphales are another order of parasitic fungi which, unlike the previous order, fits well into the typical cleistothecial series. Members of this order cause the plant diseases known as powdery mildews, a name they have earned because they produce a vast number of small white conidia on the surface of the host. The mycelium is entirely superficial and is securely anchored by haustoria in the host epidermis.

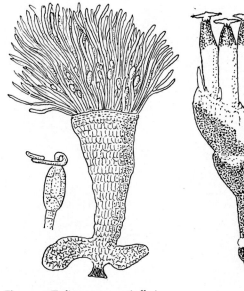

Fig. 122 *Zodiomyces vorticellarius.* Left: ascogonium with trichogyne and attaching spermatium (magnified)

Fig. 123 *Dichomyces bicolor* (highly magnified)

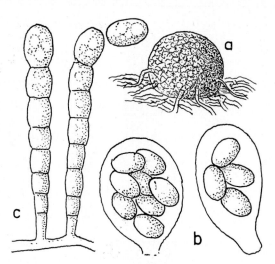

Fig. 124 *Erysiphe polygoni. a:* Fruiting body (magnified); *b:* asci; *c:* conidial stage (*oidium*; highly magnified)

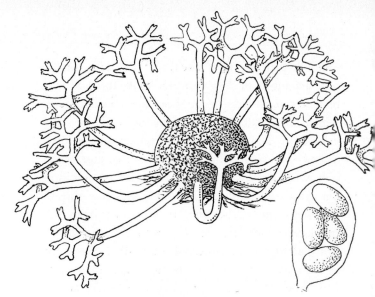

Fig. 126 *Microsphaera berberidis;* fruiting bodies with forking hyphae. Right: ascus (highly magnified)

The fruiting bodies are typically rounded cleistothecia, which remain completely closed until the ascospores mature. Their base usually bears a ring of long hyphae which facilitate dissemination, usually by the wind. In many genera, for instance in *Sphaerotheca* and *Erysiphe*, the hyphae are flaccid and bent at the tip; in *Phyllactinia* they look like bristles, each with a bulbous base. The bulbs serve as most unusual dissemination devices: their thin-walled

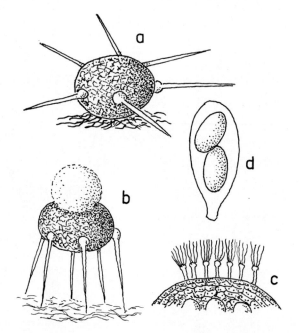

Fig. 125 *Phyllactinia guttata. a:* Fruiting body; *b:* fruiting body raised on 'stilts' above the mycelium (note the drop of mucus on top of the fruiting body); *c:* longitudinal section through the upper wall of the fruiting body, showing tufted mucus-secreting cells; *d:* ascus (highly magnified)

underside begins to shrink during dry spells, whereupon the ring of bristles is pulled downwards, with the result that the individual bristles act as stilts for the cleistothecium. In that position, it is easily caught by the slightest breath of wind and scattered abroad. The fruiting bodies of *Microsphaera*, which are also wind-disseminated, are elongated hyphae bearing numerous fork-shaped branches at their tips.

Powdery mildews attacking cultivated plants include *Sphaerotheca humuli*, which infests the hop plant, and *Uncinula necator* which attacks the grape vine with much the same dire results as downy mildew (*Plasmopara viticola*, see p. 87). Very widespread also are powdery mildews of the genus *Microsphaera*. Thus *M. grossulariae* attacks berries, particularly red currants; *M. alphitoides*, which occurs almost invariably in the conidial form, attacks oak leaves. Various sulphur preparations are available against mildew-causing fungi and have, on the whole, proved most effective.

Order

EUROTIALES

The large and highly diverse order of Eurotiales has many affinities with the Erysiphales, so much so that the two are often combined into a special group. Both have similar cleistothecia, and reproduction in both is predominantly asexual. Unlike the Erysiphales, the Eurotiales include many dissimilar forms, all of which, however, are alike in that their asci are

110

arranged in an unusual way. Whereas the asci of most Ascomycetes (with the exception of the pseudothecial fungi) constitute a clearly defined layer in the fruiting body, they are scattered in the fruiting body of Eurotiales, in which the ascogenous hyphae, whose apical cells produce the asci, are of different lengths.

The Eurotiales include several families, each with typical characters of its own. The Gymnoascaceae, a small family, represented by the genera *Gymnoascus* and *Ctenomyces*, occupies a special position among cleistothecial fungi in that their fruiting body lacks the usual closed wall; it consists of a loose web of ramified hyphae round a mass of glittering asci. Fruiting bodies are only formed in favourable conditions; many species reproduce exclusively by conidia or thick-walled chlamydospores. Most Gymnoascaceae are soil-inhabiting saprobes and feed on refuse and all sorts of animal matter; some have become parasitic and cause various troublesome skin diseases in man.

Family

Eurotiaceae

The Eurotiaceae deserve special treatment, not least because they are probably the most widespread family among all known fungi. They develop characteristic cleistothecia, though very many of them reproduce exclusively by means of conidia. This is particularly true of the genera *Eurotium* and *Carpenteles*, whose conidial forms have been given

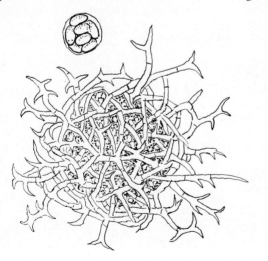

Fig. 127 *Gymnoascus reesii;* fruiting body and ascus (highly magnified)

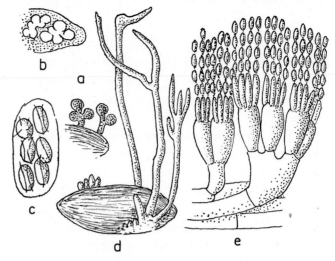

Fig. 128 *Eurotium herbariorum. a:* Fruiting body; *b:* ascus; *c:* spores viewed from above and from the side; *d:* young mycelium; *e:* conidiophore (highly magnified)

special names. Thus, while the conidial stage of *Eurotium* is known as *Aspergillus, Carpenteles* is generally described as *Penicillium. Eurotium* still comprises a relatively large number of species able to form fruiting bodies – tiny, spherical cleistothecia surrounded by a tough wall – but even these species occur chiefly in the conidial form. In the genus *Carpenteles*, however, fruiting bodies are most exceptional. Taxonomists take this fact into account when they refer to the two genera mostly by their conidial names.

Aspergillus and *Penicillium* are the most widespread moulds known to man. Most of them are saprophytic on all sorts of substrates, including bread, fruit and milk. Both genera produce richly branching mycelia, which proliferate in or on the substrate. The mycelium is covered with countless conidiophores, which cut off large numbers of conidia at their tips. The conidiophores are of characteristic shape and are the best means of distinguishing *Aspergillus* from *Penicillium*. In the former, the conidium-bearing hyphae terminate in a vesicle covered with rod-shaped unicellular organs, known as sterigmata. The conidiophores of *Penicillium*, on the other hand, are branched, each little branchlet bearing a sterigma crowned with a chain of conidia.

Unlike the mycelia, which are more or less colourless, the conidia contain a variety of pigments which give colonies of these fungi their characteristic colours: black, brown, green, yellow or white in *Aspergillus* and chiefly blue-green in *Penicillium*

(*Pl. 77, p. 144*). In *Aspergillus* the pigments vary with the distribution of trace elements in the substrate. Thus *A. niger* is black when it grows on a substrate containing traces of copper, and bright yellow on substrates devoid of copper.

When *Aspergillus* and *Penicillium* infest bread, boiled potatoes, fruits and many other foodstuffs, they cause them to go mouldy. Some species of *Penicillium*, for instance *P. digitatum*, attack and gradually destroy citrus fruits. *Aspergillus fumigatus* has become partly parasitic, infecting birds and, less frequently, man as well. The resulting aspergillosis of the lungs gives rise to symptoms that closely resemble those of tuberculosis.

Many species of *Penicillium* are, however, extremely useful. Thus they have long been employed to impart the characteristic flavour to such cheeses as Camembert and Roquefort. More recently they have been used as sources of penicillin, the now famous antibiotic. Since it became possible to obtain penicillin in its pure state, *P. notatum* and *P. chrysogenum* have been exploited on a vast scale in the fight against infectious diseases.

Besides the universally distributed genera *Aspergillus* and *Penicillium*, the Eurotiaceae also include a number of predominantly tropical genera, among them *Monascus*, an East Asian mould with a striking red colour. It is cultivated on a large scale in China, where it serves to dye a variety of foodstuffs.

The Eurotiales also include *Graphium ulmi*, a parasite which attacks and kills off elm trees. It is the conidial form of *Ceratocystis ulmi* (Family: Ceratocystaceae). The fungus lives in the sapwood of elms just beneath the bark, and is transmitted by beetles of the genus *Scolytus*. *Ceratocystis picae* attacks felled conifers, causing blue stain of lumber.

Unlike most typical Eurotiales which develop on the surface of their substrate, the Elaphomycetaceae lead an underground existence. Many of them form mycorrhizae with forest trees, especially with conifers; others live as saprobes. The family is also unique in having the largest fruiting bodies among cleistothecial fungi. These are spherical to oval in shape, have a diameter of more than 1 in., and are surrounded by a tough two-layered wall and covered with thick warts in most species. They are highly reminiscent of truffles, a fact that is reflected in the popular name of *Elaphomyces cervinus* – 'stag truffle'.

The most highly developed cleistothecial fungi are found in the order Onygenales, whose only family, the Onygenaceae, occur mainly in the tropics. They produce their fruiting bodies at the tip of erect stalks which can attain heights of up to 10 ins. The genus *Onygena*, which lives on the horns, hooves and hairs of various domestic animals, has very small, short-stalked fruiting bodies.

We now come to the perithecial fungi, whose flask-shaped fruiting bodies open by means of a preformed pore at the tip. As we said earlier, they are single-

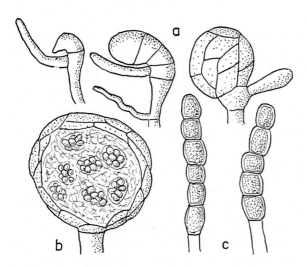

Fig. 129 *Monascus purpureus*. *a:* Fruiting bodies in various stages of development; *b:* mature fruiting body (longitudinal section); *c:* formation of conidia (highly magnified)

Fig. 130 Penicillin crystals (approx. x 100)

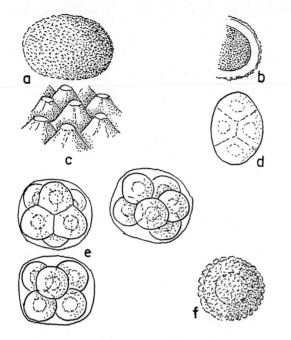

Fig. 131 *Elaphomyces variegatus. a :* Fruiting body; *b :* longitudinal section of fruiting body; *c :* part of surface (slightly magnified); *d :* young ascus; *e :* half-ripe ascus; *f :* ascospore (highly magnified)

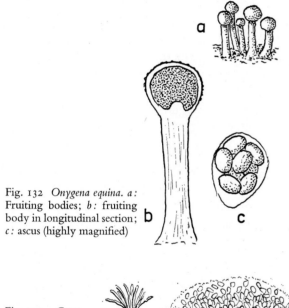

Fig. 132 *Onygena equina. a :* Fruiting bodies; *b :* fruiting body in longitudinal section; *c :* ascus (highly magnified)

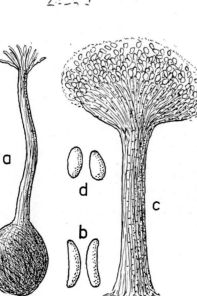

Fig. 133 *Cerato-cystis ulmi. a :* Fruiting body; *b :* ascospores; *c :* conidial stage (*Graphium ulmi*); *d :* conidia (highly magnified)

chambered; the base of each chamber bears countless club-shaped asci and sterile paraphyses. Asci and paraphyses together constitute the fruiting layer, known as the hymenium. The perithecia may be free-standing on the mycelium, or else embedded in a compact stroma.

The classification of perithecial fungi is chiefly based on vegetative characteristics, particularly on the structure of the stroma.

Order

HYPOCREALES

The Hypocreales include species with free-standing fruiting bodies; but far more frequently, their peri-thecia are embedded in the surface layer of a stroma. A special characteristic of this order is the construction of the ascospores: these are built up of two and sometimes of a greater number of cells. The Hypocreales also reproduce asexually, generally by means of conidia, which are often combined in a stroma of their own.

In the most primitive Hypocreales, the Hypomyce-taceae, the mycelium at first produces nothing but conidia; these are cut off individually from branching conidiophores. Later, fruiting bodies are developed as well – either attached to the mycelium or else enclosed in a loose mat of hyphae. Just like the mycelium which, depending on the genus and species, may be white, red or yellow, so the fruiting bodies, too, occur in a variety of bright colours. The Hypomycetaceae are parasitic on various mushrooms, including the cep (*Boletus edulis*) and related forms.

The Nectriaceae generally have their perithecia and conidia in special stromata. The perithecia are bunched together in the surface layer of what is usually a tuberous stroma; the conidia may be attached to the dense hyphae of small, spherical stromata, or else cut off by individual conidiophores. The first type of conidium is unicellular and is said to be of the *Tubercularia* form. The free-standing conidia are large, divided into several cells, have a crescent shape, and are of the *Fusarium* form.

The genus *Nectria*, one of the few Nectriaceae occurring outside the tropics, includes species with either type of conidium. *N. cinnabarina* (*Pl. 38, p. 63*) whose dark-red perithecia can often be seen on

113

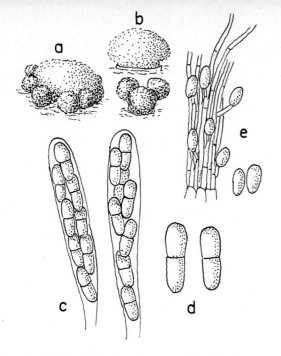

Fig. 134 *Nectria cinnabarina. a:* Stroma with perithecia and conidia; *b:* conidial stroma beside perithecial stroma (*Tubercularia vulgaris*); *c:* asci; *d:* ascospores; *e:* part of conidial stroma (highly magnified)

dead branches, reproduces asexually as *Tubercularia vulgaris*. In *N. haematococca*, a tropical genus, the conidial stage is of the *Fusarium* type. Most species of *Nectria* are saprophytic on a variety of dead plants; the exception is *N. galligena* which is parasitic on the bark of various fruit trees, causing the so-called European canker disease which leads to the gradual destruction of the bark and eventual death of the tree. The genus *Gibberella*, which is more common in warmer regions, is parasitic on the roots of rice, maize and other cereals; it causes prolific growth in the host by the production of gibberellic acid.

The Nectriaceae, many of which represent the most highly developed Hypocreales, comprise forms with the tuberous stromata characteristic of that order together with forms in which the stromata are ramified, e.g. the genus *Podostroma* from the tropics of East Asia.

Order
CLAVICIPITALES

The Clavicipitales, which are made up of a single but highly varied family, the Clavicipitaceae, are all parasitic on grasses, sedges and insects. The fruiting bodies are invariably developed in a soft stroma which, in a number of genera, is clearly divided into a basal, sterile part acting as a stalk and an upper perithecium-bearing section. The asci are exceptionally long; their walls are thickened at the tip to form a mucous plug with a long cylindrical pore. The ascospores, which arise inside the asci in groups of eight, have a characteristic shape found in only a few of the most highly developed Ascomycetes: on maturing, they grow into long threads, and form a dense bundle that fills the entire ascus. Asexual reproduction is by means of conidia, generally combined in conidial stromata.

European Clavicipitales parasitic on grasses and sedges include the genera *Epichloe* and *Claviceps*. Of the former, the most widespread species is *E. typhina* whose stromata can often be seen to surround blades of grass. The stromata are white and, at first, only produce conidia; later they also give rise to perithecia and change their colour to yellow or brown.

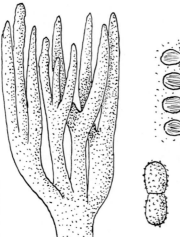

Fig. 135 *Podostroma grossum*. Left: fruiting body; top right: part of stroma in longitudinal section; bottom right: ascospore

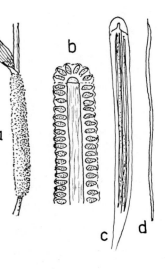

Fig. 136 *Epichloe typhina. a:* fruiting body on blade of grass; *b:* longitudinal section through a fruiting body (slightly magnified); *c:* ascus; *d:* spore

The genus *Claviceps* is best known through *C. purpurea*, one of whose stages causes the plant disease known as ergot. When the spores of *C. purpurea* germinate on rye flowers, the young mycelium penetrates into the ovary and develops into a loose conidial stroma. This organ secretes a sugary fluid and attracts insects which carry the conidia to other rye flowers. The conidial stromata gradually consume the tissue of the ovary; at the same time, their hyphae become fused into a compact tissue to form grain-like structures known as sclerotia. These represent the 'ergot' of commerce and are easily identified by their dark-purple colour (*Pl. 41, p. 64*). With their formation, which takes place at the time of the rye harvest, the fungus concludes its seasonal development, and drops to the ground where it remains throughout the winter. Next spring it produces fruiting bodies with long stalks and spherical heads bearing countless perithecia. These give rise to new ascospores, whereupon a new life cycle begins.

As we mentioned earlier, the sclerotia of *C. purpurea* are used in medicine and also cause a dangerous disease – ergotism. They contain various alkaloids, and, in the past, improper methods of cleaning flour caused a great many deaths in countries with a high consumption of rye bread. Nowadays, ergotism is generally restricted to domestic animals, especially to cattle which graze in infected fields.

In medicine, the sclerotia of *C. purpurea* are used in the preparation of a strong abortifacient which is also employed to control haemorrhage during childbirth.

Most Clavicipitaceae are restricted to the tropics, where many of them attack bamboo plants. Of those parasitic on insects, only *Cordyceps* (on the vegetable fly) occurs in Central Europe. With the exception of *C. ophioglossoides* which lives on *Elaphomyces* (stag truffle) all species are parasitic on the larvae, pupae and adult stages of various insects, which they eventually destroy. Their mycelia proliferate in the insect body, and become transformed into sclerota which later give rise to perithecium-bearing stromata. These are erect and filamentous structures usually divided into a basal 'stalk' and an upper, fertile part, in whose hyphal tissue the perithecia are partly or wholly embedded. In *C. robertsii*, which is parasitic on lepidopterous insects, the fertile upper part of the

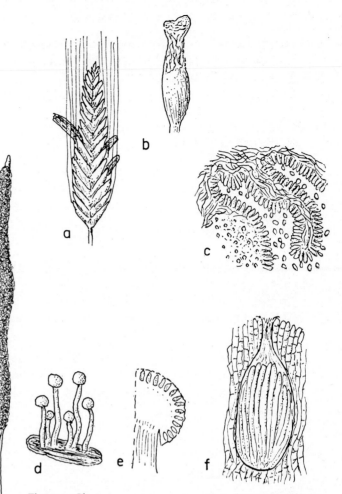

Fig. 137 *Claviceps purpurea*, ergot. *a*: Ear of rye with sclerotia (*Secale cornutum*); *b*: semi-mature sclerotium forming conidia at its tip; *c*: part of conidium-forming tissue in section (highly magnified); *d*: sclerotium after germination, with fruiting bodies; *e*: longitudinal section through a fruiting body; *f*: perithecium (highly magnified)

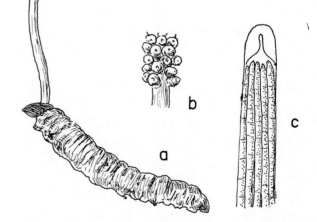

Fig. 138 *Cordyceps robertsii*. *a*: Fruiting body on *Oxycanus* larva (natural size); *b*: group of perithecia; *c*: tip of ascus (highly magnified)

115

stroma bears a stalk-like elongation as well; in other species it looks like a small head. The stromata generally have bright colours.

Order
CHAETOMIALES

The Chaetomiales, which comprise two small families, the Chaetomiaceae and the Melanosporaceae, are the only perithecial fungi that do not produce stromata. Their fruiting bodies are attached to the surface of the mycelium, and are often covered with long hairs. In the Chaetomiaceae, the tip of the fruiting body gives rise to countless curly hairs arranged in tufts round the pore. Such tufts are absent from the conspicuous, soft, bright-coloured and beak-shaped perithecia of the Melanosporaceae. All Chaetomiales live saprophytically on decaying plant material and chiefly on cellulose. The Chaetomiaceae, in particular, can cause considerable damage to paper, cotton and linen.

Order
XYLARIALES

The most primitive Xylariales show clear affinities with the Chaetomiales, like which they produce free-standing fruiting bodies. The more highly developed species, however, produce stromata of various shapes or else surround their fruiting bodies with a dense mat of hyphae. The fruiting bodies are beak-shaped as in the Melanosporaceae and open by a pore at the tip. They invariably contain a true hymenium, consisting of club-shaped asci and sterile paraphyses. A characteristic feature of the Xylariales is the presence of colourless ascospores which turn black as they mature.

The order comprises the Sordariaceae and the Xylariaceae, two families with a very large number of genera. The Sordariaceae are saprophytic on the excrement of herbivores and on dead plants; their free-standing perithecia are often embedded in the substrate, with only their necks showing.

The genus *Neurospora* is unusual in that it reproduces chiefly by asexual means. Its dense mycelium develops countless richly branched conidiophores that do not produce proper conidia but, at maturity,

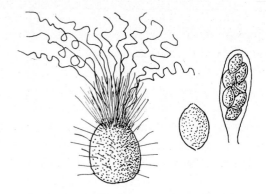

Fig. 139 *Chaetomium*. Left: fruiting body; right; ascus; centre: ascospore (highly magnified)

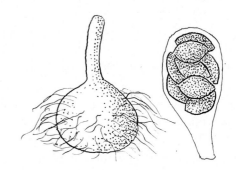

Fig. 140 *Melanospora zamiae*. Left: fruiting body (magnified); right: ascus

dissolve into individual cells which play the part of conidia. This genus used to be known only in the conidial form (*Monilia sitophila*); almost a century passed from the time that name was first coined to the discovery of the fruiting form, which is extremely rare in nature. Laboratory investigations have since shown that *Neurospora* will only reproduce sexually when two mycelia of different sex happen to meet. The genus *Neurospora* is chiefly tropical; its only European representative is *N. sitophila*. This fungus, which has bright-pink mycelia and conidia, makes bread and other bakery products unpalatable.

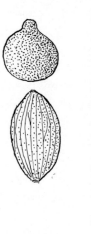

Fig. 141 *Neurospora sitophila*. Top left: fruiting body (magnified); bottom left: ascospore (highly magnified); right: ascus

Moreover, it spreads with extraordinary speed and is difficult to eradicate. These properties make *N. sitophila* an excellent object for genetic experiments.

Sordaria, *Pleurage* and *Bombardia*, three typical Sordariaceae, reproduce exclusively by means of ascospores, eight of which usually arise to every ascus. An exception is the genus *Pleurage* in which the number of spores per ascus may be as high as 512.

The Xylariaceae are a more highly developed family; their fruiting bodies are normally embedded in stromata. Only in a small number of representatives do the perithecia rise freely above the surface of the mycelium; forms of this type include the tropical genus *Rosellinia*, one of the few parasitic genera in the order. It attacks the roots of the coffee tree and of other useful plants.

The stromata of Xylariaceae vary markedly both in structure and in appearance. *Ustulina*, whose best-known species, *U. deusta*, settles on all sorts of timber, forms a flat stroma of irregular profile. At the beginning of its development, this stroma is

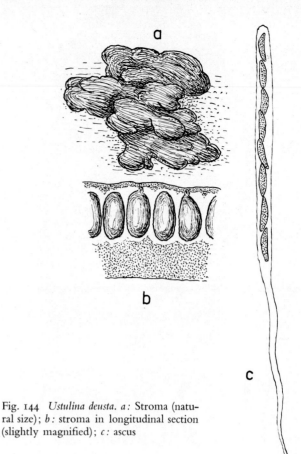

Fig. 144 *Ustulina deusta. a*: Stroma (natural size); *b*: stroma in longitudinal section (slightly magnified); *c*: ascus

conidial in character. Its surface is covered with a dense layer of short conidiophores which cut off large numbers of colourless conidia. After some time, the conidium-forming layer dissolves, and the stroma becomes transformed into a hard, black structure whose surface bears countless perithecia. *Hypoxylon* develops its tuberous and sometimes scaly stromata on dead bark and wood. They resemble those of *Ustulina* and are covered with a conidia-forming layer. In the European *H. fragiforme*, which often occurs on the bark of beech trees, the stromata are brick-coloured.

The genus Xylaria, probably the most widespread in Britain, can be identified by its cylindrical and sometimes branched stromata rising vertically above the substrate. Here, too, the young stromata are covered in conidiophores. Later, they produce perithecia which, in most species, are surrounded by a peripheral stromatic tissue from which only their necks protrude. In forests, one often meets *X. hypoxylon*, candle-snuff fungus (*Pl. 42, p. 64*), which grows on rotting tree stumps and logs and which, like its substrate, produces a weak glow in the dark.

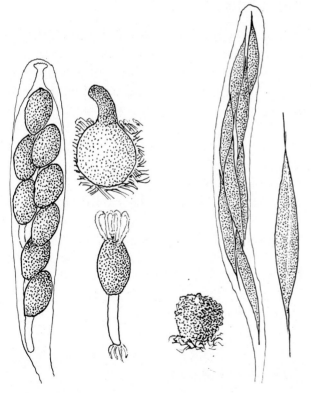

Fig. 142 *Pleurage vestita.* Top right: fruiting body embedded in manure (magnified); bottom right: ascospore; left: ascus (highly magnified)

Fig. 143 *Rosellinia bunodes.* Left: fruiting body (slightly magnified); centre: ascus; right: ascospore (highly magnified)

117

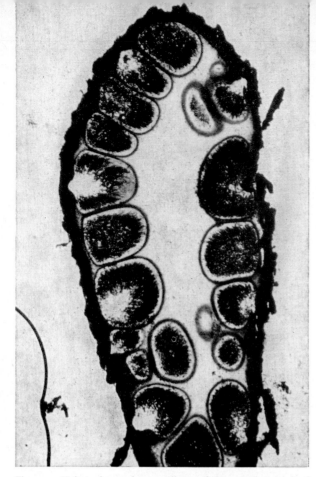

Fig. 145 *Xylaria hypoxylon*, candle-snuff fungus; longitudinal section through tip of stroma. Note the perithecia and black asci (magnified)

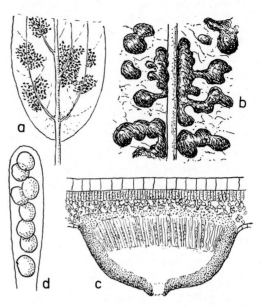

Fig. 147 *Phyllachora catervaria*. *a*: Stromata on *Ficus hispida* leaf (natural size); *b*: stromata (slightly magnified); *c*: longitudinal section through fruiting body and infested leaf (slightly magnified); *d*: ascus (highly magnified)

Order
SPHAERIALES

Taxonomists used to place all Ascomycetes with free-standing perithecia or with perithecial stromata into this order. As a result, the order became unwieldy and various genera had to be subdivided. Here we shall simply split it up into two families, both of which produce colourless, unicellular ascospores and are chiefly parasitic on the leaves of higher plants. The Polystigmataceae are best-known by the genera *Glomerella* and *Polystigma*. *P. rubrum* has a red stroma and is parasitic on various species of *Prunus*, causing severe damage, particularly to plum trees. The predominantly tropical Phyllachoraceae often spread their mycelia through the entire tissue of the attacked leaves. Their hard, black stromata partly break through the leaf epidermis to cover the surface of the leaves with a dense layer.

Order
DIAPORTHALES

The Diaporthales are predominantly saprophytic on dead branches and rotting wood. Only two genera, *Diaporthe* and *Endothia* (Diaporthaceae), also include a few parasitic forms. *E. parasitica* is the cause of

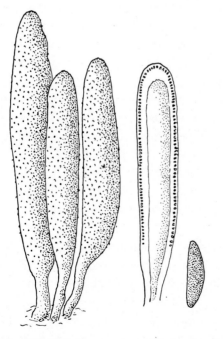

Fig. 146 *Xylaria telfairii*. Left: stroma (natural size); centre: longitudinal section of stroma; right: ascospore (magnified)

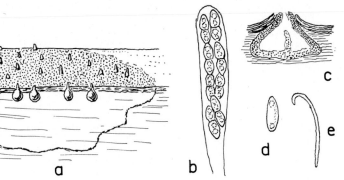

Fig. 148 *Diaporthe sp.* *a*: Stroma (slightly magnified); *b*: ascus (highly magnified); *c*: conidial fruiting body forming elliptical as well as *(d)* crook-shaped conidia (*e*: highly magnified)

chestnut blight. All Diaporthaceae form an encrusted stroma into which they incorporate parts of the substrate – dead stalks, twigs and even living leaves. Also embedded in the stroma are the perithecia and the conidial fruiting bodies, whose structure resembles that of the perithecia.

In the Ceratostomataceae, which feed exclusively on dead plant matter, free-standing perithecia are characteristically combined in groups, with only the long necks of the fruiting bodies protruding from the substrate. *Ceratostomella ulmi* produces Dutch elm disease, causing extensive die-back but not actually killing the tree.

Order
VALSALES

This order comprises two families of the most highly developed perithecial fungi. In many species the stroma is built up of hyphae and tissue derived from the surrounding substrate. In the Valsaceae, the stroma sends up a disk-shaped process, which is pierced through by the two long necks of the perithecia. In the Diatrypaceae, which live under the bark of dead branches, the stroma forces its way to the top where it appears as an elongated or rounded cushion.

The genus *Calosphaeria* (Valsaceae) does not produce stromata. Its fruiting bodies arise in wreath-shaped groups on the mycelium; the tips of their very long necks touch over the centre of the group. The necks themselves protrude through a small slit in the bark of the infested branches.

Diatrypella is a typical representative of the large family Diatrypaceae. It lives on the dead branches of oak, perforating the bark with its oval stromata.

This brings us to the end of our discussion of perithecial fungi.

All the Ascomycetes we have been describing have closed fruiting bodies. We now come to Ascomycetes in which the asci occupy the outer surface of the fruiting bodies in the form of flat disks, cups or caps. Such fruiting bodies, whether stalked or sessile, are

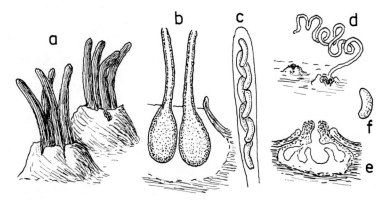

Fig. 149 *Valsa ceratophora.* *a*: Fruiting bodies breaking through bark of tree (slightly magnified); *b*: longitudinal section through fruiting body (slightly magnified); *c*: ascus; *d*: conidial stage (*Cystospora*); *e*: conidial fruiting body in longitudinal section; *f*: conidium (highly magnified)

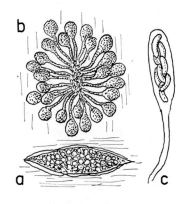

Fig. 150 *Calosphaeria pulchella.* *a*: Fruiting bodies (slightly magnified); *b*: fruiting bodies freed from substrate; *c*: ascus (highly magnified)

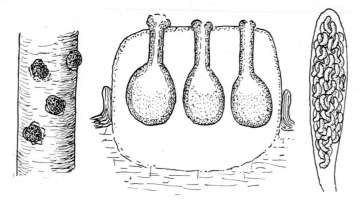

Fig. 151 *Diatrypella quercina*. Left: stromata on oak branch (slightly magnified); centre: stromata in longitudinal section (magnified); right: ascus (highly magnified)

known as apothecia, and are characteristic of the most highly developed Ascomycetes of all, the apothecial fungi or Discomycetes.

We saw that even in perithecial fungi, the asci are often combined with sterile hyphae, the so-called paraphyses, into a small hymenium. In apothecial types, the hymenium consists of a very large number of asci and paraphyses and covers the entire surface of the fruiting body. For the rest, Discomycetes are extremely varied in shape.

Order
PEZIZALES

This order includes forms with an unusually rich variety of fruiting bodies; they all agree, however, in that their asci open by means of a small lid.

The Morchellaceae, or morel family, have large fruiting bodies reminiscent of mushrooms; their knobbly or bell-shaped caps are borne on a long, erect stalk and covered on top with asci and paraphyses. In *Morchella*, the cap is divided by ridges so that it looks like a honeycomb; the 'cells' are lined with a dense hymenium. *M. esculenta*, common morel, and *M. conica*, conic morel (*Pl. 43, p. 129*) are considered great delicacies by fungus lovers. Morels like calcareous and sandy soils and burned ground. The genus *Verpa* also produces erect fruiting bodies; their bell-shaped caps bear the hymenium on their upper surface and arise on long cylindrical stalks.

Closely related to the Morchellaceae are the Helvellaceae, a family which includes the widespread genus *Helvella*; *H. esculenta*, false morel, can be identified by its large brown cap and heavy ridges.

It is still widely mistaken for an edible plant and may cause fatal poisoning. The closely related *H. crispa*, one of the most common species of saddle fungus, can be eaten with safety (*Pl. 47, p. 131*).

Cup-shaped, more or less prominently stalked fruiting bodies occur in the genera *Cyathipodia* and *Paxina*. The only sessile fruiting bodies among Helvellaceae are found in *Rhizina undulata*, which is parasitic on the roots of conifers. Its apothecia are disk-shaped and lobed at the edges. Their undersurface bears countless rhizoid organs by which they are anchored to the substrate.

Cup-shaped apothecia are also characteristic of the Pezizaceae, which include the common genera *Sarcosphaera*, *Peziza* and *Otidea*. In *Sarcosphaera*, the white fruiting bodies begin as spherical structures; later they tear open at the tip to leave a star-shaped gap which reveals a violet hymenium. The genus *Peziza* has beaker-shaped apothecia which, in several species, narrow at the base to form a short stalk. Very common species include *P. vesiculosa*, elf-cup, whose large yellow fruiting bodies grow on freshly manured fields (*Pl. 46, p. 130*). Members of the genus *Otidea* can be identified by their ear-shaped fruiting bodies, which appear in groups on the forest floor. *O. onotica* is most common in oak forests.

Unlike the Pezizaceae, whose fruiting bodies can attain considerable dimensions, the Humariaceae produce relatively small fruiting bodies – their lentil-

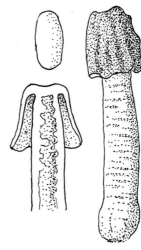

Fig. 152 *Verpa digitaliformis*. Right: fruiting body; lower left: longitudinal section of fruiting body; top left: ascospore (highly magnified)

Fig. 153 *Gyromitra esculenta*. Right: fruiting body; left: ascospore (highly magnified)

shaped apothecia rarely exceed a diameter of 1 cm. Nevertheless, these fungi are highly conspicuous, for their fruiting bodies are a glowing red, orange or yellow colour. Some of the most beautiful fungi of all are found in the genus *Scutellinia*, whose bright-red apothecia are fringed with black hairs as they break out of the bark of decaying branches (*Pl. 44, p. 130*). On the forest floor, we can often observe the orange fruiting bodies of *Aleuria aurantia*, possibly the most imposing representative of the Humariaceae. Its sessile, basin-shaped apothecia can attain a diameter of 4 ins. (*Pl. 45, p. 130*).

The smallest Pezizales are found among the Ascobolaceae, all saprobes living on dung, decaying plant remains and similar matter; their tiny fruiting bodies are lentil-shaped and have their upper surface covered in a hymenium topped by a layer of yellow or green mucus. Their characteristically broad asci protrude above the hymenium, and most conspicuously so in the genus *Ascobolus*. The best-known Ascobolaceae are found in the genus *Pyronema*. As typical 'pioneers' they settle on burned ground, particularly after forest fires. In appearance, *Pyronema* differs markedly from other Ascobolaceae: its mycelium covers the top of the ground with a dense white web. Lying flat on the mycelium are the orange-coloured, lentil-shaped fruiting bodies; they rarely attain a size of more than 1 mm., but combine into large groups visible to the naked eye. Species of *Pyronema* are extensively used in the experimental study of sexual reproduction in fungi.

The most highly developed Pezizales are found in the family Sarcoscyphaceae, a chiefly tropical group with a number of cosmopolitan species. Sarcoscyphaceae have typical lentil- and beaker-shaped, stalked or sessile apothecia. These fruiting bodies, which can attain considerable dimensions, often have a gelatinous structure and are covered with a fine layer of felt or with hairs. The dense hymenium is characteristically composed of narrow asci and delicate, fused paraphyses. In *Sarcoscypha coccinea*, scarlet elf-cup, the fruiting bodies consist of stalked beakers, lined with a scarlet hymenium. The fungus lives on dead roots but sends its fruiting bodies to the surface. The genus *Sarcosoma* can be identified by its large, urn-shaped apothecia whose broad bases lie flat on the substrate – the soil or bits of wood. The fruiting

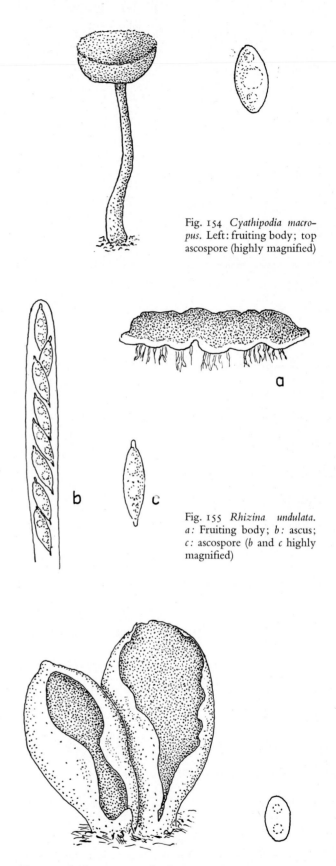

Fig. 154 *Cyathipodia macropus*. Left: fruiting body; top ascospore (highly magnified)

Fig. 155 *Rhizina undulata*. *a*: Fruiting body; *b*: ascus; *c*: ascospore (*b* and *c* highly magnified)

Fig. 156 *Otidea onotica*. Left: fruiting body; right: ascospore (highly magnified)

121

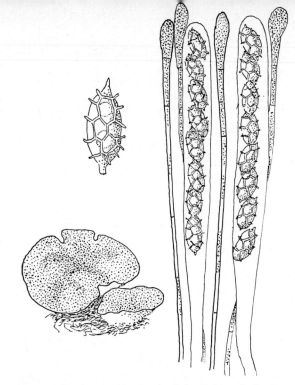

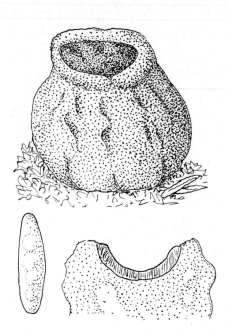

Fig. 157 *Aleuria aurantia*. Lower left: fruiting body (natural size); top left: ascospore (highly magnified); right: asci and paraphyses

Fig. 160 *Sarcosoma globosa*. Top: fruiting body (slightly reduced); lower right: fruiting body in longitudinal section; lower left: ascospore (highly magnified)

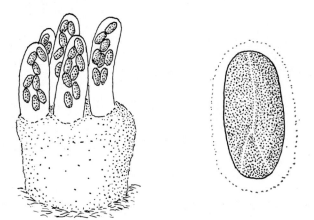

Fig. 161 *Sarcoscypha coccinea*. Right: fruiting body (natural size); left: ascospore (highly magnified)

Fig. 158 *Ascobolus immersus*; left: fruiting body with protruding asci (slightly magnified); right: ascospore (highly magnified)

bodies are built up of gelatinous hyphal tissue with a high water content; they are almost black in colour and are lined with a yellow hymenium. The genus is found throughout the world; its most common European representative is *S. globosa*.

Order
TUBERALES

The fungi combined in this order seem to have no more than the most tenuous links to one another, a fact reflected by, among other things, marked differences in the structure of their fruiting bodies. The more primitive Tuberales, i.e. the Geneaceae from the tropics of Asia, produce more or less spherical, hollow apothecia resembling those of the Pezizales. In the more typical Tuberales, however, in the

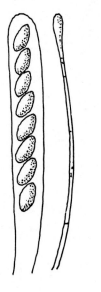

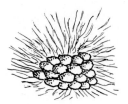

Fig. 159 *Pyronema omphalodes*. Right: fruiting body (magnified); left: ascus and paraphysis (highly magnified)

families Eutuberaceae and Terfeziaceae, the fruiting bodies are the closed and compact structures we refer to as truffles. If we cut one of them open, we shall find that it is crossed by numerous tubes of varying thickness; the tubes correspond to the central cavity in the fruiting bodies of Geneaceae. The tubes, which occasionally broaden into chambers, are hymenium-lined and the hymenium is thus greatly increased in surface area. Unlike the fruiting bodies of Pezizales and of Geneaceae, those of truffles are closed – their rudimentary aperture fuses during an early stage of development. However, as the truffle matures, pores appear at the ends of every tube. The fruiting bodies are generally broken open by animals, and the spores, too, are mainly disseminated by animals. Occasionally, however, a fruiting body may burst open by the spontaneous collapse of its wall.

Though the Tuberales produce several distinct types of fruiting bodies, all have several common characteristics. Thus, all of them produce mycelia and fruiting bodies alike in the soil. Many of them, particularly the truffles, form mycorrhizal associations with the roots of higher plants and forest-growing trees. Moreover, the hymenium generally consists of two superposed layers, the lower built up of asci and the bases of the paraphyses, the upper of the protruding tips of the paraphyses. In the Eutuberaceae and the Terfeziaceae, however, we also meet species devoid of a typical hymenium; in their case the asci are scattered loosely among the paraphyses.

The Geneaceae are tropical, and the truffles, too, are chiefly found in warmer zones. One of the few genera represented in Europe is *Tuber* (Eutuberaceae); it includes the most valuable edible fungus of all. The South European *T. melanospermum*, which is a speciality of Perigord in S.W. France, is highly prized by gourmets throughout the world. Truffles usually grow in association with the roots of oaks and, in order to get at them, the collectors use specially trained pigs or hounds, which detect them by their odour and dig them up (*Pl. 48, p. 131*). Two species native to Britain, namely *T. aestivum* and *Hydnotria tulasmei*, are also hunted with dogs. In Southern France and Italy, truffles have more recently been grown in special forest regions; for this purpose young oaks from forests rich in truffles are specially transplanted. Truffles are not only eaten as

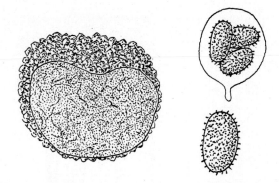

Fig. 162 *Tuber melanosporum*, truffle. Left: fruiting body cut open (natural size); upper right: ascus; lower right: ascospore (highly magnified)

such, but also go into a number of liqueurs and patés. They are also used in perfumes and to scent tobacco.

The Discomycetes are usually divided into two groups, whose asci have distinct opening mechanisms. The asci of the first group open by means of a hinged lid-like structure – the most typical representatives are the Pezizales. The second group, which comprises all other Discomycetes, release their ascospore through an apical, circular perforation. Fungi of this type belong chiefly to the order Helotiales, which is as widespread and rich in forms as the order Pezizales.

Order
HELOTIALES

Most Helotiales are typical Discomycetes; they have disk- or lentil-shaped apothecia which may be stalked or sessile. The only exception is the family Geoglossaceae, whose fruiting bodies are asymmetrical, and can moreover grow to a height of more than 2 ins. One of the most distinctive characteristics of the Helotiales is the production of bicellular or multicellular ascospores. The Helotiales are mainly saprophytic on dead plant stalks and wood in the soil. Some of them have, however, become parasitic on various higher plants, to which they often cause severe damage. Many parasitic species are capable of asexual reproduction by means of conidia.

We said that the most impressive members of the order are found among the Geoglossaceae; their stalked fruiting bodies can assume a variety of shapes. Thus the genus *Geoglossum* owes its name of 'earth-tongue' to its tongue-shaped fruiting bodies which

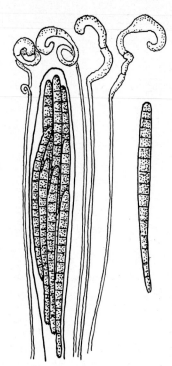

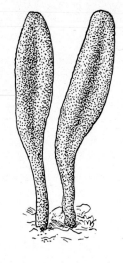

Fig. 163 *Geoglossum peckianum*. Left: ascus and paraphyses; centre: ascospore (highly magnified); right: stalked fruiting bodies

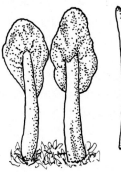

Fig. 164 *Spathularia flavida*. Left: fruiting body (natural size); right: ascospore (highly magnified)

break out in large black bunches on moss-covered forest soils. Typical of *Geoglossum* and all related species are their filamentous, multicellular ascospores. In *Leotia*, a species growing on moist forest soils, the green hemispherical cap, lobed at the rim, is borne on a bright-yellow stalk. *Microglossum* and *Mitrula* form more or less club-shaped fruiting bodies. In *Spatularia flavida*, the yellow to orange cap is fan-shaped and attached to one side of the stalk.

In the size of their fruiting bodies, the Geoglossaceae are closely rivalled by the Sclerotiniaceae, which produce typical apothecia on long stalks. The Sclerotiniaceae are, with few exceptions, parasitic on higher plants but have the ability to change over to the saprophytic habit whenever the need arises. They frequently reproduce asexually by means of conidia. In the genera *Monilinia* and *Botyotinia* the conidial form often predominates, and is known by a distinct name. Thus the conidial form of *Monilinia*, which

produces richly branched chains of conidia, is known as *Monilia*. *Monilinia* causes brown rot in various fruit trees, including pears and peaches, which latter they transform into dry 'mummies'. The 'mummies' drop to the ground completely penetrated by the mycelium and covered with conidia. The mycelium overwinters in the mummified fruit and then gives rise to long-stalked, basin-shaped apothecia. *Botryotinia* forms long conidiophores during its asexual phase; these branch out at the tips, with each little branch bearing a conidial head. The conidial stage goes under the name of *Botrytis*. The best-known species of *Botryotinia* is *Botryotinia fuckeliana* whose conidial form (*Botrytis cinerea*) causes rot in grapes. In wet years, it can lead to the complete destruction of the grape harvest; in dry years, on the other hand, it is welcomed by vintners because it causes the sugar content of the grapes to increase considerably and hence helps to produce select wines.

Very widespread in temperate zones is the family Helotiaceae whose relatively small, short or long-stalked apothecia grow on dead branches, rotting tree stumps and similar substrates. Most are saprobes, though some forms have turned parasitic. One of the latter is *Bulgaria inquinans*, Black Bulgar, whose top-shaped, fleshy apothecia have a flat upper surface covered with a shiny black hymenium. *B. inquinans* lives on the dead branches of oak trees, but occa-

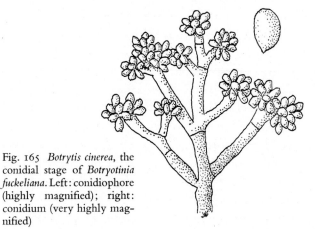

Fig. 165 *Botrytis cinerea*, the conidial stage of *Botryotinia fuckeliana*. Left: conidiophore (highly magnified); right: conidium (very highly magnified)

Fig. 166 *Bulgaria inquinans*, black bulgar. Left: fruiting bodies ($\frac{1}{2}$ natural size); right: ascospore (highly magnified)

Fig. 167 *Helotium fructigenum*

sionally attacks living oaks as well; when it does so in large concentrations it can cause severe damage. Very common also is the beautiful, cap-shaped and generally yellow fruiting body of *Helotium*, which grows in loose groups on leaf litter, old tree stumps and other plant remains. The most common and widespread species is *H. fructigenum*. The genus *Chlorosplenium* produces mycelia and fruiting bodies of a striking blue-green colour, which it imparts to the dead wood it infests. In Britain such wood is used for the manufacture of Tunbridge ware, and goes by the name of green oak.

Very small, usually unstalked and basin-shaped apothecia covered in hairs are characteristic of the family Hyaloscyphaceae which, like the Helotiaceae, live on dead wood and other plant material. While the majority are saprobes, *Trichoscyphella willkommii* is a widespread parasite, causing scab-like deformations on the branches of larch trees (*Pl. 50, p. 132*).

Unlike the typical Helotiales, which produce their fruiting bodies on the surface of the substrate, the Dermeaceae hide their apothecia until they are fully mature. In some Dermeaceae, moreover, reproduction is predominantly by conidia. This is the case, for instance, in *Diplocarpon*, a small genus of leaf parasites which usually occurs in the conidial form known as *Actinonema*. The conidia appear at the tip of short conidiophores combined in groups. Like the apothecia, the conidiophores are hidden beneath the epidermis of the infested leaves until they mature. To the naked eye, the conidiophores appear as black spots on the leaf surface, particularly of roses, which are regularly subjected to attacks by *D. rosae*.

Related to the Helotiales are three small orders which constitute the most highly developed Discomycetes.

Order
PHACIDIALES

The most important characteristic of the Phacidiales is the presence of strongly reduced fruiting bodies; in most species these are so rudimentary that the fungi consist chiefly of hymenium. The fruiting bodies, which develop inside the substrate, are embedded in a stroma, and the stroma covers the hymenium as well. As soon as the ascospores are mature, the stroma tears open just above the hymenium. Several Phacidiales reproduce asexually before they eventually produce fruiting bodies. The conidia, too, originate in the stroma. The entire order, which includes the families Hypodermataceae and Phacidiaceae, is parasitic on a variety of plants, particularly on deciduous trees and conifers. The best-known

125

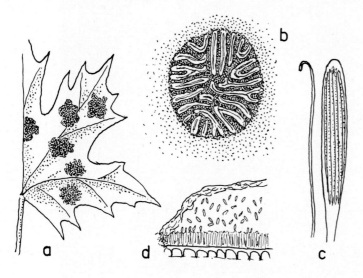

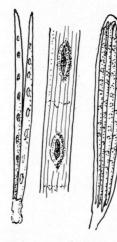

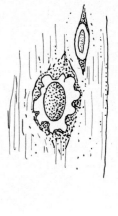

Fig. 168 *Rhytisma acerinum*. *a:* Fruiting bodies on leaf of *Acer pseudoplatanus*; *b:* arrangement of fruiting bodies; *c:* ascus and paraphysis (highly magnified); *d:* conidial stage (*Melasmia acerina*)

Fig. 169 *Lophodermium pinastri*. Left: fruiting bodies on pine needles; centre: fruiting bodies (higher magnification); right: ascus (highly magnified)

genera are *Rhytisma* and *Lophodermium*, two Hypodermataceae.

All species of *Rhytisma* are leaf parasites; the most common, *R. acerinum*, attacks the leaves of various maples, especially *Acer pseudoplatanus*. The fungus forms flat, circular stromata beneath the leaf epidermis, which eventually break out and appear as circular black spots. The genus *Lophodermium* includes several species that infest the needles of conifers. *L. pinastri*, in particular, can do grave damage to young pines, causing the premature shedding of needles.

Order

LECANORALES

Fungi in this order mainly live in symbiotic association with algae, with which they form the living communities known as lichens; only a handful of species in the two constituent families, the Lecidiaceae and Patellariaceae, have preserved their autonomy. All are small fungi with flat, basin-shaped apothecia; these are gelatinous in the Lecidiaceae and hard in the Patellariaceae. The asci are hidden under a hard crust of interwoven hyphal tips. Non-symbiotic Lecanorales generally live as saprobes on rotting wood and other plant remains. The excep-

tion is the genus *Abrothallus* (Lecidiaceae) which is parasitic on lichens.

Order

OSTROPALES

This small order, comprising only the family Ostropaceae, includes fungi with typical apothecia together with species in which the fruiting bodies are flask-shaped, and hence reminiscent of perithecia. The most important characteristic of Ostropales is the presence of very elongated asci, each with a bundle of filamentous and multicellular ascospores. Ostropales live chiefly on dead branches and stalks, and send their fruiting bodies up through the bark. The largest genus, *Stictis*, enjoys a very wide distribution.

Class

BASIDIOMYCETES
Basidium-forming Fungi

With the Basidiomycetes we reach the most highly developed of all fungi. This class, which comprises some 15,000 species, contains, side by side with a number of tiny and exceedingly harmful parasites (the smuts and rusts) almost all the fungi that are commonly referred to as toadstools or mushrooms. Their main characteristic is the presence of basidia, i.e. of organs whose surface bears a definite number of basidiospores (typically four). As in the Ascomycetes, the formation of the spore-producing organs is based on sexual processes: here, too, the fusion of the sexual nuclei occurs very shortly after the production of the young spores.

In the higher Basidiomycetes, the basidium consists of a single club-shaped cell; in the more primitive forms, it is divided by cross walls and more rarely by longitudinal walls, into (usually) 4 cells. The unicellular basidia produce 4 small papillae, known as sterigmata, by budding at their tip; each sterigma then swells up to form a bladder-shaped sporangium at its apex. In 4-celled basidia, each cell produces its own sterigma. As the sterigmata mature, the diploid nucleus of the basidium which originated from the fusion of two (binucleate) sexual nuclei, divides meiotically into 4 haploid nuclei, which migrate through the sterigmata into the sporangia. They become surrounded by a wall – which soon afterwards fuses with that of the sporangium – and are thus transformed into basidiospores. The basidiospores are subsequently shot off by means of the enlargement of a water droplet that has formed at their base.

The development of Basidiomycetes agrees with that of Ascomycetes inasmuch as it, too, involves three nuclear phases: a haploid phase, a binucleate phase, and a very brief diploid phase. Unlike the Ascomycetes, however, in whose life cycle the haploid phase predominates, Basidiomycetes are predominantly binucleate. Their cycle may be summarized as follows: the mature basidiospore, which has broken free from the basidium, germinates into a tubular hypha which contains a large number of haploid nuclei resulting from several successive divisions of the spore nucleus. The germinal hypha soon afterwards splits up into cells, each with a single nucleus. The cells now branch out and grow into a simple mycelium, known as the primary mycelium. It appears in two sexually differentiated types, known as plus and minus, and represents the gametophyte generation. If two sexually compatible primary mycelia meet, copulation occurs, with the hyphae acting as the organs of copulation. True sexual organs occur

in a few lower Basidiomycetes only. Copulation simply involves the fusion of protoplasts – the nuclei of the partners' cells draw together in pairs but do not fuse. The fungus now enters its binucleate or dikaryophase – the major part of its life cycle.

The binucleate fusion cell gives rise to a binucleate mycelium whose cells, each containing a pair of nuclei, form a lateral clamp connection. This structure, which is one of the characteristics of Basidiomycetes, has been described at some length on p. 93. It ensures that every newly formed cell is provided with a pair of nuclei. The binucleate mycelium resulting from the copulation of two haploid primary mycelia is known as the secondary mycelium. Unlike the former, it spreads profusely through the substrate and has a considerable life span. In some fungi the hyphae of the secondary mycelium are bunched together into rhizomorphs – thick strands that can attain a considerable length. After a fairly long interval, which may span several years, the mycelium, which has kept growing larger all the time, begins to form fruiting bodies.

In certain zones of the mycelium, often on its periphery, the hyphae combine into more or less compact bodies, which eventually give rise to the fruiting bodies. The mycelium responsible for this development is called the tertiary mycelium. It differs from the secondary mycelium in being more compact and more highly differentiated, but resembles it in having binucleate cells and clamp formations. Here we have one of the chief differences between Basidiomycetes and Ascomycetes: in the latter the fruiting bodies are invariably produced by a haploid mycelium. The development of the fruiting bodies in Basidiomycetes culminates in the formation of basidia, produced in the terminal cells of special, basidium-forming hyphae. Normally the basidia are combined with similar but sterile cells, the so-called pseudo-paraphyses, to form a closed hymenium. In a number of Basidiomycetes, the basidia and pseudoparaphyses are, moreover, associated with cells of a third type, the cystidia, which protrude far above the hymenium and generally serve as organs of excretion, though sometimes they also act as a protective cover for the hymenium. As in the most highly developed Ascomycetes, the hymenium of Basidiomycetes is often exposed; it is generally found on the underside of the fruiting body. In a small number of Basidiomycetes, however, it is enclosed inside the fruiting body.

The basidia are the seat of the sexual process proper, i.e. of the fusion of the dikaryotic nuclei. The binucleate phase which, as we saw, is the dominant one in Basidiomycetes, is followed by a diploid phase of very short duration; immediately upon its formation the diploid fusion nucleus divides into 4 haploid nuclei by meiosis. This reduction division goes hand in hand with sexual differentiation: two of the nuclei are of the plus type and the other two are of the minus type. The resulting basidiospores, which are shot off from the basidia, germinate into haploid plus and minus mycelia.

The fruiting bodies break up as soon as the spores have matured. The secondary mycelium, on the other hand, may survive for decades, producing new fruiting bodies every year. Some Basidiomycetes also reproduce asexually by means of conidia, but this type of reproduction is far less prevalent than it is among Ascomycetes. We have said that the life cycle we have sketched out is characteristic of the more highly developed Basidiomycetes; in principle, however, it applies to the lower Basidiomycetes as well.

The Basidiomycetes constitute the most unified group among the fungi, not only in respect of their life cycle but also in respect of their sexual reproduction: with very few exceptions random cells of the sexually differentiated primary mycelium assume the function of copulatory organs – they are said to be somatogamous (from the Greek *soma*, body, and *gamos*, marriage). There is also a high degree of correspondence in the structure of the fruiting bodies. These may vary considerably in shape, consistency and colour, but, in contrast to the Ascomycetes whose fruiting bodies can be divided into four clearly distinct types, most Basidiomycetes have a single type of fruiting body: an open structure in which the hymenium is laid bare from the start. True, some species have fruiting bodies that begin as closed organs and only open as they mature, or even remain closed throughout their history, but such species are very few and far between.

Differences in the shape of the fruiting bodies serve as important criteria in the classification of Basidio-

mycetes. Of even greater taxonomic importance is the structure of their basidia, by which Basidiomycetes can be divided into two sub-classes. Forms with 4-celled, or more rarely with 2-celled basidia, constitute the sub-class Phragmobasidiomycetidae, which is generally considered to be the more primitive of the two, since its members lack fruiting bodies and form true sexual organs – both characters associated with a lower stage of development. The second sub-class, the Holobasidiomycetidae, are chiefly characterized by the presence of unicellular basidia and of fruiting bodies, and by the absence of sexual organs.

The Basidiomycetes enjoy a very wide distribution: they are as much at home in the tropics as they are in polar regions, though they generally prefer moderately warm, moist conditions. Most Basidiomycetes are saprophytic on organic matter in the soil or on dead wood. Numerous Holobasidiomycetidae, including most of our forest-growing mushrooms and toadstools, form mycorrhizae with the roots of trees; some species are involved in the formation of lichens. Parasitism occurs chiefly among the Phragmobasidiomycetidae. Parasitic Basidiomycetes, which occupy a special taxonomic position, also deserve special mention because they are among the few fungi whose ancestry is known, at least in part. Generally speaking, we are fairly unfamiliar with the fungal fauna of past geological epochs since, being extremely delicate and perishable, fungi are rarely preserved in fossil form. Most of those that have been are parasites and as such have come down to us with their host plants.

Sub-class

PHRAGMOBASIDIOMYCETIDAE

The fungi in this sub-class are divided into two groups. The first comprises all those forms whose basidia are divided into four cells and which never produce fruiting bodies. These are all found in the parasitic orders Ustilaginales (the smuts) and Uredinales (the rusts). The members of the second group (orders: Auriculariales and Tremellales) also include species with four-celled basidia, but many show a

43 Morchella conica (Pezizales)

44 *Scutellinia trechispora* (Pezizales)

45 *Aleuria aurantia* (Pezizales)   46 *Peziza vesiculosa* (Pezizales)

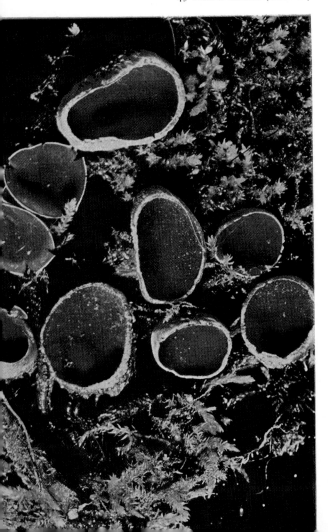

47 *Helvella crispa*

48 Pig looking for truffles (*Tuber melanospermum*) in Southern France

49 *Tremella mesenterica*

50 *Trichoscyphella willkommii* (Helotiales)

51 *Calocera viscosa* (Dacrymycetales)

52 The poisonous *Clavaria pallida*

53 *Exobasidium rhododendri* (Exobasidiales)

54 *Serpula lacrymans*, dry-rot fungus

55 A 'fairy ring'

56 *Coriolus versicolor*
(Telephorales)

57 *Fomes fomentarius,*
tinder fungus

58 *Mycena polygramma* (Agaricales)

59 *Hygrocybe conica* (Agaricales)   60 *Laccaria laccata*

61 *Clitocybe nebularis*

62 *Marasmius perforans*

63 The highly poisonous death cap
(*Amanita phalloides*)

65 *Macrolepiota procera*

64 *Coprinus comatus*, shaggy ink-cap

66 Horse mushroom
(*Agaricus arvensis*)

67 *Stropharia aeruginosa*, verdigris agaric

68 *Nematoloma fasciculare*

69 Milk-cap, *Lactarius volemus*

71 *Anthurus muellerianu*
(Phallales)

70 *Suillus grevillei*

72 *Boletus edulis*, cep

73 *Russula sp.*

74 *Phallus impudicus,*
stinkhorn

75 *Lycoperdon perlatum,* common puff-ball

76 The earth-star *Geastrum rufescens*

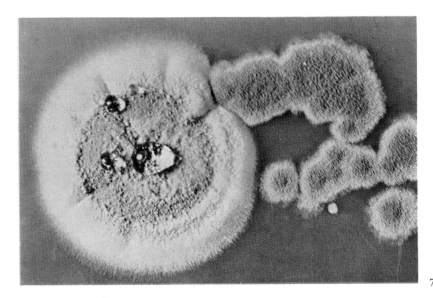

77 *Penicillium*

marked transition to the unicellular basidia typical of the Holobasidiomycetidae and involving a progressive reduction of the septa in the basidial cells. In addition, they produce fruiting bodies, and unlike the first group, they are predominantly saprophytic.

Order
USTILAGINALES
Smuts

The Ustilaginales, or smuts, live exclusively as parasites on higher plants, often causing extensive damage. A few can be grown on culture media, and hence observed at leisure. Most species develop a very profuse binucleate mycelium which often spreads deep into the host tissue. Usually, the hyphae develop between the plant cells, but some species live inside the cells or else send haustoria into them. The binucleate mycelium originates from what is usually a very short-lived primary mycelium; its formation is not, however, totally dependent on the meeting of sexually differentiated primary mycelia; it can also result from the copulation of basidiospores, of conidia or of vegetative cells produced by budding of the hyphae. Budding is particularly prevalent when smuts are grown in pure cultures: as long as the cells do not come into contact with a host, they continue to multiply by budding, but the moment a suitable host is introduced they either develop into a mycelium or else begin to copulate in pairs.

The binucleate mycelium develops thick bundles of short hyphae on various organs of the host. The protoplast of each hyphal cell rounds up and the hyphal walls gelatinize. Each protoplast now secretes a thick wall which eventually converts the protoplast into the so-called smut spores, each completely independent of its neighbours with which it is packed close together beneath the epidermis of the host. These layers are known as sori and look like small pustules to the naked eye. As soon as the sori have broken through the epidermis, the ripe spores rise up in clouds of black dust. Smut spores, like the mycelium from which they have originated, remain binucleate throughout their development. As soon as they attain maturity, however, their two nuclei fuse into a diploid one. Because fusion occurs in the

basidia, the diploid smut spores are also known as probasidia. They usually mature in the autumn and often spend the winter as resting stages, protected against the frost by tough walls. In a number of smuts, however, the resting stage is omitted and the probasidia germinate directly they are formed: they send out a short tube, which eventually develops into a basidium. The diploid probasidial nucleus migrates into the tube and usually splits into 4 haploid daughter nuclei. Septa then arise between them and divide the basidium into uninucleate cells. In the further course of development, each basidial cell gives rise to a basidiospore; at the same time, its nucleus divides and one of the daughter nuclei migrates into the spore. As soon as the spore is ripe, it breaks free from the basidium. Under favourable conditions, the basidium is capable of producing basidiospores repeatedly; this it can do because only one of its daughter nuclei migrates into the spore.

When basidiospores come into contact with a suitable host, they germinate into a haploid primary mycelium which copulates to give rise to a new binucleate mycelium. The latter gives rise to smut spores or more rarely starts its development with conidia or bud cells. As we saw, however, even these cells are capable of copulation, and hence of producing binucleate secondary mycelia.

Smut spores do not generally settle on all parts of the host but attack either the mature seeds or the young ovaries, into which they send their long germ tubes, much like pollen grains. Here, the parasites are impossible to detect at first – the infected ovaries are not particularly disturbed by the tiny mycelium. The ovules in which the fungus finally establishes itself also mature without showing any signs of damage. It is only in the young plants that the smuts demonstrate their destructive powers to the full. Smuts attack a number of important crops, particularly cereals, and a precise understanding of their particular life cycles is a prerequisite of their successful eradication. This can be effected in two ways: by spraying the crops with fungicides at flowering time, or by treating the seeds and destroying the fungal mycelia in them. To that purpose, the seeds are briefly immersed in mercury solution, or else kept in warm water for a time, when alcohol and acetaldehyde are produced by fermentation and kill the fungi. Since both methods are fairly effective, farmers no longer worry about entire crops being destroyed by smuts.

The smuts are divided into three families, the Ustilaginaceae, the Tilletiaceae and the Graphiolaceae, all with only a few but large genera. The first two of these families are cosmopolitan, but the Graphiolaceae are more prevalent in the tropics and subtropics, where they chiefly attack palms.

Family
Ustilaginaceae

The Ustilaginaceae account for by far the greatest number of smut species, the genus *Ustilago* alone comprising more than 300. Characteristic of this family are their multicellular basidia, which generally arise as short tubes from the smut spores. Septa are then laid down to divide every tube into 4 superposed cells, each of which produces a lateral bud (basidiospore).

The Ustilaginaceae are parasitic on various plants but have a predilection for grasses. Many species of *Ustilago* attack various cereals, including wheat and maize, and to a lesser extent, oats and barley. The agent of maize smut, *U. zeae*, infests the entire maize plant causing up to 8 ins. ulcerous swellings on stalks, leaves, and flowers. *U. nuda*, loose smut of wheat,

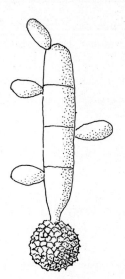

Fig. 173 *Ustilago scabiosae*; germinating smut spore (highly magnified)

so-called because it is disseminated by the wind, spreads its binucleate mycelium throughout the vegetative body of the host, but develops its smut spores exclusively in the ovaries, transforming their tissue into densely packed galls. As the spores mature, the galls break up and turn into 'dust', which settles on other wheat plants. Each spore germinates directly into a basidium which immediately starts to produce basidiospores. These attack the ovaries and develop into tiny, simply constructed primary mycelia, which winter inside the wheat grains. If the seeds are not treated, the mycelium in them will give rise to a new generation of smut spores in the spring.

Not all species of *Ustilago* are parasitic on cereals. Thus *U. scitaminea* attacks sugar canes and transforms their inflorescences into long whip-shaped tubes filled with countless smut spores. Among Ustilaginaceae parasitic on wild plants, special mention must be made of the genus *Cintractia* which chiefly attacks Cyperaceae (sedges) and Juncaceae (rushes). Very widespread is *C. caricis*, a species that attacks sedges of the genus *Carex*.

Fig. 171 *Cinctractia caricis*. Left: part of infested inflorescence of *Carex*; right: smut spore (highly magnified)

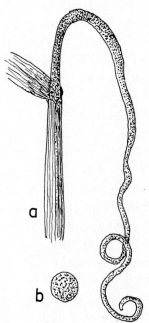

a

b

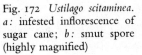

Fig. 172 *Ustilago scitaminea*. a: infested inflorescence of sugar cane; b: smut spore (highly magnified)

Family
Tilletiaceae

The Tilletiaceae resemble the Ustilaginaceae in external appearance, but differ radically from them in the construction of their basidia. These are no longer divided by septa but consist of a single cell crowned by a ring of elongated basidiospores. Normally each cell forms 8 spores, but the number can

146

be increased to as many as 50. The basidiospores form pairs that become united into H-pieces by copulation tubes, through which the cell content of one spore can migrate into the other; the nuclei of the two spores combine to form a nuclear pair. When the binucleate spore germinates, it gives rise to a number of crescent-shaped conidia, each with a pair of nuclei. The conidia eventually settle on the host plant, where they grow into a binucleate mycelium bearing new smut spores. Like the Ustilaginaceae, the Tilletiaceae chiefly attack the host's ovaries, which they often pack with dense balls of smut spores surrounded by a protective wall of sterile cells. The balls are disseminated as a whole, and do not even break up when the spores begin to germinate. Many Tilletiaceae are dangerous crop parasites; thus *Tilletia caries* and *T. foetida* cause bunt or stinking smut of wheat. Wheat-infesting Tilletaciae are found wherever wheat is cultivated.

While *Tilletia* attacks grasses, the genera *Entyloma* and *Urocystis* infest dicotyledons. *E. dahliae* is a widespread dahlia parasite, causing prominent yellow spots on infested plants; *U. violae* attacks violets.

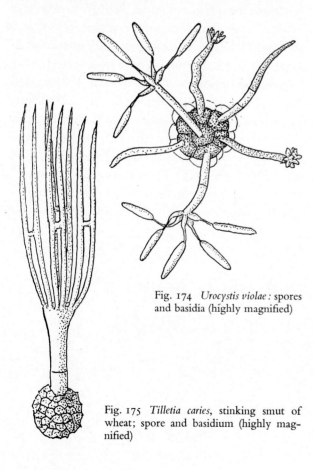

Fig. 174 *Urocystis violae*: spores and basidia (highly magnified)

Fig. 175 *Tilletia caries*, stinking smut of wheat; spore and basidium (highly magnified)

Order
UREDINALES
Rusts

Like the Ustilaginales, the Uredinales are parasitic in habit. They, too, live exclusively on higher plants, often choosing the same host as the smuts. Nevertheless, they are readily distinguished from the latter by their reddish-brown sporangia; these break through the host's epidermis, causing the condition known as rust.

The rusts are inseparably bound up with their hosts, and are not viable outside them. While smuts can readily develop on artificial media, rusts have withstood all attempts to grow them in cultures. Other distinctions from the Ustilaginales are that Uredinales do not produce fruiting bodies and that their spores are invariably divided into 4 cells. Moreover these so-called teleutospores undergo a long resting stage before germination.

Even more characteristic of the Uredinales is the formation of true sexual cells. This feature not only distinguishes the rusts from the smuts, but gives them a special position among Basidiomycetes in general. A second remarkable characteristic of rusts is their peculiar life cycle. In most species it involves five distinct stages, each with a characteristic spore. The haploid gametophyte and the binucleate sporophyte generations complete their development in a period lasting from one spring to the next. In some species, both generations develop on one and the same host plant. Very often, however, the alternation of generations goes hand in hand with a change of host at the end of the haploid phase – the new host invariably belongs to a different group of plants. Here the fungi develop their sporophytes, which reproduce vegetatively until the autumn, when they go over to the formation of teleutospores, with whose germination during the following spring the life cycle can begin anew. The host of the gametophyte, which starts its development in the spring and which has a very short life span, is called the alternate or secondary host; the sporophyte host is known as the primary host and its generic name is often used in the description of rusts. Thus *Puccinia graminis* owes its name to the fact that its primary host is invariably one of the grasses. Changes of host, or heteroecism as biologists call this phenomenon, result from the fact that gametophytes and sporophytes have different food requirements.

In typical rusts with alternate hosts the life cycle proceeds roughly as follows: in the spring, the haploid and sexually differentiated basidiospore germinates on the leaves of the alternate host and produces a short germ tube, which enters through a crack in the leaf tissue and develops into a haploid mycelium. The mycelium then begins to proliferate between the leaf cells and later sends haustoria into the cells themselves. Just beneath the epidermis of the leaf upper surface, the hyphae of this primary mycelium become concentrated into flask-shaped structures, the so-called spermogonia or pycnia, which later break through the leaf. The spermogonia are provided with numerous short hyphae that produce small unicellular cells at their tip – these are known as spermatia or pycniospores. They are male reproductive structures and when they leave the spermogonia, they are exuded in a droplet of nectar.

The edges of the spermogonia meanwhile develop into so-called receptive hyphae, which behave as female reproductive structures; they can also originate in the mycelium, in which case they grow out through cracks in the leaf upper surface. Insects, attracted by the nectar, pick up the mature spermatia and transfer them to the receptive hyphae of the next spermogonium they visit. If the spermatia and receptive hyphae come from separate individual hosts, spermatization now takes place: the cell content of the spermatia passes into the receptive hyphae by a pore dissolved in the walls at the point of contact. Spermatization concludes stage 1 in the life cycle of the rusts.

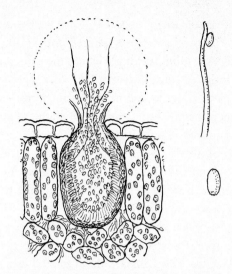

Fig. 176 Spermogonium of Uredinales (stage 1); left: longitudinal section of spermogonium with drops of nectar; upper right: receptive hypha with spermatium from another spermogonium (highly magnified); lower right: spermatium (very highly magnified)

After spermatization, the mycelium which produced the spermogonia develops a second type of structure – the so-called aecial primordium. It appears on the under surface of the infested leaves and its originally haploid nuclei are dikaryotized by the passage of the spermatial nuclei through the receptive hyphae. The aecial primordium is transformed into an aecium, a beaker-shaped structure consisting of hyphal cells and surrounded by a single-layered wall – the pseudoperidium. The basal cells of the aecium give rise to long chains of rust-coloured binucleate spores, known as aeciospores. The chains quickly grow in length and break through the pseudoperidium and, soon afterwards, through the epidermis of the infested leaf. Like the spermogonia, the aecia, in which the transition from sporophyte to gametophyte generation occurs and which are known as

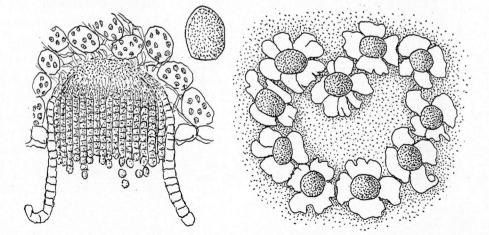

Fig. 177 Aecidial stage (stage 2). Right: top view of a group of aecidia; left: longitudinal section through an aecidium (magnified); centre: aecidiospore (highly magnified)

148

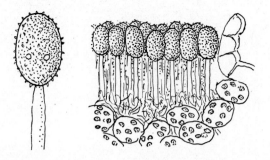

Fig. 178 Spore formation in Uredinales (stage 3). Right: uredospore-sorus (highly magnified); left: uredospore (very highly magnified)

stage 2, spend their entire life on the alternate host. The aeciospores, on the other hand, are carried by the wind to the primary host, and continue their development on it.

The aeciospores germinate into a binucleate mycelium which quickly spreads round the focus of infection in the plant tissue, and begins to form pustules of oval, orange-brown, thick-walled, binucleate conidia, the so-called uredospores. They represent stage 3 in the life cycle of rusts, which lasts the entire summer and plays a particularly important role in the dissemination of these fungi. The mature uredospores burst through the epidermis of their host, and infect other plants on which they germinate to produce a new uredospore-forming mycelium, able to produce new uredospores within 10–14 days. As a result, several generations of uredospores can be produced in a single season.

In the autumn, stage 3 is supplanted by stage 4, which begins with the formation of masses of teleutospores. These form pustules and arise from the same mycelium as the uredospores, but appear in a variety of different shapes and colours and may be unicellular or multicellular. Because of these differences, teleutospores are of particular importance in the classification of the Uredinales. In contrast to all other rust spores, they are resting stages. After a binucleate stage, the teleutospores undergo nuclear fusion, and it is as diploid probasidia that they winter in the dead remains of their hosts or in the soil, protected against the frost by a very thick wall. In the spring, they germinate to produce long, filamentous basidia divided into 4 superposed cells, each of which produces a colourless, lateral basidiospore on a sterigma. With the formation of the basidiospores,

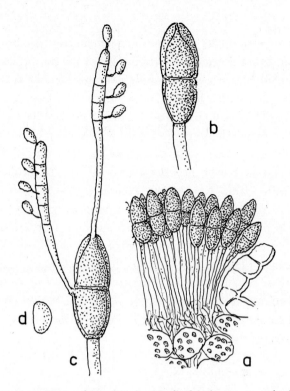

Fig. 179 Spore formation in Uredinales (stages 4 and 5). a: Section through group of teleutospores (highly magnified); b: teleutospore; c: germinating teleutospore (a, b, c = stage 4); d: basidiospore (very highly magnified; this is stage 5)

the rusts enter stage 5 of their development which concludes their life cycle.

Stages 4 and 5 (teleutospores and basidiospores) occur in all rusts; the other stages can be partly or completely omitted. This is yet another reason why the teleutospores are so important in the classification of rusts: they are divided into two main types, according to whether their teleutospores are stalked or sessile.

Sessile teleutospores, which are considered the more primitive, arise directly from the mycelium; the stalked types arise at the tips of special, erect hyphae. The former are found in the family Melampsoraceae, the latter in the family Pucciniaceae.

The teleutospores of Melampsoraceae are often so crowded together that they form crusts beneath the epidermis of the infested plant. This happens, for instance, in *Melampsora lini* which attacks flax plants. In other species, the teleutospores may form long chains, fused into columns. A case in point is the genus *Cronartium*, whose columns may attain a length of several millimetres. Frequently these strange concentrations of spores appear on the leaves of various species of *Ribes*, for instance of *R. grossularia* (gooseberry). In the genus *Cronartium*, the teleuto-spores are not the usual resting stages but germinate directly; as a result the spore columns become surrounded with a loose layer of basidia. We have said that Melampsoraceae can be identified by the fact that their teleutospores are sessile; another characteristic is their choice of conifers as alternate hosts. Some have even become specialized to a particular genus – thus *Cronartium* develops its spermogonia and aecia on *Pinus* causing tumorous galls, and *Milesia* infests *Abies* (firs). *Melampsora* is a little less selective for it attacks the larch (*Larix*), the hemlock spruce (*Tsuga*), the Douglas fir (*Pseudotsuga*) and *Abies*; occasionally the first two stages also occur on species of leek (*Allium*) and on *Ribes*. The last two of these hosts are Angiosperms, normally the primary hosts of rusts.

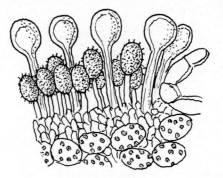

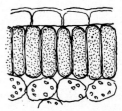

Fig. 181 *Melampsora helioscopiae* on leaf of *Euphorbia helioscopia*. Left: section through group of uredospores (with paraphyses); right: teleutospores beneath the epidermis of the host plant (highly magnified)

Despite their relatively wide choice of hosts, Melampsoraceae are not usually harmful to crops. The exceptions are *Melampsora lini* which, as we saw, is parasitic on flax, and the tropical *Phakopsora desmium*, which attacks *Gossypium* and can cause serious damage to cotton plantations.

The Pucciniaceae, on the other hand, include a considerable number of dangerous crop parasites. This family of common rusts is characterized by the production of stalked teleutospores originating from the tips of single or bunched hyphae. Only in a very few species is the stalk missing; in these species, the teleutospores form long threads which break through the epidermis of the infested plants. While unicellular teleutospores predominate among Melampsoraceae, most Pucciniaceae have their teleutospores divided by septa into several cells. The number of cells varies considerably: often there are no more than 2 (e.g. in *Puccinia*), but there may be as many as 10 (e.g. in *Phragmidium*, which attacks roses and raspberry bushes). In the genera *Triphragmium*, which also attacks rose plants, and *Nyssopsora*, which attacks umbellifers and aralias, the teleutospores consist of 3 cells arranged into a spherical structure with three distinct humps.

The Pucciniaceae live exclusively on Angiosperms. The only exception is the genus *Gymnosporangium* which chooses junipers as its primary host.

Of the numerous genera in this family, many are exclusive to the tropics. Quite a few, however, have spread further afield with their hosts. Their minute

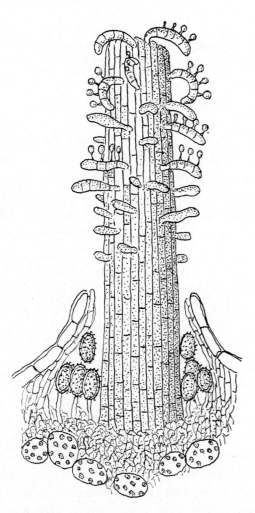

Fig. 180 *Cronartium flaccidum* on *Cynanchum* leaf. Uredospores and teleutospore column bearing numerous basidia

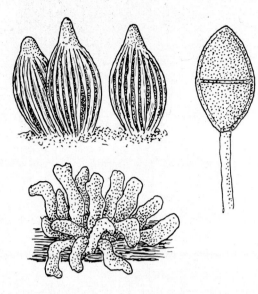

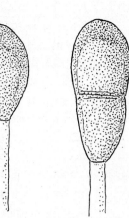

Fig. 184 Left: teleuto-spore of *Uromyces fabae*; right: teleutospore of *Puccinia graminis*, cereal rust

Fig. 182 *Gymnosporangium sabinae*; top left: aecidia on pear leaf; lower left: teleutospores on branch of juniper, *Juniperus sabina* (natural size); right: single teleutospore with part of its 'stalk' (highly magnified)

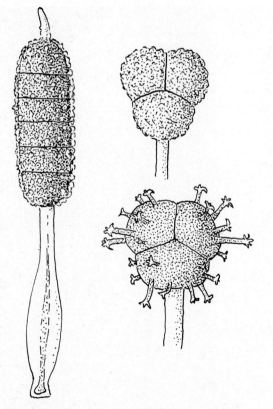

Fig. 183 Left: teleutospore of *Phragmidium tuberculatum*; top right: teleutospore of *Triphragmium ulmariae*; bottom right: teleutospore of *Nyssopsora clavellosa* (all highly magnified)

uredospores are readily scattered by the wind over vast distances. The best-known cosmopolitan genera are *Uromyces* and *Puccinia*, which include some of the most harmful of all rusts. *Uromyces* (600 species) has a predilection for leguminous plants. *U. fabae*, bean rust, can seriously impair the bean harvest; the equally widespread *U. pisi* attacks the garden pea (*Pisum sativum*) and the wild-growing vetch (*Lathyrus*). This rust does relatively little damage to the pea crop, but causes malignant deformations ('cedar apples') in the alternate host, the spurge, *Euphorbia cyparissias*: the infested plants do not form branches and produce relatively short, fleshy leaves that grow sparsely from the stem and never combine into whorls. Worse still, the host usually loses its capacity to produce flowers (cf. p. 82).

The genus *Puccinia* includes close on 4000 species and is by far the largest in the entire order. Most *Pucciniae* live on grasses. The most harmful of all is *P. graminis*, cereal rust, which occurs in four sub-species, all of which have the common barberry bush as their alternate host: *P. graminis tritici* attacks wheat; *P. graminis hordei* attacks barley; *P. graminis avenae* attacks oats; and *P. graminis secalis* attacks rye. The sub-species are, in turn, made up of a large number of physiological races which differ in their parasitism on various agricultural varieties of the host – *P. graminis tritici* alone consists of over 150 known races. This marked tendency to form races gives farmers a serious problem. Since no effective chemical treatment against cereal rusts has as yet been developed, attempts have been directed at breeding cereal varieties that are rust-resistant. Unfortunately, what successes are scored are generally short-lived, since new races of rusts keep appearing

151

to infest the new varieties. Another method of attack, first used in the seventeenth century, the eradication of the barberry host, reduces the danger of infestation considerably, but does not remove it altogether, since in warmer regions, the fungus can survive the winter in the uredospore stage and infest the grain directly, i.e. in the absence of an alternate host. Hence cereal rusts pose a particularly serious threat in warmer countries; in Northern Europe, they cause much less harm than other species of *Puccinia* such as *P. glumarum*, which mainly attacks wheat but can also cause damage to barley and rye. *Pucciniae* also attack asparagus, onions and carrots. In the tropics, the related *Hemileia vastatrix* attacks and destroys the coffee flower; it has, however, ceased to pose a serious threat since planters have been able to breed resistant coffee races.

Order
AURICULARIALES

With the Auriculariales we come to the more highly organized Phragmobasidiomycetidae, all of which produce true fruiting bodies. These structures, which vary considerably in size, generally form thin dry crusts close to the substrate, or organs with a gelatinous consistency. Their upper side bears basidia, usually combined into a hymenium. The basidia of Auriculariales closely resemble those of Uredinales; they are divided by septa into 4 superposed cells, each of which produces a lateral sterigma bearing a basidiospore. In a number of species, the basidia are produced by the germination of the thick-walled probasidia, which correspond to the teleutospores of the rusts. In all other respects, however, the Auriculariales are clearly more advanced than the rusts. They are divided into two main families, the Auriculariaceae and the Septobasidiaceae, which differ markedly in the structure of their fruiting bodies.

The Auriculariaceae, for the most part, produce gelatinous fruiting bodies, usually in the shape of irregular flat cushions. In *Auricularia*, however, the fruiting body is earshaped (*Fig. 186*), and rises erect from the substrate. The Auriculariaceae are predominantly saprophytic on decaying plant remains and dead wood. The exception is the genus *Helico-*

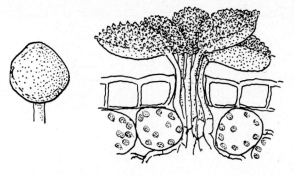

Fig. 185 *Hemileia vastatrix*. Left: teleutospore; right: uredospores on leaf of coffee plant

basidium, which has turned parasite. Its mycelium creeps along the ground and penetrates the roots of trees and other plants. The fruiting bodies develop above the ground; they are compact, matted crusts and often surround the base of the host's stem. *H. compactum* causes damage to coffee and tea. *Auricularia auricula*, Jew's ear, which is the chief European representative of this predominantly tropical family, is an occasional parasite on elder trees.

Fig. 186 *Auricularia auricula*, Jew's ear

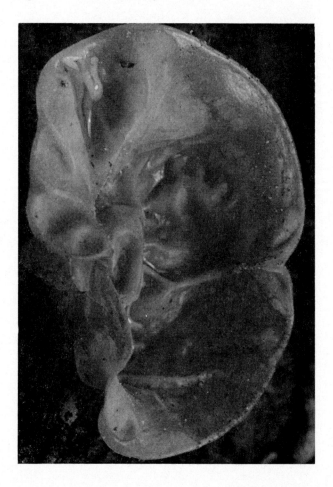

The Septobasidiaceae, which are also a predominantly tropical and sub-tropical family, form peculiar associations: they live on the bark, leaves and fruits of orange and other citrous trees infested with scale insects and cover the latter with a crust-like mycelium. In the genus *Septobasidium*, the mycelium is divided into a basal layer of hyphae rising up in columns and a covering mat of closely intertwined hyphae. The top of the mycelium, which can attain considerable dimensions, bears a dense hymenial layer. Vegetative mycelium and fruiting body are so closely united that it is extremely difficult to distinguish them. The part-parasitic and part-symbiotic association of Septobasidiaceae and scale insects has already been mentioned during our general discussion of symbiosis in fungi (see p. 88). Here we need merely repeat that while the fungi and insects reach a kind of mutually satisfactory equilibrium, both behave as pure parasites towards the host plant. Species of *Septobasidium*, in particular, whose mycelia are very large, often cause severe damage to the trees they infest.

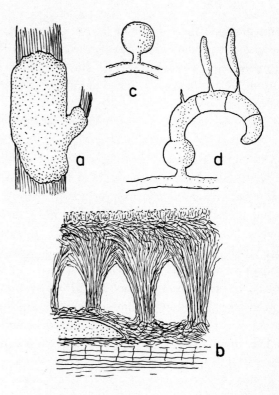

Fig. 188 *Septobasidium bogoriense. a:* Growing on bark (natural size); *b:* cross-section of fungus (scale insect on left); *c:* probasidium; *d:* germinating probasidium

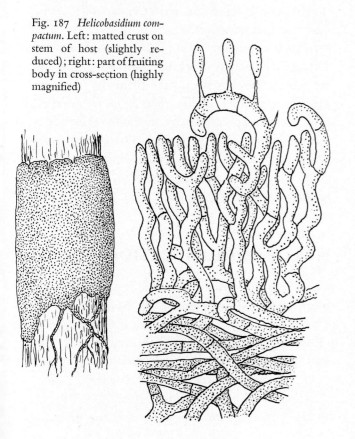

Fig. 187 *Helicobasidium compactum.* Left: matted crust on stem of host (slightly reduced); right: part of fruiting body in cross-section (highly magnified)

Order

TREMELLALES

The Tremellales, or jelly fungi, are Basidiomycetes whose fruiting bodies have the consistency of jelly or wax and tremble upon being touched. They may be cushion-shaped, lobular or resemble mushrooms in appearance, and come in all sorts of colours, with various shades of yellow predominating.

This order occupies an intermediate position between the Phragmobasidiomycetidae and the more highly developed Holobasidiomycetidae. The presence of multicellular mycelia relates it to the first group, from which, however, it differs both in structure and in the way it produces its basidia. These are divided by longitudinal walls, which usually intersect to form 4 cells arranged cross-wise. Every basidial cell is crowned with a basidiospore borne on a long sterigma. In most Tremellales, the basidiospores are capable of multiplying by a kind of budding process; they develop a sterigma that cuts off a new basidiospore at its tip and repeats this process several times. Unlike the smuts, rusts and

153

Auriculariales, the jelly fungi do not develop pro-basidia, but produce their basidia directly from the terminal cells of special hyphae. This development constitutes a milestone in the evolution of Basidiomycetes.

The order includes three families of which two, the Sirobasidiaceae and the Hyaloriaceae, are confined to the tropics. The most important family, however, the Tremellaceae, are also represented in temperate regions. They comprise a large variety of wood- and soil-inhabiting fungi of the most varied shapes. On dead trunks and on bark one occasionally finds orange-coloured, convoluted fruiting bodies of *Tremella mesenterica*, witches' butter (*Pl. 49, p. 132*). *Sebacina*, which also grows on wood, spreads its pale-yellow, cushion-shaped fruiting bodies flat on the substrate. One of the most beautiful of jelly fungi, *Phlogiotis helvelloides*, occurs in warmer parts of Europe, where its pink to rust-coloured,

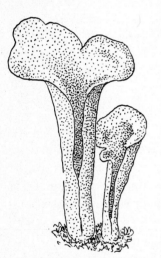

Fig. 189 *Phlogiotis helvelloides*; fruiting body (slightly reduced)

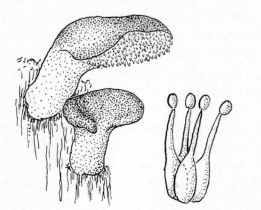

Fig. 190 *Pseudohydnum gelatinosum*. Left: fruiting body (slightly reduced); right: basidium (highly magnified)

funnel-shaped fruiting bodies break out from the forest floor in groups. It is the only edible jelly fungus. In *Pseudohydnum gelatinosum* (*Fig. 190*) the gelatinous, grey-brown, stalked fruiting bodies spread out into semicircular caps whose underside is covered with countless tooth-like protuberances. The teeth, which help to increase the surface of the fruiting body considerably, are lined with hymenium. This structure, which is unusual among jelly fungi, is characteristic of the more highly developed family Hydnaceae (see pp. 157–158).

The path entered upon by the Tremellales is pursued further by the Dacrymycetales and Tulasnellales, two related orders with clear affinities to the sub-class Holobasidiomycetidae. Most of their constituent species produce unicellular basidia, though a few transitional forms are septate. In the Dacrymycetales, the basidia are elongated and provided with two long arms that thin out into pointed sterigmata bearing basidiospores. This type of basidium is said to be of the tuning-fork type. In the Tulasnellales, the basidia are pear-shaped and produce 4 basidiospores each, perched on bladder-shaped sterigmata. The sterigmata are usually divided from the basidium by a septum, and later snap off together with the mature spores.

In their appearance, the Dacrymycetales and the Tulasnellales greatly resemble the Tremellales and are often treated as such. Like them they produce gelatinous fruiting bodies that do not, however, grow to any appreciable size. The only exception is *Calocera viscosa* (*Pl. 51, p. 132*; Dacromycetaceae) whose attractive yellow fruiting bodies look like corals and may sometimes be seen on rotting wood in the autumn.

Sub-class

HOLOBASIDIOMYCETIDAE

With the Holobasidiomycetidae we come to the most highly developed of all Mycophyta: the mushrooms and toadstools with their multiform, often magnificently coloured, fruiting bodies. Despite their great variety, all Holobasidiomycetidae share a common character: their unicellular, club-shaped basidia are crowned by (usually) 4 basidiospores borne at the tip of a delicate sterigma.

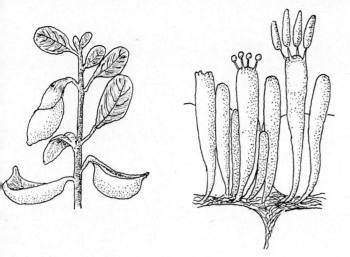

Fig. 191 *Exobasidium vaccinii*. Left: leaves of infested host (natural size); right: mycelium and basidia (highly magnified)

Another characteristic feature of most Holobasidio-mycetidae is that they produce their basidia in vast quantities – a single lamella may give rise to hundreds of thousands. The basidia are combined in a closed hymenium usually covering the entire underside of the fruiting body. Only in the Gasteromycetes – which also differ from the remaining Holobasidio-mycetidae in having closed fruiting bodies – is the hymenium weakly developed or completely missing.

By the structure of their fruiting bodies, Holo-basidiomycetidae can be divided into two large groups. The first includes all species with open fruit-ing bodies, in which the hymenium is freely dis-played; the best-known representatives of this group, which we may call the typical Holobasidiomycetidae, are the mushrooms. The second group comprises the Gasteromycetes (puff-balls, etc.) which, as we saw, have fruiting bodies that are completely closed (at least in the juvenile stage) and which accordingly do not release their spores until maturity.

A special position among the Holobasidio-mycetidae is held by the small order Exobasidiales, which is usually placed first as the most primitive in the sub-class: members of this order do not produce fruiting bodies and, in contrast to most higher Basidiomycetes, they are parasitic rather than saprophytic. Their mycelium proliferates in the stems and leaves of higher plants; the basidia are formed between the epidermal cells of the host, push through the cuticle, and form a layer on the surface. Infected organs show striking malformations and partly change into galls. Of the two genera constituting the family Exobasidiaceae, the most common is *Exobasidium*, which mainly attacks Ericaceae. *E. vaccinii* is a widespread bilberry parasite; *E. rhododendri* (Pl. 53, p. 134) attacks rhododendron plants; the tropical *E. vexans* causes severe damage to tea bushes.

The Exobasidiales are succeeded by the very large order Telephorales, in which the development from very simple to relatively complex fruiting bodies can be readily followed.

Order

TELEPHORALES

The fungi in this order produce a variety of fruiting bodies whose shape ranges from thin hyphal layers in the simplest to mushroom-like caps in the most highly developed. But whatever their shape, all the fruiting bodies are open structures, their surface partly or completely covered with a hymenium. Moreover, they are open and begin to produce basidia as soon as they are formed, with the result that the hymenium grows in size with the fruiting body. Various types of special hyphal cells participate in the construction of these fruiting bodies, among them paraphyses and cystidia (see p. 125). In the Telephorales, hyphae occur in association with other special cells scattered in the fruiting body and often spreading into the hymenium. Thus many species have large, thin-walled, yellow cells filled with oil – these are known as gloeocystidia. Other species are characterized by the possession of forked hyphae, the so-called dichophyses, or of acanthophyses – short, laterally branched hyphae with a very tough wall. In addition, we also meet pigment cells – star-shaped asterophyses and unbranched, thick-walled setae. Finally, some Telephorales contain special cells filled with red sap, which oozes out whenever the fungus is wounded.

The Telephorales are distributed all over the world and include a very large number of families. Most species are saprophytic on dead wood or on leaf litter, but some are parasitic on various plants and particularly on trees, often causing considerable damage.

The lowest representatives of the Telephorales constitute the family Corticiaceae, whose crusty or

155

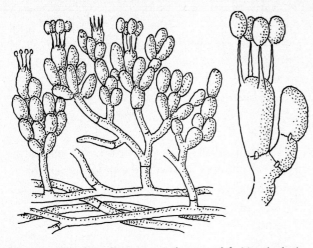

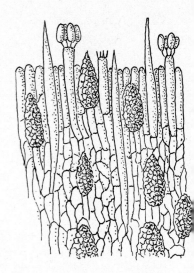

Fig. 192 *Pellicularia filamentosa*. Left: part of fruiting body in cross-section (highly magnified); right: basidium (very highly magnified)

bark-like fruiting bodies lie flat on the substrate – dead branches and tree trunks – with the hymenium on the free surface. The simplest example of this kind of fruiting body is found in the genus *Pellicularia*. Here the fruiting bodies consist of a loose web of hyphae, topped by erect, branching basidium-bearing structures combined in groups, but not into a closed hymenium. Most species of *Pellicularia* are parasitic on higher plants. Thus *P. filamentosa* causes black scurf in potatoes. This fungus rarely fruits; instead it develops a sterile web of hyphae which produce sclerotia, hard resting bodies resistant to unfavourable conditions; in this form the fungus is known as *Rhizoctonia solani*.

In the more typical Corticiaceae, the fruiting bodies are built up of a more or less dense and often

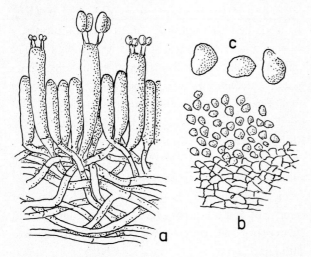

Fig. 193 *Corticium salmonicolor*. *a*: Part of fruiting body in cross-section; *b*: part of conidial fruiting body in cross-section; *c*: conidia (all highly magnified)

tissue-like web of hyphae divided into several layers; the uppermost is formed of basidia and associated cells, which are invariably combined into a hymenium. Such multi-layered fruiting bodies are found, for instance, in the genera *Corticium* and *Peniophora*, each represented by more than 100 species all over the world. *Corticium* includes a large number of species with beautifully coloured fruiting bodies – blue in *C. caeruleum*, a common species on dead wood, and salmon-pink in the tropical *C. salmonicolor*, the only parasitic species in this group.

The next family, the Stereaceae, also produce thin-layered fruiting bodies which, in contrast to those of the Corticiaceae, are attached to the substrate by one side only, or by their centre. In the genus *Stereum*, the most important in the family, the fruiting bodies have the shape of flat or fan-shaped caps and are of a leathery consistency. If we open one, we can see that it consists of three superposed layers; the upper is relatively thin and crusty and often covered with hair; the middle layer is very thick and has a tough, leathery consistency; the lowest represents the hymenium. In a number of Stereaceae, particularly in the genus *Stereum* itself, the whole fruiting body is filled with hyphae containing a sap, usually red, that oozes out when the fungus is injured. The Stereaceae are exclusively wood-inhabiting; most are saprophytic on decaying tree stumps and other wood fragments. The family does, however, include a number of tree parasites; one of the worst among them is *S. purpureum*, which causes silver leaf, a common disease of plum and related fruit trees.

156

The semicircular, cap-shaped fruiting bodies of *S. purpureum* and its relatives are also found in members of the families Schizophyllaceae and Hymenochaetaceae. *Schizophyllum*, the only genus in its family, produces relatively flat, fan-shaped fruiting bodies, often with slit edges. Lamellae radiate out from the point of attachment, and are covered by hymenium. In dry conditions the lamellae bend downwards to close the under-surface of the fruiting body completely, thus preventing the desiccation of the delicate basidia. In the Hymenochaetaceae, the fruiting bodies are attached by their side; here new growth can be readily identified as a semicircular band at the top of the cap.

In the Telephoraceae, we first meet the type of fruiting body characteristic of mushrooms; they are generally divided into stalk and cap. The cap of some species, particularly of *Telephora*, is funnel-shaped and leathery, but as we go up the family, the cap becomes increasingly more spherical. The under-side of the cap is covered with countless warts or short, soft spines bearing the hymenium. (We met similar structures, all involving a marked increase in surface area, in *Pseudohydnum gelatinosum* (p. *154*). Among the Telephoraceae such structures are particularly prominent in the genera *Phellodon* and *Sarcodon*, both of which include a number of fairly common species growing on conifers and to a lesser extent on deciduous trees. *Phellodon zonatus* owes its specific name to the circular zones into which its large fruiting body is divided. The cap is rust-coloured, and grows paler towards the edges. In all other species of *Phellodon*, too, the edge of the cap is considerably lighter in colour than the rest.

The best-known representative of the genus *Sarcodon*, *S. imbricatus*, is a rather imposing fungus, whose chocolate-coloured cap is made up of large concentric circles and covered by overlapping scales. This fungus, which is fairly common in dry pine forests, is highly esteemed for its spicy taste, particularly when young; as they grow older, the fruiting bodies often acquire a bitter taste.

As we have said, the formation of spines or teeth is particularly well developed and characteristic of the Hydnaceae, which, like the Telephoraceae, generally produce stalked, cap-shaped fruiting bodies bearing masses of long white teeth or spines on the

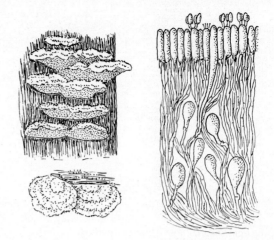

Fig. 195 *Stereum purpureum*. Top left: fruiting body (natural size); lower left: top view of fruiting body (natural size); right: section through fruiting body (highly magnified)

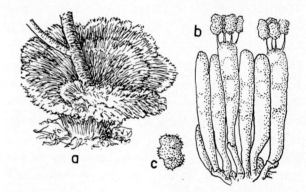

Fig. 196 *Telephora terrestris*. *a*: Fruiting body (natural size); *b*: basidia and spores (highly magnified); *c*: basidiospore (very highly magnified)

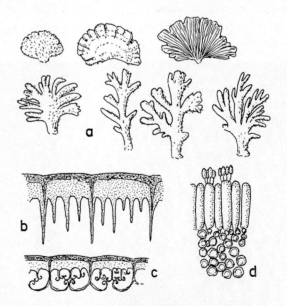

Fig. 197 *Schizophyllum commune*. *a*: Fruiting bodies viewed from below and from the side (somewhat reduced); *b*: section through moist fruiting body; *c*: section through dry fruiting body (*b* and *c* slightly reduced); *d*: section of hymenium (highly magnified)

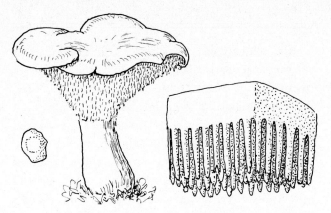

Fig. 198 *Sarcodon imbricatus*. Left: fruiting body (slightly reduced); right: basidiospore (highly magnified)

Fig. 200 *Hydnum repandum*, wood hedgehog. Centre: fruiting body (slightly reduced); right: part of cap under-surface (slightly magnified); left: basidiospore (highly magnified)

under-surface. The most beautiful of these fungi, *Hericium coralloides*, produces large white fruiting bodies whose structure differs considerably from that of other Hydnaceae. They are attached laterally, and consist of a large number of coral-shaped branches tipped with long spines. Another species of unusual shape is *Auriscalpium vulgare*, a small fungus that lives on fallen pine cones. Its fruiting bodies consist of a flat, kidney-shaped cap perched sideways on a slim stalk. Stalk and cap alike are densely covered in hair and are of an inconspicuous browny-black colour. The cap under-surface is covered with long, cone-shaped spines.

The commonest of these spinous fungi, *Hydnum repandum*, wood hedgehog, grows in mixed woods in autumn and often occurs in large concentrations.

It produces small to medium-sized, fleshy fruiting bodies with a pinkish-buff cap of irregular shape. The cap under-surface is densely covered in long yellow spines, which run down part of the stalk as well. The spines are extremely brittle and break off very easily. Wood hedgehogs are edible when young and are greatly sought by connoisseurs.

Completely different in appearance from all the Telephorales we have been describing so far is the family Clavariaceae (club and coral fungi) which includes a number of forest species with unusual and striking fruiting bodies. Some of these are cylindrical or club-shaped and fine down more or less regularly into a stalk-like base. Even the smallest of them are conspicuous, because they break out from the forest floor in very large groups, all glowing in bright

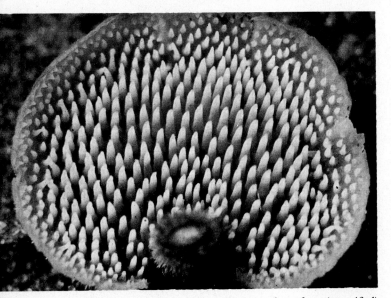

Fig. 199 *Auriscalpium vulgare*; under-surface of cap (magnified)

Fig. 201 *Auriscalpium vulgare*

158

colours. This type of fruiting body is characteristic of club fungi, particularly of the genus *Clavaria*.

Probably the most imposing species in this genus is *C. pistillaria*. Its fleshy fruiting bodies, whose colour ranges from bright-yellow to dark-brown, can attain a height of 8 ins., and look like miniature clubs standing upright on the forest floor. The fungus is edible. Similar in shape but much smaller and slighter is *C. ligula*, which grows exclusively in pine forests, usually in large groups. It, too, is edible, but it does not rank highly among edible fungi.

In club fungi, the hymenium covers the entire cap, but the stalk is sterile, at least in its basal part. In the related coral fungi, which constitute the majority of Clavariaceae, the fruiting body is made up of a cylindrical, more or less tuberous, fleshy stalk that gives rise to branches of various thickness and shape, often terminating in feathery lobes. The main and lateral branches are completely covered in hymenium; only the stalk is bare.

Some coral fungi produce loosely branched fruiting bodies, among them *Clavulina cristata*, a small white fungus that appears in groups in mixed woods. Its diverging branches have crested tips – hence the specific name of *cristata*. This characteristic, and also the white colour of the fruiting bodies, help to distinguish this tasty fungus from its unpalatable or poisonous relatives.

Clavulina cristata is the smallest of all European coral fungi. Most other species, and particularly those in the genera *Clavaria* and *Ramaria*, form highly ramified fruiting bodies, up to 6 ins. high, many of them beautifully coloured. In the striking *Clavaria botrytis*, the fruiting bodies have an unusually thick and fleshy stalk and are divided into countless white branches, each with a flesh-coloured tip. *C. botrytis* is an extremely tasty mushroom. Similar in habit are the lemon-yellow *C. flava* and the golden *Ramaria aurea*, whose richly branched, brightly coloured fruiting bodies are a beautiful sight in autumnal woods. The last two corals can be eaten when young, but are not particularly tasty. In beech forests one occasionally comes across *Clavaria pallida*, whose pale-yellow to flesh-coloured fruiting bodies are borne on short stalks and start branching just above the ground. This species is poisonous and causes violent digestive upsets.

Fig. 202 *Clavaria ligula*

Closely related to *Clavaria* is the genus *Sparassis*, which includes one of the strangest of common species, *S. crispa*, the cauliflower fungus. Like coral fungi, it has richly branched fruiting bodies borne on a thick, tuberous stalk. Here the branches are, however, flattened into bands with fused tips, so that the fungus comes to look like a cauliflower. This impression is enhanced further by its pale-yellow to brownish colour. The fungus grows round the base of pine stumps and the fruiting bodies, which have a tough and fleshy consistency, may weigh more than 10 lb. Young fruiting bodies are considered a great delicacy.

In addition to the club and coral fungi, the Clavariaceae also contain a number of genera (e.g. *Typhula*) with small fruiting bodies divided into long, unbranched stalks and spherical or conical heads. These fruiting bodies arise from small sclerotia embedded in the substrate – the soil or dead plants.

The Cantharellaceae are another family with cap-shaped fruiting bodies. The cup under-surface bearing

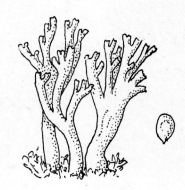

Fig. 203 *Clavulina cristata*. Left: fruiting body (slightly reduced); right: basidiospore (highly magnified)

the hymenium is characteristically studded with ridges or ribs which give a considerable increase in surface area. The family comprises the two genera *Craterellus* and *Cantharellus*, which though closely related have quite distinct fruiting bodies. In the former, the relatively short stalk fans out into a trumpet-shaped cap, whose edge is bent outwards and often split. The outer surface of the trumpet, which is covered with hymenium, is divided by more or less prominent ridges that continue right down to the stalk. The best-known species in this genus, *C. cornucopioides*, horn of plenty, sometimes grows in large groups on the floor of deciduous woods; its fruiting bodies look like so many small, dark-brown horns. The fungus is edible and makes an excellent seasoning.

The genus *Cantharellus* includes *C. cibarius*, chanterelle, one of the most popular edible mushrooms, sold in large quantities on French markets. It is a small to medium-sized plant with bright-yellow, conical fruiting bodies, their entire outer surface – from the edge of the cap to the stalk – covered with numerous forked ridges. Chanterelles grow in woods, generally in large clumps and usually reappearing in the same spot year after year. Closely related is *C. friesii*, which is easily identified by its orange-coloured, velvety fruiting bodies. It, too, is edible, but relatively rare. *C. infundibuliformis*, whose

Fig. 205 *Sparassis crispa*, cauliflower fungus

trumpet-shaped fruiting bodies are reminiscent of *Craterellus*, bears forked ridges on the outer surface of its cap, which stamp it clearly as a species of *Cantharellus*. The fruiting body is brownish-yellow on top and pale-yellow underneath, and appears in mixed forests in late autumn. Since it is generally overlooked in the dense moss it is rarely collected, but is, in fact, a great delicacy and also makes an excellent seasoning.

Like the Cantharellaceae, the Meruliaceae achieve

Fig. 207 *Typhula variabilis*; fruiting body arising from small sclerotium (natural size)

Fig. 204 *Cantharellus cibarius*, chanterelle

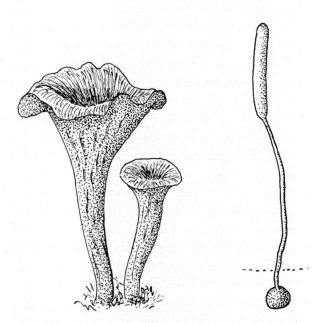

Fig. 206 *Craterellus cornucopioides*, horn of plenty; fruiting body (slightly reduced)

160

a considerable increase in hymenial surface by folds in the fertile tissue of the fruiting body. However, instead of straight ridges, these fungi have reticulate ones; as a result, their fruiting bodies, which often have a wide, semicircular cap, are reminiscent of those of more primitive Telephorales. The family comprises the two genera *Merulius* and *Serpula*, which are sometimes treated as a single genus. *M. tremellosus* grows on the decaying stumps of deciduous trees; its semicircular fruiting bodies, attached laterally to the substrate, are light-grey and matted on the upper surface. The lower side bears a network of flesh-coloured folds. The fruiting bodies have a tough, gelatinous consistency.

The far better known genus of *Serpula* includes the notorious wood-destructive *Serpula lacrymans*, dry rot (*Pl. 54, p. 134*). This fungus, which lives on moist roof beams, wooden walls and panels and beneath floor boards, can destroy the woodwork of an entire building in a short period. Its mycelium forms a white or grey woolly layer on the infested wood, or else combines into thick strands that grow through cracks in the wood or walls. The characteristic fruiting bodies are flat, spongy and disk-shaped; their white edges are often slightly raised. With the exception of the broad edge, the entire upper surface of the fruiting bodies is covered with reticulated folds; these are clothed in hymenium and bear prominent, rust-coloured basidiospores. The fruiting bodies secrete a watery fluid – hence the specific name of *lacrymans*, meaning 'tearful'. Dry rot can only settle on moist wood, but once established it quickly spreads to dry wood as well. To eradicate it completely the infested wood must be torn out and the substrate treated with special chemicals. To forestall attacks, floorboards, etc. should be well ventilated.

The Cantharellaceae and Meruliaceae, which as we saw increase their hymenial surface by means of ridges or folds, are relatively primitive fungi yet foreshadow one of the most important characteristics of the Agaricaceae, or mushrooms proper. The Telephorales, moreover, also comprise the large family Polyporaceae, which has clear affinities with the boletes. Polyporaceae produce fruiting bodies in a great variety of shapes and sizes; in many genera, and particularly in the more primitive, the fruiting bodies are resupinate, that is to say, twisted right round and lying flat on the substrate. The vast majority, however, produce cap-shaped fruiting bodies; the caps are generally attached to the substrate by their sides and are semicircular or bracket-shaped. Quite a few species also produce a stalk. While annual Polyporaceae have soft and fleshy fruiting bodies, those of perennial species have a leathery consistency and grow larger every year.

But though the fruiting bodies of Polyporaceae vary so widely in shape, they all have a common feature: their under-side (or in resupinate forms, the upper side) is invariably covered with countless round or sometimes oval pores, to which the family owes its name. The pores are the openings of tubes or labyrinthine canals running close to the under-surface of the fruiting bodies. The family used to be lumped together with the Boletaceae (boletes), from which, however, they differ in having an unprotected hymenium; this applies to all other Telephorales as well. Many Polyporaceae, particularly the perennial species, produce spores at periodic intervals. The spores mature simultaneously and pour out from the pores as clouds of dust. Often there is a considerable time-lag before new spores are produced; during the resting period, the fruiting bodies are completely devoid of spores.

With few exceptions, Polyporaceae live on wood. Most of them are saprophytic on decaying tree trunks or on fallen stems and branches; some species occasionally settle on old telephone poles. They break down the dead wood, and thus play an essential part in the formation of humus. However, not all Polyporaceae content themselves with dead timber – quite a few are parasites on living trees which they gradually destroy, often causing widespread damage. Numerous genera are found in the tropics, but the great majority prefer more temperate latitudes. In Europe, the family is chiefly represented by the sub-families Fomitoideae, Polyporoideae and Corioloideae.

The best-known species among the Fomitoideae is *Fomes fomentarius*, tinder fungus (*Pl. 57, p. 135*). This remarkable fungus, which lives on old birch and less often on old beech stems, produces hoof-shaped caps projecting a long way from the side of the bark. Their conspicuously arched upper surface is covered with a very hard grey or black crust,

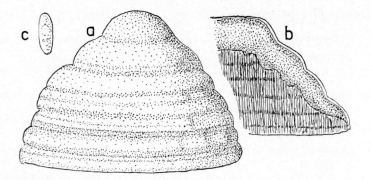

Fig. 208 *Fomes fomentarius*, tinder fungus. *a*: Fruiting body seen from the side (reduced); *b*: longitudinal section of fruiting body (reduced); *c*: basidiospore (highly magnified)

divided into concentric annual grooves. Fruiting bodies with 10 to 15 grooves are far from rare, and in old fungi the cap can attain a diameter of up to 17 ins. Under the crust lies a relatively soft, downy hyphal tissue; it is fawn-coloured and known as the tinder layer. It covers numerous hymenium-lined tubes divided into several horizontal layers. Modern forestry techniques have helped to suppress this fungus, which attacks injured trees and gradually destroys them. Tinder fungi used to be collected, cut up, boiled in water, saturated with saltpetre and finally beaten soft. The resulting substance would catch light at the very first spark and continue to smoulder for a very long time. The tinder layer also served to stanch the flow of blood; hence medieval treatises refer to this fungus as *Fungus chirurgorum*.

The related *F. annosus* is a common and very destructive parasite, causing red rot in conifers; its mycelium spreads upwards from the roots of infested trees and transforms the wood into a soft rust-coloured mass. The fruiting bodies, irregular and relatively flat caps, red to dark-brown on top and cream-coloured at the edge and under-surface, break out from the roots once the tree has been killed.

Among the more important representatives of the Fomitoideae, mention must also be made of the genus *Phellinus*, which includes a number of tree parasites. Very widespread indeed is *P. igniarius*, also known as the false tinder fungus, which, despite its name, is not suited to the manufacture of tinder but resembles *Fomes fomentarius* in external appearance. Unlike the latter, however, it has a hard, dark-brown fruiting body. Moreover, it attacks poplars, willows

and various fruit trees, including the apple, whereas the tinder fungus has a predilection for beeches. *P. igniarius* enters the host through wounds, destroys the wood by producing white rot, and kills the tree within a few years. Trees infested by this fungus are often chosen by woodpeckers, which build their nest in the decaying wood, usually beneath the fruiting bodies whose wide-brimmed caps help to protect the fledglings from the rain.

Another well-known member of the Fomitoideae is *Piptoporus betulinus*, razor-strop fungus, which attacks birches and causes grave damage particularly to older and ailing trees. Its semicircular or kidney-shaped fruiting bodies, which die after a year, break out in a vertical line from the trunks and branches.

The sub-class Polyporoideae consists exclusively of forms with stalked fruiting bodies, and is divided into the genera *Polypilus* and *Polyporus*. The former includes some of the largest known fungi. Their fruiting bodies consist of a large number of flat caps that rise up from a common stalk and spread out in all directions. A particularly imposing species is *P. ramosissimus*, which grows at the base of decaying oak and beech stumps. Its fruiting bodies arise from tuberous sclerotia hidden in the ground. The thick white stalk is divided into a large number of up-turned branches, each bearing an almost perfectly circular fawn cap. The caps can attain a diameter of just under 2 ins.; the whole fungus may be more than 18 ins. in width. Closely related is *P. frondosus* which also grows at the foot of old oaks. It differs from *P. ramosissimus* in having fan-shaped caps attached to the side of the stalk. When the fungus is shaken the caps knock against one another to produce an audible rattle.

The most imposing of all European fungi is *Polypilus giganteus*. Its fan-shaped caps, which rise directly from the main stalk, grow to a width of 1 ft. and combine into branches often more than 3 ft. in diameter. The caps are yellowish-brown on top; their under-side is white but turns black on being pressed, a characteristic which helps collectors to identify this common fungus, which grows prolifically on the stumps of foliage trees.

Unlike *Polypilus*, *Polyporus* species produce fruiting bodies with only a single cap, perched on top or on the side of the stalk. The best-known representative is *P. squamosus*, dryad's saddle, a sizeable fungus which grows on the stems of deciduous trees. Its broad, fan-shaped caps are perched laterally on the stalk, and are extremely colourful – the yellow upper side is covered in broad brown scales arranged loosely in concentric circles.

The fungi in the third sub-family, the Corioloideae, mostly produce unstalked fruiting bodies, whose semicircular or fan-shaped leathery caps protrude from the substrate like so many brackets. The upper side of these brackets is generally marked with concentric rings which are not, however, indications of age, since most Corioloideae produce annual fruiting bodies. Occasionally these zones, which appear as smooth or matted bands, are set off against one another in different colours. Particularly characteristic of the Corioloideae is the relatively simple structure of their fruiting bodies; though these are often covered with a thin, rudimentary crust or skin, they are not differentiated internally into sterile and fertile layers. Instead, they are built up of a homogeneous tissue, perforated by tubes carrying the hymenium. The pores by which the tubes open on the lower surface of the cap are often fused to form elongated straight or twisted grooves. In some genera, the surface tissue between these grooves has become folded into ridges. The marked differences in shape resulting from the presence of these structures helps considerably in the identification of the several genera, many of which are very common. The most widespread of these, *Coriolus*, includes the beautiful *C. versicolor* (*Pl. 56, p. 135*), which grows on old stumps in deciduous woods. Its flat, fan-shaped, multicoloured caps break out from the bark of trees in dense many-storeyed colonies or in flat rosettes and make a most colourful spectacle. Particularly beautiful are specimens with yellow or dark-red bands, or those in which grey zones alternate with bright blue. The fruiting bodies of *C. abietinus* have a bright-violet under-surface; this species lives on fallen branches or the dead stumps of pine trees.

More impressive still are various species of *Trametes*, all of whose fruiting bodies are bracket-shaped. The white brackets of *T. gibbosa* are common on beech stumps, but can also be found growing on dead lime trees and horse chestnuts. They have pronounced humps at their point of attachment to

Fig. 209   *Trametes gibbosa*

the substrate; another characteristic feature is the presence of rays of rectangular pores. Similar in appearance is *T. suaveolens*, which grows in isolated groups on poplars and willows; the two species are easily distinguished because the fruiting bodies of *T. suaveolens* smell strongly of aniseed.

As we said earlier, the fruiting bodies of some Corioloideae have a lamellate structure. Among British species this particular type of structure is found in *Daedalea quercina*, a fungus that lives exclusively on dead oak trees; its fruiting bodies are relatively large brackets, the colour and consistency of cork. Their under-side, which tapers strongly towards the point of attachment, is covered in a confused mass of straight and spiral plates of various length, with the pore channels running in between. In the related genus of *Lenzites*, the under-side of the fruiting bodies is split up into a large number of thin, leathery or corky ridges. *L. saepiaria* produces black fruiting bodies, edged in cream, on fence posts, bridge railings and other woodwork in which coniferous wood has been used. The rarer *L. betulina*, which grows on dead stumps of birches and beeches, has bright-coloured fruiting bodies covered with concentric layers with a hairy consistency.

Closely related to the Polyporaceae is the small genus *Fistulina* which, because of marked peculiarities in the structure of its tubes, has been raised to the rank of a family, the Fistulinaceae. The tubes, which

163

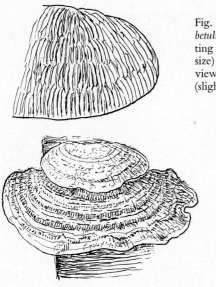

Fig. 210 *Lenzites betulina*. Below: fruiting body (natural size); top: partial view of under-surface (slightly reduced)

do not communicate with each other, appear as wart-shaped humps, but grow longer as the fruiting bodies develop until, finally, they emerge from the under-side of the fruiting body. They open as soon as the spores are mature.

The only British species, *F. hepatica*, poor man's beefsteak, is one of the most peculiar sights among local fungi. Its fruiting bodies, which grow on the stems and stumps of old oaks, bear a strong resemblance to beef. This impression is enhanced further by the fleshy consistency and the warty structure of

Fig. 211 *Fistulina hepatica*, poor man's beefsteak; cap under-surface (magnified)

their under-side. The fruiting bodies can grow to a foot across, and are edible when young, but must first be soaked in water to get rid of the tannin.

Order

AGARICALES

The large order Agaricales includes the fungi whose fruiting bodies we commonly call mushrooms or toadstools. Most are soil-dwelling saprophytes, and feed on organic substances in the humus layer. However, the order also includes several species, particularly of forest-inhabiting fungi, that form mycorrhizal associations with the roots of various trees. Parasitism is extremely rare among Agaricales.

The Agaricales are divided into two main groups. In the first (the mushrooms), the basidia are borne on gills (lamellae) or plates; in the second (the boletes) the basidia line the inside of tubes. In contrast to the Telephorales, Agaricales have fruiting bodies of a marked uniformity: with very few exceptions these consist of an erect stalk and a horizontal cap. Usually the cap is fleshy and perched centrally on the stalk; in some species, however, it is attached to the side.

The most important characteristic of Agaricales is the structure of their hymenium. While that of Telephorales is open, that of most Agaricales develops inside the fruiting body and only comes to the surface during the final stages of development. Moreover, while the gills and tubes are growing they are usually covered by a protective layer. In some species this protection is provided by the edge of the cap which, in young fruiting bodies, is folded inwards and covers the under-side of the cap.

In most Agaricales the edge of the cap is joined to the stalk by the velum partiale or inner veil, which may take the form of a delicate weft of membrane or of a tougher annular structure. As soon as the cap of the growing fungus begins to spread outwards, the inner veil tears; it may become severed completely or remain attached to the stalk as a ring-shaped membrane, the annulus. In certain mushrooms, however, portions of the torn web may hang down as a thin curtain, the cortina. In yet other species, for instance in *Amanita muscaria*, Fly Agaric (Family Amanitaceae) stalk and cap are jointly enclosed in a tough white membrane, the velum universale. As the fruiting body enlarges, the velum universale tears to leave a beaker-shaped body, the volva, around the base of the stalk; remnants of it also appear on the cap in the form of white scales or spots (*Fig. 220*).

Although all Agaricales have fruiting bodies of corresponding structure, they nevertheless assume a surprising variety of shapes. More than 2000 distinct species are at home in Northern and Central Europe, and of these the vast majority are Agaricaceae. Boletaceae account for less than 50 of these species, and many of them have become so rare that they have had to be placed under special protection.

Many Agaricales are choice edible fungi, and quite a few have been known since antiquity. Unfortunately many edible species resemble their poisonous relatives so closely that the two are often confused, particularly by non-experts. The risk is relatively small with boletes, whose only poisonous representative, *Boletus satanas*, is extremely rare. However, gilled Agaricales include several highly poisonous species that cannot be identified by their taste, smell or colour – hence it is absolutely essential for every mushroom collector to know them by sight.

In classifying the Agaricales, taxonomists rely on the structure of the flesh, the nature and arrangement of the gills, the presence or absence of veils, and particularly on the colour of the spores. These may be light or dark, and since they impart their colour to the gills, it is possible to distinguish light-coloured from dark-coloured Agaricales. The light-coloured types constitute the small families Hygrophoraceae and Amanitaceae, and the very large family Tricholomataceae; the dark-coloured types are distributed into a number of small families.

Family
Hygrophoraceae

The Hygrophoraceae occupy a special position among the pale-spored mushrooms, thanks to a unique property of their gills: these continue a long way down the stalk in most species, are thickened by a fleshy intermediate layer, and have a waxy appearance in mature specimens.

Hygrophoraceae are fairly common in Britain, where they occur in woods, fields and meadows.

On the Continent one of the best-known wood-dwelling genera is *Limacium*, which is readily identified by its slimy fruiting bodies. These are invested in a velum universale when young; remains of the velum form a slimy layer on mature caps and stalks or more rarely combine into small tufts. Edible species include *L. eburneum*, whose ivory-coloured fruiting bodies often break out from the autumnal forest floor in groups.

Hygrocybe, a genus of relatively small and fragile fungi with vitreous caps, mostly red or yellow, occurs in fields and meadows, where its various species form a striking contrast to the grass. They are among the most colourful of European fungi. A particularly beautiful species is *H. punicea* with scarlet to orange caps up to 4 ins. across. This fungus grows chiefly on alpine meadows. Another magnificent species is *H. conica* (*Pl. 59, p. 136*); it is easily identified because its yellow flesh turns dark blue at the slightest touch.

In the same sites as, and often growing in association with, *Hygrocybe* we often meet various species of *Camarophyllus*. They are medium-sized, relatively thick-fleshed mushrooms of an inconspicuous colour. Most are highly prized edible fungi, for instance *C. pratensis*, whose conical fruiting bodies grow throughout the autumn at the edge of woods, in fields and in meadows. Another favourite of fungus collectors is *C. marzuolus*, which lives in alpine woods. Its fruiting bodies have an attractive black cap and a white stalk; they break out of the ground soon after the snow has melted.

Family
Tricholomataceae

The large family Tricholomataceae comprises all white-spored mushrooms having fibrous fruiting bodies and thin gills fused firmly to the stalk. They are a highly diverse group, whose family relationship is not yet fully established. However, by the nature and formation of their stalk we can divide them into three main types: (1) those with fleshy stalks attached to the centre of the cap; (2) those with fleshy stalks attached to the cap eccentrically or laterally; (3) those with gristly stalks attached to the cap eccentrically or laterally.

The first type is by far the most widespread. It contains mushrooms of a variety of forms, among them some of the very smallest; the majority, however, are of medium size, and some have very large fruiting bodies.

The smallest include the genus *Asterophora*, which grows on the caps of old specimens of *Russula* (*Fig. 213*). The delicate white fruiting bodies of these tiny fungi are covered with brown dust, representing the thick-walled chlamydospores which, in *Asterophora*, frequently take the place of the basidiospores. Small, delicate fruiting bodies are also found in *Laccaria laccata*, one of the commonest and most diversified species in Britain (*Pl. 60, p. 136*). It occurs in red, brown and violet varieties.

Among the more imposing representatives of this group is a whole series of common forest mushrooms. One of these is *Hygrophoropsis aurantiaca* which, from a distance, is often confused with the true Chanterelle but can be readily distinguished from it by its flaccid, thin-fleshed cap and orange lamellae. This group also includes the genera *Clitocybe*, *Tricholoma* and *Colybia*, each with an exceptionally large number of species.

The genus *Clitocybe*, with some fifty British species, most of them fairly large, is readily identified by its funnel- or top-shaped cap and dense, generally white lamellae, decurrent in many species. Young

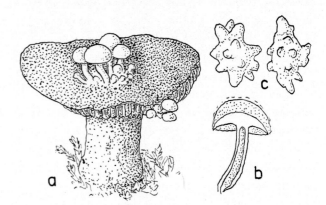

Fig. 213 *Asterophora lycoperdoides*. a: Fruiting body growing on *Russula adusta* (natural size); b: longitudinal section through fruiting body (natural size); c: chlamydospores (highly magnified)

fruiting bodies, which generally lack the typical funnel shape, have the edge of their caps rolled down – a useful distinguishing mark. The genus generally occurs in large groups. Many species will form ring-shaped colonies, the so-called fairy rings: their mycelia spread out laterally in all directions to give rise to fruiting bodies at the tips of the hyphae. Whenever such a mycelium can develop undisturbed, it will spread further and further, so that the ring grows larger every year. Fairy rings are produced by other fungi as well, but they are most conspicuous in *Clitocybe*.

The most imposing European representative of this genus is *Clytocybe gigantea*, which produces off-white caps, smooth on the upper surface, and up to 1 ft. in diameter. They are attached to a relatively short but very strong stalk. *C. gigantea* is particularly common in mountain pastures and sunny forest clearings. It is a choice edible mushroom and also yields the antibiotic clytocybin, whose effects resemble those of penicillin. The related *C. geotropa* (*Fig. 212*) makes its appearance in late autumn, among deciduous trees, under bushes, and occasionally in parkland. Its large, leathery, yellow fruiting bodies make a striking contrast to the leaf litter around them.

While *C. gigantea* is relatively rare, the smaller species of *Clitocybe* are fairly common. Thus *C. nebularis* (*Pl. 61, p. 137*) can often be seen in autumnal forests. It is easily identified by its fleshy, slightly

Fig. 212 *Clitocybe geotropa*

convex, brownish or pale-grey caps, often covered in a white bloom, and giving off a sweet aroma. In some areas it is regarded as a good edible mushroom. *C. odora* is easily recognized by its bluish-green colour and its strong and fragrant smell of aniseed.

Though most species of *Clitocybe* are edible, it is best to avoid the small white types, which include a number of poisonous toadstools.

Distantly related to *Clitocybe* is *Armilariella mellea*, honey fungus (*Fig. 214*), which is very common in forests and gardens, where it attacks and eventually kills the roots of all sorts of trees. The mycelium develops rhizomorphs, thick strands of densely packed hyphae, underneath the bark. Wood attacked by this fungus is luminous in the dark. The fruiting bodies are yellowish-tawny to deep brown in colour, and the centre of the cap is covered with small dark scales that are easily peeled off. Young fruiting bodies have a near-spherical cap joined to the stalk by a velum; the cap subsequently spreads out to form a large umbrella, with the velum as a white ring. Young honey fungi are prized by mushroom collectors as great delicacies; foresters, on the other hand, known them as dangerous parasites, particularly in pine plantations.

One of the most widespread genera of mushrooms, *Tricholoma*, includes some seventy British species. They do not, however, form a homogeneous group, and modern taxonomists tend to split them up into several distinct genera.

Apart from a few smaller species, most members of this genus are fairly large and strong. They have broad, often centrally flattened caps, in a host of beautiful colours. One of the chief distinctions of this genus is the presence of sinuate gills, i.e. gills that show a certain curvature as they reach the stalk. These fungi smell strongly of cucumber or new meal.

Of the large number of British species, mostly common in woods, we shall merely mention some of the more striking or important. *T. equestre*, which is prized as an edible mushroom, occurs in large groups and is easily identified by its greeny-yellow cap with brown central spots, and its sulphur-yellow gills and stalk. There is little danger of confusing this mushroom with its sulphur-yellow relative, *T. sulphureum* (*Fig. 215*), common in deciduous forests, since the latter smells strongly of gas-tar.

Fig. 214 *Armillariella mellea*, honey fungus

T. gambosum, St George's mushroom, so called because it appears round about St George's Day (April 23), is another favourite edible species. It grows among grass in pastures, usually on calcareous soils. Its fruiting bodies are ivory-coloured and smell of new meal. *T. nudum*, wood blewit, has a rounded cap and is amethyst in colour. It, too, is a good edible species and can be readily grown on garden compost. Many taxonomists combine *T. nudum* with a number of related species into the genus *Lepista*, characterized by the presence of pale-red gills.

Apart from edible, or at least harmless, mushrooms, the genus *Tricholoma* also includes a highly

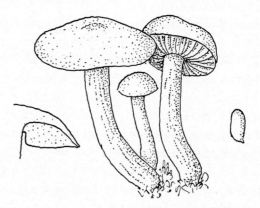

Fig. 215 *Tricholoma sulphureum*. Centre: fruiting body (natural size); left: longitudinal section through right half of cap (slightly reduced); right: basidiospore (highly magnified)

167

Fig. 216 *Pleurotus ostreatus*, oyster mushroom. Centre: fruiting body (slightly reduced); right: longitudinal section through right half of cap (slightly reduced); left: basidiospores (highly magnified)

poisonous, albeit rare, species, namely *T. tigrinum*, which grows exclusively on calcareous soils. It is of medium size, brightly coloured, and its silvery cap is loosely covered in grey-brown scales. Its gills and the tip of its stalk exude droplets of water. Since it is easy to confuse *T. tigrinum* with other grey species, particularly with the mouse-coloured, scaly *T. terreum*, it is best to avoid grey species altogether, the more so as *T. tigrinum* can cause severe intestinal complaints and lead to general debility.

Tricholomataceae which have their caps attached to the side or edge of the stalk are best known through three small genera of wood-infesting fungi, namely *Panellus*, *Pleurotus* and *Lentinus*.

Panellus is represented in Europe by a small number of fairly common species. All form densely bunched colonies on the trunks and stems of decidu-ous trees. Their fruiting bodies, generally small in size, consist of a kidney- or fan-shaped cap, with wavy or serrated edges, and a short stalk that nar-rows markedly at the base. Cap and stalk are clearly differentiated; the gills do not continue into the stalk. The fruiting bodies have a leathery consistency and generally shrivel up with age; when they are moistened, however, they quickly return to their original shape. *P. stipticus* is common on oak trunks and stems, where its small yellowish-brown fruiting bodies are combined into dense bunches. *P. conchatus*, which grows on beech and birch trunks, is a very beautiful species, with violet fruiting bodies that turn a cinnamon colour on top.

Pleurotus, with some 40 species in Europe, bears a superficial resemblance to *Panellus* from which it is,

however, easily distinguished by its fleshy fruiting bodies and also by the fact that its gills continue into the stalk. Moreover, the stalk is not invariably attached to the edge of the cap, as it is in *Panellus*, but is often no more than slightly off-centre. The best-known species, *P. ostreatus*, oyster mush-room, has a striking, thick-fleshed fruiting body. Its short, stout, white stalk is attached to one side of the black or greyish-brown cap; the gills are pale-coloured. *P. ostreatus* (*Fig. 216*) grows in bunches on the trunks and stems of various deciduous trees, chiefly beeches, poplars and willows. It is considered a good edible mushroom, though, for cooking, only young specimens are generally used.

Lentinus strongly resembles *Pleurotus*, from which it differs in having serrated, or at least irregularly notched, gills. In general, this genus is far less com-mon than the last two. Probably the best-known species is *L. cochleatus*. Its rust-coloured fruiting bodies smell strongly of aniseed and grow in dense clumps on beech trunks.

The third group of Tricholomataceae – those having a gristly stalk – is chiefly represented by three genera, all fairly closely interrelated, namely *Collybia*, *Marasmius* and *Mycena*. All are small fungi and grow partly on the soil and partly on wood.

Collybia, with just under 40 species in Britain, is a very heterogeneous group, though all its constituent species share a smooth, elastic, hollow stalk rather like a rubber tube. The edge of the cap is invariably inrolled in young plants; subsequently, it spreads out to form a flat, arched, or buckled umbrella.

Numerous species of *Collybia* live on tree trunks and dead stems. They may grow directly from the wood, as for instance *C. mucida*, whose white, slimy fruiting bodies break out in bunches from the bark of dead or diseased beeches, or else directly from the soil in the close vicinity of tree trunks, to which they are joined by an underground extension of their stalk, known as the 'root'. A typical representative of such root-forming species is *C. radicata*, rooting shank, which is common in woods from early sum-mer to late autumn. It is a medium-sized, yellowish-brown fungus, with a flat, furrowed cap on a tall stalk which tapers into a very long 'root'. *C. tenacella*, which grows exclusively on decaying pine cones, produces long and hairy roots.

Fig. 217 *Marasmius rotula*

Species living on the forest soil include the medium-sized yellow or reddish-brown *C. dryophila*, which is very tasty when fried. Closely related to *Collybia* is *Flammulina* (= *Collybia*) *velutipes*, winter fungus or velvet-stemmed agaric, a honey-coloured plant with a dark-brown, velvety stem. This fungus appears at the end of autumn and persists into the winter. It grows in clusters on the stems and trunks of decaying willows and other deciduous trees, and less frequently on healthy trees. It is one of the few fleshy mushrooms capable of withstanding long spells of frost; as soon as the weather grows milder, the frozen fruiting body thaws out again and immediately continues to grow. The thin, soft-fleshed caps make a highly prized delicacy.

Marasmius is chiefly distributed in the tropics, but includes more than a score of representatives in Britain. Most species are very small, with a long, thread-like stalk and a very attractive cap. The fruiting bodies are remarkably resistant, particularly to desiccation; they may be dried without injury and will revive directly they are moistened. Most species live on the forest floor, feeding on humus or dead plants. Thus pine forests are often densely covered in *M. perforans* (*Pl. 62, p. 137*), whose tiny white caps on slender, dark-brown stalks make a striking contrast to the green needle litter. Each fungus is attached to an individual pine needle. The particularly attractive *M. rotula* (*Fig. 217*) lives on

leaf litter, dead branches and other plant detritus of deciduous forests, where its white caps look like so many little parachutes. In this species, the gills are fused into a ring-shaped collar some distance from the stalk.

Two species well known to be edible are *M. scorodonius* and *M. oreades*, fairy-ring champignon. The first of these tastes of garlic, and its dried fruiting bodies ('true mousseron') may be added to various dishes as seasoning. In external appearance, *M. scorodonius* resembles *M. perforans* with which it, moreover, often grows in association. However, it is easily distinguished from the latter by its garlic smell and shiny, reddish-brown stalks. *M. oreades* can also be used as a seasoning, but is mainly eaten fried. It is one of the most imposing members of this genus; its tan, bell-shaped caps can attain a diameter of 2 ins. and its matted stalks are relatively massive as well. This species is common on meadows and lawns. It is highly gregarious and generally forms fairy rings.

The genus *Mycena* includes a great many dwarf forms: only a few of the 80 or so species found in

Fig. 218 *Mycena galericulata*

Central Europe can be identified with the naked eye. Most have long, delicate stalks and thin, cone-shaped or bell-shaped caps (*Figs. 218, 219*). The tiny *M. rosella* has extremely beautiful fruiting bodies in a delicate pink hue. Another attractive species is the pink or violet *M. pura*, which smells of radishes. The remaining species of *Mycena*, too, have a characteristic odour; some have their stalks filled with milk sap, which oozes out in the form of large yellow or red drops from broken or injured stalks. White milk sap of the kind found in so many higher plants is present in only one species of *Mycena*, namely *M. galopus*. It has a pale-grey to pale-fawn cap, and gills that change from white to pink with age. This fungus grows in clusters on old stumps throughout the year, when conditions are favourable. Somewhat less common is *M. polygramma* (*Pl. 58, p. 136*), another beautiful mushroom inhabiting old stumps, but easily identified by its slim, silvery, furrowed stem, and its light-brown, bell-shaped cap.

Family
Amanitaceae

Like the Hygrophoraceae and the Tricholomataceae, the Amanitaceae are white-spored mushrooms. However, apart from the colour of their spores they share few other characters with the rest. They are unusual in that their stalks and caps are built up of two distinct tissues; as a result, the cap is very easily separated from the stalk. Another characteristic is the presence of free gills, developed exclusively from cap tissue. The young fruiting bodies of all Amanitaceae are enveloped in a velum universale; often there is also a velum partiale.

Among the Amanitaceae, the genus *Amanita* deserves special mention because it contains a number of extremely poisonous species – in fact, very few species of *Amanita* are harmless, let alone edible. Since these fungi are so often confused with others, mushroom collectors should learn to recognize them at sight. Luckily *Amanitae* have a number of distinguishing marks that facilitate their identification. To begin with, they all have two veils, the velum universale which leaves a more or less distinct cup or volva on the swollen base of the stalk and some-

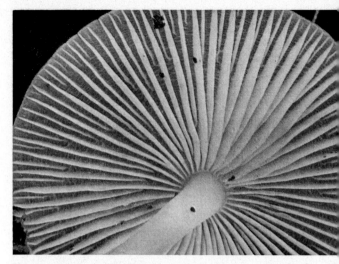

Fig. 219 *Mycena galericulata*; cap under-surface (magnified)

times loose patches on the cap, and the velum partiale which forms a membranous ring round the stem. Now the presence of a ring or girdle of scales together with a volva clearly distinguishes *Amanita* from all mushrooms of similar shape. Specimens should therefore be dug up with care and the base of the stalk examined for the presence of a volva.

A. phalloides, death cap, is responsible for most of the recorded deaths from fungus poisoning. Appearing in autumn on all sorts of soil in deciduous forests, the death cap is a fairly large fungus with a tall, slender stalk and a slightly arched, grey or olive-topped cap. The tip of the pale stem is marked with fine vertical lines due to gills and also bears a finely striate ring. The related *A. virosa*, destroying angel, prefers coniferous forests and is generally smaller in size than *A. phalloides*. Moreover, its cap does not expand nearly so much, with the result that it retains its conical shape. Its fruiting bodies are pure white and can be seen from far afield. Both species have a prominent volva completely surrounding the swollen base of the stem; in *A. virosa*, the volva is generally hidden beneath the ground but in *A. phalloides* its lobate edges occasionally protrude from the soil. Both fungi share yet another feature: their gills remain pure white even in age. Only if all these factors are remembered is there no risk of confusing either fungus with such white mushrooms as for instance the champignon, whose gills are never white but vary from pinkish grey to chocolate brown.

Fig. 220 Young fly agaric (*Amanita muscaria*)

A single *Amanita phalloides* cap is enough to kill an adult. The poisons involved are phalloidine and amanitine, which latter attacks the heart, kidneys and liver and is particularly dangerous in that its effects do not appear for several hours and sometimes not for two days. When the symptoms – severe intestinal upsets, damage to the heart and circulation – are not identified in time the patient generally dies.

Two other poisonous fungi in this genus are *A. muscaria*, fly agaric (*Figs. 220, 221*), and *A. pantherina*, panther cap. They, too, are often confused with edible species, and every collector should be familiar with them. The fly agaric, probably one of the most attractive-looking fungi of all, is so well-known that it hardly needs description. It has a slender, tall, white stalk bearing a white volva, and a scarlet or orange cap with numerous snow-white, wart-like scales – remains of the universal veil. The swollen base of the stem, too, is covered in scaly remains arranged in several rows. The gills are a

brilliant white. Fly agaric may also appear in other colours – the chief reason why fly agaric poisoning occurs at all. In the Mediterranean region, however, even the red fly agaric is often confused with the edible *A. caesarea*, a glorious mushroom with a glowing red cap, yellow gills, a yellow stalk and a pure white volva. Since this species is restricted to southern climes its resemblance to the crimson fly agaric poses few dangers in Western Europe.

Things are quite different with the brown fly agaric (*A. muscaria* var. *umbrina*) which closely resembles *A. rubescens*, the blusher, a highly prized edible mushroom. The latter is one of the commonest fungi, and grows in early autumn in woods of all kinds. It differs from the brown fly agaric chiefly in that its cap scales are reddish or pale grey, its stalk bears red spots particularly towards the base, and its volva is represented by small scales forming broken rings.

The toxic substance in *A. muscaria* is muscarine, a poison that attacks the nervous system and subsequently the heart. Unlike phalloidine and amanitine, muscarine is quick-acting: the symptoms appear within half an hour of eating and take the form of intoxication, hallucination and strong delirium. In severe cases, heart and respiratory failure may lead to death. Normally, however, fly agaric poisoning does not prove fatal, not only because it is quickly

Fig. 221 *Amanita muscaria*, fly agaric, forming a fairy ring

171

Fig. 222 *Amanita vaginata*

diagnosed, but also because the body can cope unaided with small quanties of muscarine (several Siberian tribes even use this drug as a narcotic).

Far more dangerous than *A. muscaria* is *A. pantherina*, which can boast not one, but two, edible doubles. It is a medium-sized fungus with a relatively slender, tall, white stalk and a flat or slightly concave, dull brown or greyish-brown cap, bearing numerous pure white warts. The edge of the cap is striate. The volva is represented by two or three girdles just above the swollen base of the stem, and the ring is attached near the middle of the stem. Volva and ring alike are white.

The two edible species with which *A. pantherina* is so often confused are *A. rubescens*, mentioned above, and *A. spissa*. To tell them apart, the collector should remember that *A. pantherina* alone has a volva, and that whereas the ring of *A. pantherina* has a smooth surface, that of the other two is furrowed.

Panther cap poisoning is very similar to fly agaric poisoning – in both cases the active substance is muscarine. The panther cap, however, contains yet another poison, namely muscaridine, which has similar effects.

Two other genera of Amanitaceae common in Europe are *Volvaria* and *Pluteus*, both of them pink-spored. *Volvaria speciosa*, a large, off-white fungus, likes rich soil, and hence occurs chiefly on compost and dung heaps.

The genus *Pluteus* differs from all other Amanitaceae in that its stalk is without a visible trace of a ring or volva. Moreover, it is one of the few genera in its family to live on wood. However, the chief character of the Amanitaceae – free gills – is particularly marked in this genus: the gills are separated from the stalk by a prominent furrow. The best-known British representative, *P. cervinus* (*Fig. 223*), has a dark-brown cap, 2 to 4 ins. in diameter, flattened and with a boss in the centre. The stalk is white but streaked with fine radiating fibrils. This fungus is fairly common from late spring to autumn, particularly on the stumps of deciduous trees. It is the only edible member of its genus but far from tasty.

The Amanitaceae also include the genus *Termitomyces*, which inhabits the comb cells of the nests of certain termites. The fungus spreads its mycelium on the wood passed through the intestines of these animals, and covers the comb cells with a hoary layer, which was formerly thought to serve as food for the larvae. In places, the hyphae combine into fleshy structures that later develop into fruiting

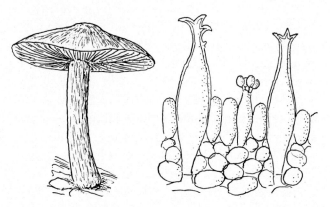

Fig. 223 *Pluteus cervinus*. Left: fruiting body (slightly reduced); right: cross-section through a gill (highly magnified)

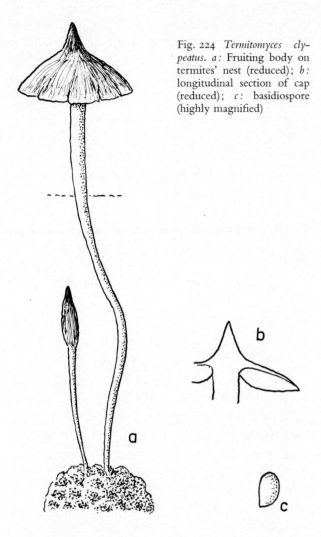

Fig. 224 *Termitomyces cly-peatus. a:* Fruiting body on termites' nest (reduced); *b:* longitudinal section of cap (reduced); *c:* basidiospore (highly magnified)

bodies. These break out of the nest by means of a highly elastic stalk that can grow to a length of 7 ft., and a cap with a very hard and pointed boss. In their external appearance, the fruiting bodies of *Termito-myces* correspond largely with those of other Amani-taceae, and, when expanded, may attain a fairly large size (*Fig. 224*).

We have said that the hoary covering of the comb cells was formerly believed to serve as food for the larvae. Recent French studies have suggested that the larvae cannot eat the fungus because of the peculiar structure of their mouth parts. Even so, the termites have a vital need for these fungi: whenever young queens are about to form a new colony, they invariably take with them a lump of the fungus-infested wood and introduce it into the first comb of the new nest.

Family
Agaricaceae

The Agaricaceae are closely related to the Amanita-ceae, like which they have free gills (with few ex-ceptions) and fruiting bodies built up of two distinct types of tissue. Unlike the Amanitaceae, however, most Agaricaceae have coloured spores. They also differ from the former in their velum formations – only the tropical genus *Clarkeinda* has a volva. In the remaining genera, the velum universale leaves a few scales or no remains at all. The velum partiale on the other hand is well developed. It is built up of tissue from the cap margin – unlike the velum partiale of *Amanita* which is constructed of gill tissue – and remains on the stalk in the form of a membranous ring which, in many species, is easily peeled off. All Agaricaceae are soil-dwelling fungi, growing chiefly in open woods, meadows, pastures and other grass-land. Though they enjoy a very wide distribution, they prefer temperate zones.

The family consists in the main of the three small genera *Macrolepiota*, *Lepiota*, *Cystoderma* (parasol-mushrooms) and the large genus *Agaricus* which includes some of the best-known mushrooms of all.

The first three genera occupy a special position in the family: except for a single species they have white spores and white gills. All have a parasol-shaped cap and a slim stalk, thickened at the base and surmounted by an attractive ring. Another character of this group is the fact that their cap skin tears upon expansion. For the rest, the three genera differ mark-edly in the size and structure of their fruiting bodies.

The genus *Macrolepiota* includes the largest parasol mushrooms of all. *M. procera* (*Pl. 65, p. 138*), which is often seen in early autumn at the edge of copses or in clearings, is easily recognized by its slim and generally very tall stalk and its imposing cap, which may attain a diameter of 1 ft. The cap, except for the central boss, is covered with brown scales which make a striking contrast to their white background. The scales are constructed from the skin of the cap which tears inwards from the margin as soon as the oval or spherical young fruiting bodies expand. The stalk, too, is covered in brown scales arranged in jagged belts, and also derived from broken skin. As in all parasol mushrooms, the stem of *M. procera* has a ring, though in this species the ring is movable and has a double edge; the upper margin is generally broader than the lower. *M. procera* is highly prized by mushroom collectors; its size and snake-like stem easily distinguish it from poisonous species with which it might otherwise be confused.

Lepiota resembles *Macrolepiota* in all respects other than size – some species have caps no more than an inch or so in diameter. Some of the larger species are sought by mushroom lovers, particularly *L. excoriata* and the pink-fleshed *L. naucina* which occur chiefly on meadows, grassland and sandy soils. *L. excoriata* has a brownish cap whose edge is broken up into fibrous scales. Its whitish stalk, covered in fine felt, bears a thick-skinned, movable ring with a jagged edge. *L. naucina* is very similar in shape, but is easily distinguishable by its white and completely smooth cap, its narrow, smooth-edged ring, and particularly by the fact that its gills turn pink with age – an unusual feature in this group of fungi. It is a favourite edible species, but must be collected with care – odd specimens grow in pine forests where laymen may easily confuse them with the destroying angel.

Species of *Cystoderma*, another genus of medium-sized to small parasol fungi, resemble the rest of the group chiefly in the colour of their spores and gills, but not in the shape of their fruiting bodies. Here, cap and stalk have a homogeneous structure, i.e. they are built up of identical tissue and cannot be easily separated. Moreover, the skin of the caps splits up into countless 'cysts' instead of scales – whence the generic name. Despite their relatively small size, these fungi, which grow chiefly in coniferous forests, are highly conspicuous: their caps, which are bright red or yellow, form a striking contrast to the white gills. A particularly beautiful species, *C. cinnabarina*, has a glowing vermilion cap up to 4 ins. in diameter and a rust-coloured, scaly stalk. Another beautiful species is *C. amianthina* whose cap and stalk are both bright-yellow. It is the commonest of European *Cystodermae*.

The genus *Agaricus* includes *A. campestris*, the common or field mushroom, which is often confused with the thick-fleshed, cultivated kind sold in the shops. On the Continent, the various species are commonly referred to as champignons, and proba-

bly constitute the tastiest and also the most nourishing mushrooms of all. They vary considerably in size, shape and colour. In different species, the cap may be more or less rounded, smooth or covered with scales, white, yellow or brown. The stalk is massive and often thickened at the base, and invariably has a ring. The spores and gills of all champignons are dark chocolate-coloured when mature, and pink or red in young specimens. This characteristic deserves special attention, since it enables collectors to distinguish champignons from a number of poisonous species, including the death cap and its near relatives. Another distinguishing feature is the tendency of the fruiting body to become discoloured upon pressure: it may turn yellow or various shades of red.

Champignons differ markedly in their choice of habitat. Some species inhabit forests, particularly pine forests; others flourish both in woods and meadows; others again live exclusively in richly manured fields, pastures and gardens.

A. campestris, the field mushroom, belongs to the last group. It is a medium-sized white or off-white fungus with a stout stalk, and a hemispherical fleshy cap that expands to about 4 ins. across. The margin of the cap often bears a cortina, a curtain-like cobwebby, torn veil derived from the velum partiale. The gills of young specimens are rose-pink, but turn chocolate-brown or nearly black with age. The field mushroom grows most profusely on paddocks, and less commonly on rich meadowland and in gardens. It does not recur at regular intervals and there may be years in which it does not grow at all, particularly when there are prolonged spells of rain after long periods of drought.

Closely related to the field mushroom is *A. arvensis*, the horse mushroom (*Fig. 225*), which also grows in meadows and pastures, but more frequently in coniferous forests. It has a characteristic smell of aniseed and a conspicuously large and tough ring. It is exceedingly good to eat, but is all too often confused with the destroying angel. A great many cases of mushroom poisoning rest on this confusion, hence the collector must make a point of examining the gills: they are pure white in the destroying angel, and yellowish-grey, later turning brown, in the horse mushroom.

Fig. 225 *Agaricus arvensis*, horse mushroom

special cellars, caves or disused tunnels (e.g. the Scotland Street Tunnel, which runs from Waverley Station in Edinburgh to the north of the city, and was used for intensive mushroom cultivation from 1887 to 1903). The best culturing medium is well rotted horse manure, piled up to form a long ridge. The top of the bed is then flattened and the mushroom mycelium applied. As soon as it has spread through the manure, the culture is covered with sand, through which fruiting bodies will begin to protrude within a matter of weeks. Every bed can be harvested for three months; thereafter the culturing medium must be renewed .

Apart from a few small tropical genera, *Agaricus* is the only genus in this family to have dark chocolate-coloured or black spores.

Family
Coprinaceae

Black spores, however, are typical of the family Coprinaceae, fungi of various sizes, all with delicate fruiting bodies that grow as quickly as they disappear again. The cap of young specimens has a pronounced egg or bell shape, and many species bear remains of the velum universale in the form of scales or grains on the cap margin. Many Coprinaceae also display remains of the velum partiale, in the form of a narrow ring on the stalk.

The most important representative of the Coprinaceae is the genus *Coprinus*, ink-cap, so called because the gills deliquesce into a black, inky liquid that drips from the disintegrating cap, particularly during warm weather.

Coprinus comprises a considerable number of species throughout the world. There are about 40 British types, mostly small, extremely delicate and short-lived. Some are rarely seen, because they develop during the night and disappear at sunrise. The best-known of the smaller species is *C. micaceus* (*Fig. 226*), which grows in groups at the foot of old tree stumps. It is an unusually attractive species with a yellow-brown cap densely covered with glittering grains when young.

Among the larger species, two of the best-known are *C. comatus*, shaggy ink-cap, and *C. atramentarius*, common ink-cap. Both like rich ground, and are

Horse mushrooms may also be confused with the related yellow-staining mushroom (*Agaricus xanthoderma*), which is slightly poisonous. The two are not only similar in external appearance but also grow in the same spots. *A. xanthoderma*, however, has a distinct smell of carbolic and can also be identified by the rapid change to bright yellow when its skin is rubbed.

Two further edible species are *A. edulis* and *A. bisporus*. The former grows exclusively in villages and towns, has a white, swollen fruiting body and a stalk that apparently bears a double ring (the lower 'ring' is, in fact, the edge of a tight-fitting sheath). It grows from early summer to late autumn, mostly in parks, on lawns, refuse sites and sometimes at the edge of unmade roads. *A. bisporus*, a brown species with a (mostly) scaly cap, grows in gardens, where it prefers compost heaps. This fungus occupies a special position among champignons in that its basidia produce two spores each instead of the usual four.

Two spores per basidium are also produced by the cultivated mushroom, which suggests that it was bred from *A. bisporus* which, moreover, it resembles very closely. Mushroom cultivation is widely practised throughout Europe and the U.S.A. Since cultivated mushrooms flourish best at temperatures of from 10° C to 15° C, they are usually grown in

Fig. 226 *Coprinus micaceus*

often found in gardens, on lawns and refuse dumps and by the roadside. *C. comatus* (*Pl. 64, p. 138*) which, on occasion, can attain quite considerable dimensions, has a distinct brownish cap with shaggy white scales all round. At first, the cap is barrel-shaped, but as it expands, its margins begin to roll up. The gills are first white, then pinkish and finally turn black, liquefying as the spores ripen from below upwards. *C. atramentarius*, which is the commoner of the two, has a conical, fleshy grey, radially ribbed cap. Both species are edible when young, and *C. comatus*, in particular, is considered a great delicacy. Though edible, these fungi may cause considerable discomfort if alcohol is consumed at the same meal.

The Coprinaceae comprise several other genera as well, all of them black-spored, but none subject to gill liquefaction ('autolysis'). Most are small, very high-stalked fungi with bell-shaped caps and grow chiefly on dung (e.g. *Panaeolus*) or on old tree stumps (e.g. *Psathyrella*).

Brown-spored fungi, which are far more common than the black-spored, are divided into several families, all represented in Britain by a number of genera.

Family

Strophariaceae

This family includes fungi with dark-brown or browny-violet spores, and is also characterized by the fact that the skin of their caps is built up of horizontally arranged hyphae. The best-known genera are *Stropharia* and *Pholiota*, both of them fairly common in British woods. *Stropharia aeruginosa*, verdigris agaric (*Pl. 67, p. 139*), grows amongst grass in

pastures and in woods in summer and autumn. The broad conical cap of this strikingly beautiful fungus is covered in green slime and adorned with whitish scales round the edge – the remains of the velum universale. The bluish-green stalk bears a large ring, which is gradually turned violet-brown by the dropping spore powder.

The genus *Pholiota* differs from other Strophariaceae in that its fruiting bodies are built up of homogeneous tissue. The various species differ in size and shape – several are treated as separate genera by a number of modern taxonomists. The typical representatives have their caps and stalks covered in scales up to the ring, which is very large in most species. Another characteristic is the rust-coloured to muddy-brown colour of the spores. Most species live on wood; some attack living trees, causing considerable damage. Thus *P. squarrosa* (*Fig. 227*) infests various deciduous trees including the apple. It is a fairly large fungus with a yellow cap covered in brown scales,

Fig. 227 *Pholiota squarrosa*

and a stalk that is scaly up to the ring, but smooth on top. The scales usually stick out like so many small barbs. This fungus grows in clusters at the bottom of the trunks of broad-leaved trees, or of old stumps. Its mycelium causes the wood to rot or to turn brittle, with the result that infested trees gradually die.

P. mutabilis is also common on fallen trunks and stumps. It is a small or medium-sized fungus with a honey-coloured or brownish, completely smooth cap. The cap has a hygrophanous margin. The brown stalk is studded with rust-coloured scales beneath the ring. The gills change from light to dark brown as the fungus matures. *P. mutabilis* is very common in deciduous woods, where its fruiting bodies appear in large clusters from spring to winter. Its spicy flavour makes it a great delicacy. Moreover, it continues to produce fruiting bodies time and again – one and the same stump can be harvested up to four times a year.

Another edible species in this genus is *P. caperata*, one of the few species to grow directly on the soil. It also differs from the remaining species in external appearance, so much so that some taxonomists prefer to treat it as a separate genus (*Rozites*). This fungus, which often grows to a considerable size, has a bright-yellow expanding cap covered in white felt, particularly towards the centre. The cap is borne on a stout yellow stalk, with a white, skinny ring, topped with white specks. This fungus grows chiefly in coniferous forests, and less frequently in deciduous woods. It generally appears in small clusters.

Family
Cortinariaceae

The Cortinariaceae constitute the most important group among the brown-spored Agaricaceae. They comprise a large number of species, characterized by the presence of rust-coloured or yellow-brown spores and of homogeneously constructed fruiting bodies. They owe their name to a character common to only a few species but of very great systematic importance, i.e. to the presence of a cortina which, as we saw, is a curtain-like veil hanging from the margin of the cap and representing the remains of the velum partiale. The cortina is particularly prominent in the genus *Cortinarius*, with some 170 species

in Britain alone. Because this genus is so large, taxonomists have thought it best to divide it into a number of subspecies which, in what follows, will be indicated by parentheses. The genus consists of medium to large mushrooms, mostly with thick-fleshed caps and stalks. Though they vary considerably in shape and colour, most have rust-coloured spores. They also correspond in habit: all are forest-dwellers. Many species are exceptionally beautiful, among them the violet *C. (Inoloma) traganus* and *C. (Inoloma) violaceus* (*Fig. 228*), two particularly large species with swollen stalks. In them, the violet cap forms a striking contrast to the rust-coloured gills (of mature specimens).

Another beautiful species is *C. (Dermocybe) sangineus*, a small, thin-skinned fungus found occasionally in deciduous forests. Here, cap, gills and stalk are blood-red. Closely related is *C. (Dermocybe) cinnamomeus*, a small or medium-sized fungus with a flat, cinnamon-colour to yellow cap, often bearing a central boss. The stalk is of similar colour and slim. This species, too, prefers coniferous forests.

Oddly enough, this large genus contains only a few edible species, or rather, only a few known edible species. One of these is *C. (Myxacium) mucosus*, a medium-sized fungus with a brownish, slimy cap and a whitish stalk whose slimy sheath stretches halfway up from the base. This fungus grows on sandy soil in coniferous forests, and is particularly widespread on heath land in north Germany. We have said that few species of *Cortinarius* are edible;

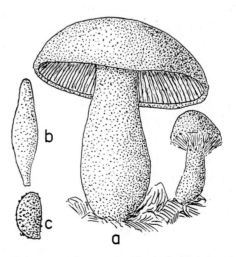

Fig. 228 *Cortinarius violaceus. a*: Fruiting body (slightly reduced); *b*: hair from marginal gill tissue (highly magnified); *c*: basidiospore (highly magnified)

177

similarly the genus includes few poisonous species – most are as harmless as they are tasteless.

Things are much the same with *Hebeloma*, a very small genus of medium-sized fungi with pale reddish-yellow caps. *H. crustuliniforme*, a fairly large species, has a broad, thick-fleshed cap, with a bright reddish-yellow, greasy top and muddy-brown gills. The upper part of the relatively stout white stalk is covered in white scales. The fruiting body exudes a strong smell of radishes, a characteristic of the entire genus. All species are slightly poisonous.

Inocybe, a large genus of fungi growing on the ground, is widely represented in Britain. The various species are extremely difficult to distinguish from one another. Most are medium-sized fungi, with a slim stalk that is slightly thickened towards the base (*Fig. 229*). The cap is somewhat conical at first and later flattens out. It bears a central boss, and the margin is often lobed and split. In most older specimens, the cap is brown and has a silky sheen due to rays of delicate fibres. The stalk, which is much lighter in colour, is silky as well. The gills are white at first and then turn muddy or olive. In contrast to *Cortinarius* and many species of *Hebeloma*, *Inocybe* lacks any trace of velum remains. True, the fruiting bodies are at first protected by a sheath, but this subsequently dissolves. The genus includes a large number of poisonous species, all of which contain varying amounts of muscarine, the poison of the fly agaric (see p. 171). One of them, *Inocybe patouillardi*, red staining inocybe, is one of the most poisonous fungi of all: it contains twenty times as much muscarine as the fly agaric. It is particularly dangerous because young specimens are easily confused with a number of edible species, including field mushrooms and *Tricholoma gambosum*, St George's mushroom (see p. 167). When *I. patouillardi* breaks out of the ground, its cap is more or less white, and its colour and oval shape resemble those of the common field mushroom. As it grows older, its identity becomes far clearer: the cap flattens out, begins to tear at the margin and turns brown on top, while the gills assume the typical muddy colour. Moreover, older specimens have two further distinguishing marks: their white flesh turns brick-red when pressure is applied or in places where the flesh is torn; e.g. at the edge of the cap. In addition, older specimens begin

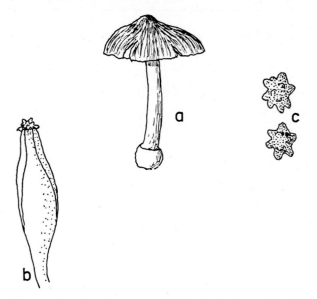

Fig. 229 *Inocybe asterospora*. *a*: Fruiting body (natural size); *b*: cystidium (highly magnified); *c*: basidiospores (highly magnified)

to exude a smell of rotten fruit, which becomes more and more repulsive. Every mushroom collector ought to familiarize himself with these characteristics. Admittedly, even field mushrooms have red flesh, but this is blood- rather than brick-coloured. Field mushrooms can also be told apart from *I. patouillardi* by their ring, their pink or chocolate-coloured gills, and by their pleasant aroma. St George's mushroom, again, differs from *I. patouillardi* in being ivory-coloured throughout its life and by its strong smell of cucumbers or fresh meal. The reason why *I. patouillardi* is nevertheless so often mistaken for edible species is that it grows side by side with them – in clusters among grass beside paths, and at the edges of woods and clearings.

We have said that we know of only a few species of *Inocybe* that are free of muscarine. One of these is *I. fastigiata*, a small or medium-sized wood-inhabiting fungus with a yellow cap shot through with brown fibres, and a brownish stalk tipped with white floc. Its gills have a distinct olive-green colour, but since it resembles other species in so many respects, it is best avoided altogether. True, fatal results have only been recorded from the red-staining species, but the others may produce very serious conditions as well, and all should be treated with the utmost suspicion.

Closely related to the Cortiniaceae are the Crepidotaceae, a small family, mostly living on wood. The best-known genus in this family is *Crepidotus*, a group of delicate fungi with shell-shaped caps attached laterally to a very short stalk or directly to the substrate – fallen branches or old stumps. The most common species is *C. variabilis*. Its tiny fruiting bodies have a white-topped cap and rust-coloured gills. This fungus grows in dense colonies, particularly in coniferous forests.

The brown-spored mushrooms finally include a small group of fungi which, in addition to the usual characteristics of fleshy mushrooms, have tubular structures commonly associated with boletes. They belong to the genera *Paxillus* and *Gomphidius* which, though they comprise a relatively small number of species, are so widespread that they are generally treated as two distinct families.

Family
Paxillaceae

This family, most of whose species attain fairly considerable dimensions, are easily identified by the inrolled margin of their caps. Another distinguishing mark is the fact that the gills, which in most brown-spored mushrooms are restricted to the cap, run a long way down the stalk, often uniting by means of conspicuous veins. The gills are easily separated from the flesh of the cap by slight pressure. It is this last character, in particular, which points to a close relationship with the boletes, in which the gills are easily stripped from the context of the basidiocarp.

The Paxillaceae, which live partly on wood and partly on the ground, are widely distributed in coniferous and mixed woods. *Paxillus involutus*, the commonest of all (*Fig. 230*), is a fairly large fungus with a flat, often centrally depressed cap, and a tall, strong stalk. Cap, gills and stalk come in various shades of yellowish-brown, but turn darker the moment pressure is applied. Sensitivity to pressure is, in fact, one of the chief distinguishing marks of this fungus, which is very tasty when blanched and cooked. (It should not be eaten in its raw state, when it is poisonous.) The closely related *P. atrotomentosus* resembles *P. involutus* in size and colour, but has a matted, dark-brown, relatively squat stalk. Another distinction is that whereas *P. involutus* grows on the forest soil, *P. atrotomentosus* grows exclusively on old stumps of conifers. This fungus is rather tasteless and hence not suitable for cooking.

Family
Gomphidiaceae

This family comprises five British species, all of which grow on the ground in coniferous woods, where they form mycorrhizal associations with the roots of trees. They are medium-sized fungi with a fleshy cap usually covered in a layer of slime – the remains of the velum universale – and with a stout stalk, yellow at the base, and also covered in slimy velum remains. Another characteristic is the presence of unusually thick, decurrent gills, dark brown to black in colour. The close relationship of this family to the boletes is reflected in the spindle-shaped form of their basidiospores, and also in the association with specific trees, which is far more common among Boletaceae than among other Agaricales.

Gomphidius viscidus, the commonest British species, grows singly in pine woods in autumn. Its dull-brown, bell-shaped cap is fleshy, has a strong central boss and a flush of purple at the margin, and is very slimy when wet. The stem is yellow, streaked with dull purple, and tapers below. The broad gills change from brown to purple with age; they are distant and deeply decurrent. The flesh is reddish-yellow, and bright-yellow towards the base. *G. glutinosus*, which also grows in pine forests, has a top-shaped cap, grey to black in colour and covered in a thick transparent layer of slime. The stalk is bright yellow at

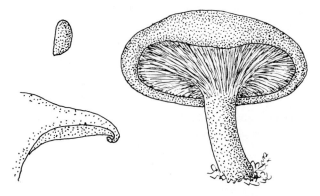

Fig. 230 *Paxillus involutus*. Right: fruiting body (slightly reduced); lower left: longitudinal section through right half of cap (slightly reduced); upper left: basidiospore (highly magnified)

the base. In young specimens, the slimy layer covers the gills as well, but as the cap expands, the layer tears and leaves a skin on the upper surface of the cap and a ring on the stalk. Another species deserving special mention is *G. maculatus*, whose bright-red cap, spotted stalk, and browny-red gills turn wine-coloured the moment pressure is applied.

Family
Russulaceae

While the last two families differed from the Agaricaceae in having a tubular structure, the Russulaceae, which comprise the genera *Russula* and *Lactarius*, differ in yet another way: their flesh is exceptionally brittle, granular rather than fibrous, so that it can be broken like chalk. Whereas the fruiting bodies of all the mushrooms we have been discussing were built up exclusively of longitudinal hyphae, those of Russulaceae include countless spherical cells, the so-called sphaerocysts, which lend the tissue a grainy and hence a brittle consistency. Russulaceae also differ from Agaricaceae in the shape of their spores which, instead of being oval, are almost perfectly spherical and covered with warty, spinous or other processes, which stain blue with iodine. Judging purely by the colour of the spores, we should have to classify the Russulaceae among the white-spored mushrooms, with the majority of which, however, they have nothing else in common.

Russulaceae can be divided into two distinct groups, according to whether or not they contain milk sap. Those that do not, constitute the genus *Russula*; the rest makes up the genus *Lactarius*. The sap, which is watery in a few species but white or coloured in the majority, is produced in tubular hyphae, which form a kind of network in the fruiting body. If the latter is injured, the milk sap pours out in drops; in a number of 'white-milked' species, the sap changes colour the moment it oozes out and comes into contact with the air. Certain substances (which are also present in *Russula*) lend the sap a mild or sharp flavour.

Russula and *Lactarius* differ markedly in external appearance as well.

Russula, with some 70 species in Britain, comprises medium-sized to large fungi, with a stout,

usually short stalk and a broad, flattened cap. Most species have glowing caps in a variety of colours on white or less often on coloured stalks. The white or yellow gills are in striking contrast to the top of the cap. *Russula* species are unusual not only in the brightness but also in the unrivalled range of their colours. They occur in every conceivable shade of red (*Pl. 73, p. 142*), brown or yellow; some are violet, off-white, and even green, a most unusual colour among plants lacking chlorophyll. Colour is of the utmost importance in the identification of the various species. Since many of them, however, change colour in the course of their development, other characters must be taken into consideration as well, for instance the consistency of the cap (dry or sticky), the colour of the gills or of the spore powder (white or yellow), and the taste (mild, sharp or bitter). Even so, it is extremely difficult to tell the various species apart, if only because there are so many of them. Luckily, collectors need not be deterred, for they can rely on a rule of thumb that applies to this family alone: all mild-tasting species of *Russula* are edible; all the rest are not. The taste is easily discovered by chewing a piece of gill which, moreover, can be done without fear, since the genus includes no highly poisonous fungi.

All species of *Russula* grow on the ground but need the vicinity of trees (some are restricted to a given species). They are extremely common in woods, particularly during dry summers, when they appear in large masses. Here we have space to mention only a few of the most important.

R. ochroleuca is found in woods of all kinds early in the season. It has a conspicuous ochre-yellow to light-brown cap, white gills and a white stalk which, however, becomes greyish with age. It is one of the acrid-tasting group, though the flesh loses its bitterness upon boiling. *R. nigricans*, which is very common as well, has thick gills, flesh that reddens when cut, and a cream-coloured cap that turns black as the fungus matures. Its stem is short, thick and white, and blackens when bruised. Another common British species, *R. atropurpurea*, has a purplish cap, showing yellow spots with age, and is smooth and slimy when moist. The stem is white, yellowish or rusty at the base, and turns grey with age.

R. emetica, finally, the sickener, causes sickness

when eaten raw. It is one of the most beautiful fungi of both coniferous and deciduous woods, and prefers moist sites. The cap, which is bright scarlet with a darker centre, can be seen from far away; the gills and stalk are pure white. The fruiting body exudes a pleasant smell of fruit, but has an acrid taste. This species is often confused with *R. fragilis*, which is slightly poisonous as well, and grows in similar sites. Both species have given the genus its bad reputation, but there is no reason for rejecting the many edible species, the more so since, as we saw, they can easily be distinguished from poisonous relatives by their mild taste, and from other genera by their brittle consistency.

Brittleness is equally characteristic of *Lactarius*, milk-cap, the second genus in this family, whose flesh also breaks cleanly without trailing fibres. This genus differs from *Russula* in that its fruiting bodies contain milk sap – whence its popular name. It also differs from *Russula* in having a funnel-shaped, in-curved cap, particularly when young, and in that its gills continue in part of the stalk. Moreover, few species of *Lactarius* have bright-coloured caps – most are an inconspicuous brown, grey or yellow. *Lactarius* occurs in much the same sites as *Russula*, like which it can only grow in the vicinity of trees, and quite often of particular species, with which alone it can form mycorrhizae.

Fig. 231 *Lactarius torminosus*, woolly milk-cap

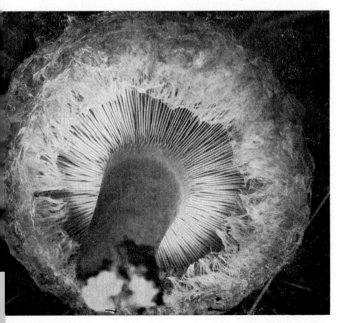

Lactarius, though widely represented in Britain, is less common than *Russula*, due mainly to its exclusive association with certain species of trees and also to the fact that it prefers colder regions, for instance the Lower Alps. The best-known species is the edible *L. deliciosus*, saffron milk-cap, one of the most beautiful representatives of its genus. The cap is orange or carrot-red and marked with concentric circles of a darker colour, becoming paler with age; the entire fruiting body turns green when pressure is applied. Another distinguishing mark is the fact that the sap is orange – in most other species it is white or colourless. As a result, it is almost impossible to confuse the saffron milk-cap with any of its less palatable relatives.

Non-edible British species include *L. torminosus*, woolly milk cap (*Fig. 231*), which grows on the ground in mixed woods and is easily identified by the pinkish colour and woolly surface of its cap; *L. plumbeus*, a large, olive-brown species, very common under birches; *L. blennius*, which is very common in deciduous woods in autumn and has a slimy grey cap marked with zones of darker spots; and *L. rufus*, which occurs in pine woods and can be identified by its brownish-red cap, at first convex then flattened, by its brownish red stem, and by its peppery taste.

Family
Boletaceae

With the Russulaceae we have come to the end of the group of Agaricales in which the hymenophore, or hymenium-bearing part of the fruiting body, is made up of gills (lamellae). As we saw, the order also includes a group of fungi in which the hymenophore consists of tubes, combined into a layer on the under surface of the cap, and is easily peeled off. In the past, this group used to be classified among the Polyporaceae; today it is generally agreed that it should be combined with the Agaricales, with which it has far greater affinities. In particular, this group corresponds with other Agaricales in the general structure and development of its fruiting bodies and in having flesh of a soft consistency. Beyond that, this group lives on the ground like the majority of Agaricales, while Polyporaceae live exclusively on wood. The close relationship between the two groups is corroborated by the existence of fungi combining certain characters of both, viz. the Paxillaceae and the Gomphidiaceae (see pp. 179–180).

Compared with the Agaricaceae, the Boletaceae constitute a very small group: whereas the former number close on 1500 species in Central Europe, the latter account for no more than 50 or so. Boletes are favourites among collectors with little experience, for they are easily identified by the pores by which their vertical tubes open on the under-surface of the cap. To avoid poisonous species, the collector need only ignore all boletes with a red under-surface and red stalk (this is merely a rule for beginners). For the rest, those that taste acrid (e.g. the small *Suillus piperatus*) or bitter should be discarded as well, for though non-poisonous they will remain unpalatable even after cooking. The fact that a bolete may turn blue when cut or pressed, is no sign that it is poisonous – the blue colour results from the oxidation of boletol. *Boletus satanas*, which is highly poisonous, hardly turns blue at all.

Fig. 232 *Boletus rufus*

Boletes have fruiting bodies varying considerably in size, and clearly divided into cap and stalk. The veil is skinny or slimy and its remains may be preserved in the form of a ring round the stalk. The grainy, soft-fleshed cap may have a scaly, matted, velvety, smooth, slimy or dry upper surface. The tubular layer generally comes away quite easily from the rest of the cap. The stalk may be cylindrical, spherical or swollen, smooth, reticulate or scaly. The spores look yellow to dark-brown inside the hymenium, and colourless, pink, yellow, or brown under the microscope. They are smooth and oval to spindle-shaped. Many boletes form mycorrhizae with trees, e.g. *Suillus elegans* with larches.

In the past, all boletes used to be combined into the genus *Boletus*, but today they have been divided into several genera, and of those listed here, each contains several which make good eating.

Medium-sized, soft-fleshed boletes, with a hemispherical or convex brown cap, often covered with mucus, belong to the genus *Suillus* (sometimes described as *Ixocomus*). Its yellow tubes are fused to the stalk; the pores are small; the stalk cylindrical, firm, and often provided with a ring. The basidia produce four spindle-shaped spores each. This genus forms mycorrhizae with conifers. The best-known species is the tasty but highly perishable *S. luteus* (*Fig. 233*), whose 2–5-in. cap is covered with a thick, brownish layer of mucus in the dew and during moist weather; under dry conditions, it looks browny-yellow to yellowish-green. The 4-in. stalk is studded with yellow or brown dots above the ring. This fungus grows from summer to late autumn, chiefly in pine forests and among young firs. The related *S. grevillei* is shown in *Pl. 70, p. 140*. *S. bovinus*, another species abundant in pinewoods, has a buff-coloured cap, smooth and slimy, measuring 2 to 4 ins. across, with a whitish edge when young. The stalk may be up to 4 ins. high and is similarly coloured. The tubes are decurrent, and the pores large and angular and often divided by small septa; their colour is yellow to light brown. Very similar in appearance is *S. variegatus*, whose browny-yellow cap is, however, densely covered in hairy, reddish-brown scales; the browny-yellow, later olive-brown, tubes have small, angular, undivided pores. This species is common among pines with which it forms mycorrhizae.

The genus *Xerocomus*, which can be identified by the velvety or matted surface of its cap, contains many fine edible fungi. The tubes may be fused or free, the pores large, angular, and whitish to greeny-yellow. The solid stalk is cylindrical or swollen, with fine ribs or veins that may be combined into a network. Each basidium produces four brown, spindle-shaped spores. *X. subtomentosus* (*Fig. 233*) is a cosmopolitan species, appearing in coniferous and deciduous forests and at the edge of woods from June to October. Its cap, 2–5 ins. wide, is hemispherical or flat, velvety, dark-yellow to cinnamon, and becomes torn into segments with age; the tubes are lemon-yellow but gradually turn a muddy green; the pores are large and angular; the cylindrical stalk is 2–5 ins. high, and tapers slightly towards the base. This tasty fungus has a fruity smell, but is highly perishable. Because its tubes do not become discoloured upon pressure, it is easily distinguished from the otherwise similar, though somewhat smaller *X. chrysenteron*, which is common in coniferous and deciduous

Fig. 234 *Xerocomus subtomentosus*

Fig. 233 *Suillus luteus*; cap under-surface (magnified)

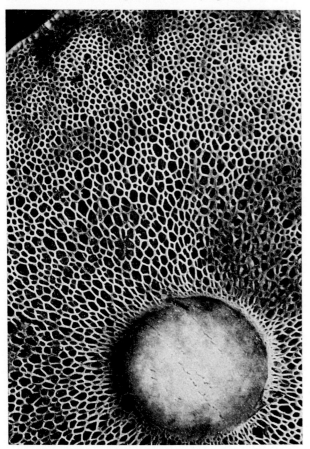

woods from June to November, and whose tubes turn greenish-blue the moment they are touched. This fungus, too, is tasty and highly perishable. *X. badius*, another edible, has much firmer flesh, and a chestnut-coloured, spherical cap that later expands to 2–6 ins. across and has an upturned margin. The tubes are greenish-yellow and have angular, whitish to greenish-yellow pores. The cylindrical or swollen stalk is yellowish-brown and has longitudinal veins, sometimes combined into a net. This species, which has a fruity aroma and a delicious taste, grows near the roots of firs and pines and more rarely in deciduous forests. It does not form mycorrhizae. As a curiosity, we might also mention *X. parasiticus*, which lives as a parasite on species of *Scleroderma*.

The tropical genus *Phlebopus* deserves special mention because of its inordinately large fruiting bodies; *P. colossus* from Africa has a cap measuring up to 2 ft. across, and is the largest mushroom of all.

The genus *Boletus* contains species whose cap can measure up to 1 ft. across. Most species have medium

183

sized to large fruiting bodies, with a thick-fleshed, smooth or velvety upper surface, long tubes and rounded pores, and a thick and swollen stem marked with fine raised lines or dots. The flesh is firm and turns blue on being cut or squeezed. Each basidium produces four spindle-shaped, brown spores. It has not yet been fully settled to what extent this genus forms mycorrhizae. The best-known species, *B. edulis*, cep (French *cèpe*; German *Steinpilz*) has grainy white flesh with a nutty flavour, a toast-brown cap, and yellow tubes that later turn green (*Pl. 72, p. 142*). It grows from May to October in woods of all kinds. Various subspecies apparently form mycorrhizae under certain conditions, for instance *B. e. reticulatus* which grows among oaks and beeches and *B. e. fuscoruber* which grows among pines and mountain conifers. Young ceps are easily confused with *Tylopilus felleus*, which tastes of gall and is completely inedible. Its tubes are depressed like a cushion; they are white at first and later turn pink; the stalk has a conspicuous network of lines. This species grows in clusters from June to October, in light coniferous forests everywhere.

But back to the genus *Boletus*, and particularly to the poisonous species. One of the most dangerous is the rare *B. satanas*, which we mentioned earlier. It is a very beautiful fungus which grows in late summer in woods and pastures on chalky soil. The cap is dirty white to greenish grey, soft and smooth to the touch. The short swollen stem is generally yellow above and below and bright-red in the middle, the whole covered with a network of red veins. The flesh when broken changes from yellow to pink and blue. This species is often confused with the edible *B. erythropus* (in which, however, the stalk has orange to carmine scales or dots running crosswise instead of a network of lines), and also with *B. luridus*, whose stalk does have a network, but whose cap is olive-green and feels like suede. *B. satanas* may also be confused with *B. calopus*, which is slightly poisonous, bitter, and has an unpleasantly sour smell. It has a velvety-grey to yellow cap, and a stalk that is yellow on top, carmine to dark-red beneath, and covered in a creamy to pink network of veins.

The genus *Leccinum* (sometimes described as *Trachypus*) includes three tasty and very common edibles. All can be recognized by their long, relative-ly slim, cylindrical stalks covered in dark scales. The very long tubes carrying whitish to brown spores are easily separated from the flesh. This genus is characteristically mycorrhiza-forming, and favours the roots of birches, poplars, hornbeams and willows. *L. scabrum*, which grows from June to October, grows exclusively at the foot of birch trees. Its hemispherical cap, which later flattens out, measures up to 5 ins. across, and varies in colour from whitish grey to reddish or dark brown, depending on the environment. The tubes are white at first and later turn grey. The slim white stalk, up to 8 ins. high, is covered with blackish fibres and scales. This species is tasty, but must be eaten soon after it is picked. Equally well-known are *L. aurantiacum* and *L. testaceum-scabrum*, which used to be combined as *L. rufum*. The cap, up to 8 ins. across, whose upper skin hangs down in lobes over the edge, is dark orange in *L. aurantiacum* and somewhat lighter in *L. testaceum-scabrum*. The latter has grey to nut-brown pores; *L. aurantiacum* has whitish ones. The white stalk of *L. aurantiacum* has creamy to reddish-brown scales, while that of *L. testaceum-scabrum* has black ones. The former grows chiefly in deciduous woods, the latter in coniferous forests; both species appear in large numbers from June to October.

We conclude with *Strobilomyces strobilaceus* (= *floccopus*) which some taxonomists combine with its African relatives (genus *Boletellus*) into a separate

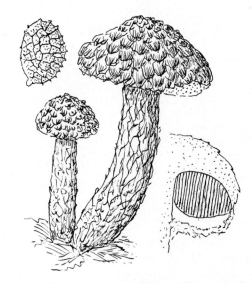

Fig. 235 *Strobilomyces floccopus*. Centre: fruiting bodies (reduced); right: longitudinal section through young cap; top left: basidiospore (highly magnified)

family, the Strobilomycetaceae. This fungus (*Fig. 235*), which is fairly widespread in North America but rare in Europe, has a number of unusual features: its broad cap, measuring 3–6 ins. across, is covered in large dark-brown scales, and its tubes are at first enclosed in a velum universale, whose flaky remains often hang down from the edge of adult specimens. The tubes are long and the pores, which at first are the colour of chalk, later become grey; pressure causes them to turn black. The dark-brown cylindrical stalk, measuring from 3 to 6 ins., is rough and furrowed and also turns black with pressure; the velum partiale is often preserved as a grey ring. The flesh is tough, pink at first and later black; it contains numerous vessels carrying the milk sap. Each basidium produces four broadly oval, dark-brown spores, covered in a network of warts. The fungus usually appears singly from summer to autumn in woods of all kinds; it is edible but not very palatable.

Order
GASTERALES

Let us recall what we have said about the classification of Basidiomycetidae. We saw that they are commonly divided into the sub-class Phragmobasidiomycetidae (p. 128) and the sub-class Holobasidiomycetidae (p. 154). Among them, we have examined the orders Exobasidiales (p. 155), Telephorales (p. 155) and Agaricales (p. 164).

While the parasitic Exobasidiales produce no fruiting bodies, the Telephorales and Agaricales all have open fruiting structures and a freely displayed hymenium. Unlike them, the Gasterales have their basidia and hence their spores tucked away inside what are usually (and in young specimens invariably) closed and swollen (angiocarpous) fruiting bodies; though a hymenium is generally present it need not necessarily be so. The fruiting bodies are enclosed in a simple or multi-layered outer wall, the peridium. The sporogenous or fertile portion inside the fruiting body, the gleba, may be variously divided into chambers, honeycomb cells or irregular segments. When the spores are mature, they are released in different ways; most readers will have observed species of *Scleroderma* at a time when their peridium tears to release a cloud of dark spores. In the stink-

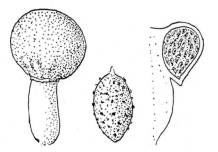

Fig. 236 *Secotium porphyreum*; left: fruiting body (somewhat reduced); right: longitudinal section through right half of fruiting body (somewhat reduced); centre: basidiospore (highly magnified)

horn (*Phallus impudicus*), the closed fruiting body, which resembles an egg, is eventually pierced by a 'stalk' bearing a bell-shaped 'cap' (which does not, however, represent the cap of a normal mushroom). The 'cap' bears the slimy, spore-filled gleba which exudes the well-known fetid odour, and is attractive to flies. These quickly consume the entire spore-bearing mass, thus ensuring the dissemination of the spores.

Sexual reproduction among Gasterales usually involves the fusion of two nuclei in the young basidium. The basidia may be spherical, oval or club-shaped, and are provided with long or short sterigmata; sometimes, however, sterigmata are completely missing. The spores are attached symmetrically to the sterigmata; where these are absent, the spores arise directly at the tip or sides of the basidia, generally 4, sometimes 6, 8, 12, even 14 at a time.

Some families in this order show affinities with the Agaricales; this is not surprising when we remember that the Gasterales do not constitute a phylogenetically homogeneous group, but simply comprise all Holobasidiomycetidae whose fruiting bodies are closed. Thus of the 190 Central European species, few share any characteristics with the rest. It should be mentioned that some authorities treat this group as a sub-class, the Gasteromycetidae, and its constituent families as separate orders.

Among the families with affinities to the Agaricales, we must mention the Secotiaceae, represented in New Zealand by *Secotium porphyreum* (*Fig. 236*), which has a distinct stalk and dark-violet cap.

The best-known Gasteromycetes of all are undoubtedly the earth-balls, which taxonomists divide into two families: the hard-skinned Sclerodermataceae and the soft-skinned Lycoperdaceae.

Family

Sclerodermataceae

In this family, represented in Britain by the common earth-ball, the hymenium is rudimentary or entirely absent. The peridium of the hard fruiting body is generally tough and built up of several layers. When the spores are ripe, the peridium tears, often at the tip of the fruiting body, to release the dark-brown spore powder. Microscopic sections show that the spores are formed in groups of four in pear-shaped basidia which arise in spherical chambers of the gleba.

The common earth-ball, *Scleroderma vulgare* (= *aurantium*), is one of the commonest British fungi, growing on the ground in woods or on heath from July to November (*Fig. 237*). Its body is bun-shaped, 2–3 ins. across but usually not so high. The peridium is leathery or cork-like, ochre-yellow, and covered with irregular warts. The gleba is greenish to creamy at first, then purplish black, marbled with sterile white hyphae. The fungus exudes a smell of radishes when young and a more pungent smell as it grows older. The earth-ball is a poisonous fungus and should be avoided; only absolute tyros confuse it with the truffle which, moreover, grows below the ground.

An interesting, though rare, relative of the common earth-ball is *Astraeus hygrometricus*. It resembles the earth-star in that its outer peridium splits up into 7–15 segments, which open out in the form of a star, while the inner peridium remains closed round the fruiting body. In earth-stars, the spores are released through an aperture at the tip of the inner peridium, while the inner peridium of *Astraeus* tears irregularly. The outer peridium is hygroscopic, opening and closing with alternate wet and dry periods. *Scleroderma* is represented by some 20 species throughout the world; *Astraeus* comprises only one species, which is restricted to temperate zones.

Family

Lycoperdaceae

This family consists of the common puff-balls. Their fruiting bodies are enclosed in 2 to 4 peridial layers, the outermost being smooth or bearing fragile spines or warts that gradually disappear. The inner layer, or endoperidium, is paper-thin but tough. In some species, it is provided with a small central aperture from which the spores are puffed out the moment the fruiting body is shaken in any way; in other species, the entire upper part of the endoperidium falls away. Depending on the species, spores may either be formed throughout the inner part of the fruiting body or else in the upper part alone. The numerous chambers within the gleba are lined with hymenium; the oval basidia bear 4 to 8 spores on sterigmata of different sizes. When the spores are ripe, the basidia break up, and some of the hyphae forming the gleba become thick and pitted to make a sterile capillitium which, in the mature sporophore, is found intermingled with the spores. Microscopic examination of these structures helps to identify the various species. The gleba of all young Lycoperdaceae is pure white, and at that stage all species are edible. However, as spore formation proceeds and the gleba turns yellowish-green or olive-brown, puff-balls lose their taste. None are poisonous.

A veritable monster among European species is *Calvatia gigantea*, the giant puff-ball. It is spherical and flattened on top; its diameter may be 18 ins. and more, and its weight may exceed 30 lb. When the spores are mature, the entire upper part of the peridium, which is white and smooth at first but later turns yellowish-brown, decomposes. The gleba of each giant can form up to $7\frac{1}{2}$ million million spores. Somebody once calculated that if all these spores

Fig. 237 *Scleroderma vulgare = aurantium*, common earth-ball. *a*: Fruiting body (slightly reduced); *b*: longitudinal section; *c*: basidia (highly magnified); *d*: mature basidiospore surrounded by hyphal remains (highly magnified)

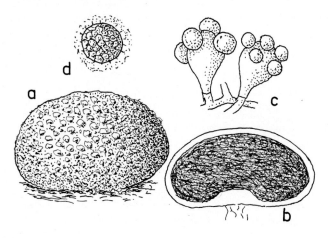

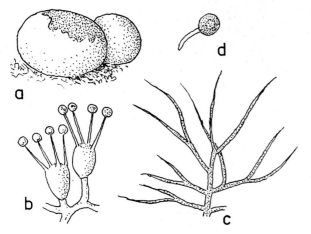

Fig. 238 *Bovista plumbea*. *a*: Fruiting body (slightly reduced); *b*: basidia (highly magnified); *c*: part of capillitium (highly magnified) *d*: basidiospore (highly magnified)

developed into fruiting bodies, whose spores would give rise to new giant puff-balls, the second daughter generation would represent a fungal mass 800 times the volume of the earth. This species, which is at home in Europe and North America, grows in grassland and parks and at the edge of woods from May to October, developing with astonishing speed whenever the weather is sufficiently warm and moist. This species has recently come into prominence with the discovery of calvacin, a tumour-inhibiting substance present in the basidiocarps. The related *C. caelata*, mosaic puff-ball, may attain a diameter of up to 6 ins. Its outer peridium becomes cracked into more or less hexagonal areas, and the bottom of its constricted base is sterile. *C. saccata*, too, which is 3 to 6 ins. tall, is divided into a fertile upper part, which tears away when the spores are mature, and a sterile 'stalk' that may persist for a long time.

In the genera *Lycoperdon* and *Bovista*, the spores escape through an ostiolum at the tip of the fruiting body. In *Lycoperdon*, only the upper part of the fruiting body is fertile; the sterile, lower part is constricted, to give the fruiting body a pear shape. *Lycoperdon perlatum*, the common puff-ball (*Pl. 75, p. 143*), is 3–4 ins. in height, at first snow-white but soon turning brown. It grows in pastures and grassy places in woods. When young it is often studded with fragile spines, each surrounded by a ring of warts. When the spines fall off, they leave a small network of scars.

L. piriforme is the only British species in its genus to grow on wood. Its pear-shaped fruiting bodies are white at first and covered with tiny grains, which soon rub off, leaving a smooth, pale brownish surface. *L. echinatum*, which grows chiefly in beech woods, has a diameter of less than 2 ins. and is densely covered in brown spines.

In the genus *Bovista*, the entire gleba is capable of producing spores. The outer peridium of the spherical fruiting body eventually peels off; the tough endoperidium is white at first and later turns brown, black or lead-grey. The spores are released through a narrow, jagged aperture at the tip. *B. nigrescens* grows to the size of a hen's egg; its white endoperidium eventually turns dark-brown. This species, which grows in large numbers on grassland from June to November, is edible while its gleba is white, and so is *B. plumbea*, which is up to 1 in. wide; its inner peridium changes from white to grey (*Fig. 238*). In autumn, the small balls of various species of *Bovista* are blown about by the wind, scattering their spore powder far and wide.

Family

Geasteraceae

The earth-stars or Geasteraceae invariably arouse interest because of their most unusual shape. They appear on the forest floor as pink, creamy or yellow rays round a spherical peridium, often crowned with a conical tip. These attractive fungi strongly resemble *Astraeus hygrometricus* to which, however, they are not closely related. In earth-stars, the outer peridium (exoperidium) consists of three layers, mycelial to the outside, fibrillose in the centre, and fleshy within. At first, the exoperidium closely invests the endoperidium. At maturity it separates and splits from the apex downwards to form 4 to 12 rays which either expand or become inturned, thus exposing the rounded endoperidium which is often borne on a stalk. The spores – 4 to 8 per basidium – are released through a conical pore (ostiolum) or pores at the tip of the endoperidium.

Of the 30 or so species, only a few are at home in Britain. In *Geaster rufescens* (*Pl. 76, p. 144*), which grows on heathland, the exoperidium is flesh-coloured and splits into 6 to 9 segments. The stars measure 1–6 ins. across. A particularly attractive species is *G. coronatus*, in which the 4 or 5 rays of the

187

Fig. 239 *Geaster triplex*, earth-star

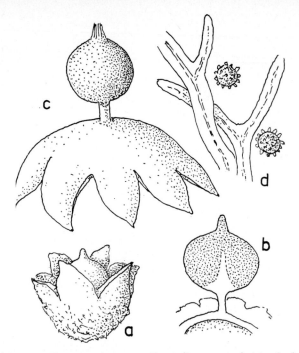

Fig. 241 *Geaster pectinatum. a:* Expanding young fruiting body (slightly reduced); *b:* longitudinal section through endoperidium (slightly reduced); *c:* old fruiting body with open exoperidium; *d:* basidiospore and capillitium fibres (very highly magnified)

exoperidium arch over a central mycelial 'sheath' to form a small crown tipped by a short stalk bearing the 1-in. spore container. The pale reddish-brown to white 'crown' and the greyish-blue 'imperial globe' above are in striking contrast to the yellow mouth of the conical ostiolum. In *G. fimbriatus*, possibly one of the commonest British species, the yellow mouth is absent; here 6–8 and sometimes 12 reddish-brown rays curl downwards, and the onion-shaped fruiting body, measuring just under an inch across, is sessile and surrounded by a wreath of rays measuring 2–4 ins. across. The ostiolum is often projecting and slightly torn. *G. triplex* (*Fig. 239*), finally, which measures more than 6 ins. when fully expanded, is one of the largest species in its genus. It is frequent in

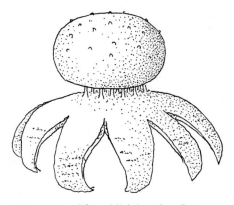

Fig. 240 *Myriostoma coliforme* (slightly reduced)

beechwoods of southern England, and is easily identified by the collar round the base of its endoperidium.

In the most unusual *Myriostoma coliforme* (*Fig. 240*), the only species in its genus, the endoperidium has several stalks and several mouths, and looks as if it were composed of numerous stars.

Family

Phallaceae

The fungi comprising this family are quite different in appearance from, and much more diversified than, those constituting the last family. Their unusual features are best illustrated by looking at *Phallus impudicus*, stinkhorn (*Pl. 74, p. 143*), in cross-section. Here the young fruiting body looks like an egg, 1 to 2 ins. across, and contains in rudiment all the structures characteristic of the mature fungus. The 'egg' is surrounded by a tough peridium whose gelatinous middle layer prevents desiccation. Right in the centre lies the receptacle containing the rudiment of the hollow, spongy stalk and of the bell-shaped, pitted cap, both built up of hyphal tissue. The receptacle (which incidentally corresponds to the velum partiale of Agaricales) is surmounted by an olive-green gleba whose numerous chambers are lined with hymenium. The basidia usually bear 8 or more sessile spores each. At maturity, the stalk expands with astonishing speed and breaks through the top of the peridium, carrying the gleba up on its cap, and leaving the remains of the peridium as a sheath round the base. The gleba then begins to decompose and to ooze down, at the same time giving off its fetid odour. This odour attracts carrion-loving flies, which disseminate the spores partly in their excreta and partly on their legs. Once the entire gleba mass has dried up or has been consumed, the stalk begins to wilt and finally disappears.

While the receptacle of *Phallus impudicus* resembles a morel (Ascomycetes), that of many tropical and subtropical Phallaceae resembles a lattice-work basket (*Clathrus*), or is divided into several free arms (*Anthurus*). Their bright-red colour gives these fungi a most attractive appearance – their putrid stench notwithstanding.

In *Mutinus caninus*, dog stinkhorn, which grows in British woods in summer and autumn, the expanded receptacle is 4 to 5 ins. long, whitish or pinkish-buff in colour, with an orange-red tip which, at first, is covered in a slimy, dark-green mass of spores. The stalk is salmon-pink.

One of many exotic species recently discovered in Central Europe is *Dictyophora duplicata*, which is common in deciduous forests of the eastern United States. It resembles *Phallus impudicus*, except for a beautifully perforated white skirt – the indusium – which hangs down from the base of the receptacle. The related *D. indusiata* (Fig. 242) is widespread in tropical forests. Specimens of the Australasian *Anthurus muellerianus* (Pl. 71, p. 141) have been discovered in various parts of southern Germany, including the Black Forest and Upper Bavaria, to the complete surprise of botanists. Here the receptacle has 4 to 7 blood-red lobes, which stretch out from the 'egg' like the arms of an octopus.

Perhaps the strangest fungus of all is *Clathrus ruber* (Fig. 243), the only European representative of its genus. In all the 10 or so predominantly tropical species, the expanded receptacle shows itself as a vermilion or coral-pink, hollow, spherical lattice-work. The arms are finely ribbed outside but the inside is covered with olive-brown mucus giving off an exceptionally putrid smell.

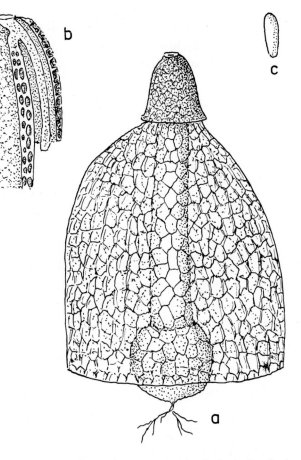

Fig. 242 *Dictyophora indusiata. a*: Fruiting body (reduced); *b*: longitudinal section through upper half of fruiting body showing unfolded indusium beneath the cap (natural size); *c*: basidiospore (highly magnified)

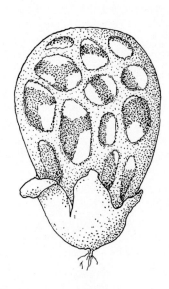

Fig. 243 *Clathrus ruber* (slightly reduced)

Though no one in his right senses would treat the stinkhorn as edible, some collectors have established that it tastes of radishes; some have even been able to overcome their natural disgust to discover that its repulsive gleba has a sweet taste.

Family
Nidulariaceae

This family comprises the bird's nest fungi, which owe their popular name to the fact that their mature fruiting bodies contain a number of small, hard, lentil-shaped structures resembling eggs.

The 'nest' is the peridium which, as in all Gasteromycetes, is originally closed; at maturity, however, the thin skin covering its top tears open.

The lentil-shaped 'eggs' or peridioles originate from the gleba, each of whose chambers is lined with hymenium and eventually becomes separated from the peridium and surrounded by several walls, the outer one of which is hard and waxy. The peridioles are attached to the inside of the 'nest' by means of a thin, coiled mycelial thread, the funiculus.

The method of peridiole dissemination in bird's nest fungi is as unusual as it is interesting. In *Cyathus*, for instance, the cups of the nest are so constructed that, as soon as a drop of rain falls on them, the peridioles are ejected with great force to a distance of

some 3 feet. As they escape, the funiculus uncoils behind them; its terminal section, the hapteron, is extremely sticky and as soon as it strikes an object such as a blade of grass it adheres to it, whereupon the funiculus winds round the object. Once the peridiole is thus firmly anchored, the spores are released.

Of the 40 or so universally distributed species of bird's nest fungi, all of which live on the ground, on dung, rotting wood or dead plant remains, three species (of *Cyathus*) occur in Central Europe and two are found in Britain. *Fig. 244* shows the cosmopolitan *C. striatus*, whose cylindrical fruiting bodies, 4–8 mm. high, grow on sticks, cones and other debris in woods, sometimes in large numbers, from spring to autumn. The cups are matted and yellowish-brown at first, but later turn grey and smooth and contain 8 to 10 light-coloured peridioles. This species is considered the most beautiful bird's nest fungus of all.

Family
Sphaerobolaceae

In this small but universally distributed family of only two genera, the fruiting body is so constructed that the entire gleba and its surrounding endoperidium, and not only the peridioles, are violently shot out. The exoperidium of the tiny glebal ball (only

Fig. 244 *Cyathus striatus*

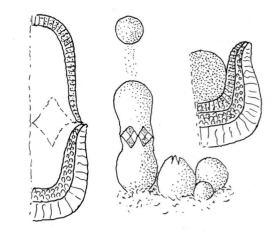

Fig. 245 *Sphaerobolus stellatus*. Centre: fruiting body ejecting gleba by sudden inversion of peridial layer (slightly reduced); right: diagrammatic section through right half of expanding fruiting body (magnified); left: the same section with peridial layer reversed

2.5 mm. across) is built up of several layers. At maturity, it splits into 6 to 8 rays, whereupon stored glycogen becomes transformed into reducing sugar. The increased osmotic pressure then stretches and reverses the peridial layer beneath the gleba, thrusting it upwards with explosive force and propelling it through the air to a distance of several feet (cf. the ejection mechanism of *Pilobolus*, described on pp. 100–101). The fruiting bodies of *Sphaerobolus*, which is sometimes called the fungal cannon, grow on decaying wood and dung (*Fig. 245*).

Class

DEUTEROMYCETES

No less than 20,000 species of fungi are included in this 'class' which – unlike the categories of the natural system – has been established quite artificially, and thus yields no information as to the natural affinities of its members. Mycologists accordingly refer to the Deuteromycetes as a form-class. In it are combined all those fungi in which sexual reproduction is unknown, i.e. in which no oospores, zygospores, ascospores or basidiospores have been discovered and which, as far as we can tell, reproduce exclusively by means of imperfect stages (conidia). For that reason the Deuteromycetes are also called 'imperfect fungi'. The conidial stages of most of them are strongly reminiscent of the conidia of Ascomycetes, and many taxonomists do, in fact, feel that the Deuteromycetes ought to be treated as Ascomycetes, the more so as some have been discovered to be capable of producing sexual stages (asci) both in nature and in the laboratory. Moreover, conidia and asci often occur at distinct periods of time or in distinct regions. Hence it is quite possible that the ascus stage may have been overlooked, or else that imperfect fungi, in the course of their evolution, may have 'lost' their ability to form asci or basidia.

The fact that several Deuteromycetes which had been named after their conidial stages were subsequently discovered to produce sexual stages as well has caused taxonomists a great many headaches. Thus *Botrytis* (*Fig. 165*) was found to be not a genus in its own right, but the conidial stage of *Botryotinia*, Family Sclerotiniaceae, Order Helotiales, Series Discomycetes. For reasons of convenience (not least connected with the identification and eradication of fungal pests) the International Botanical Congress, meeting in Stockholm in 1950, nevertheless decided to leave *Botrytis* among the Deuteromycetes.

The vegetative spores, or conidia, which are the chief characteristics of Deuteromycetes, arise in a variety of ways. Some develop directly from the mycelium on special conidiophores; others are enclosed in more complex 'containers'. In a large number of species, these take the form of spherical or flask-shaped structures with a small aperture at the tip; they resemble the perithecia of many Ascomycetes and are known as pycnidia. Another group of Deuteromycetes forms acervuli, a hyphal mat covered with conidia close beneath the epidermis of the plants on which they live as saprobes; the conidia are freed when the host tissue subsequently tears. In yet another group, densely packed conidiophores form cushion-shaped clusters on the substrate; such structures are known as sporodochia. Like the whole class, its subdivisions are wholly artificial; the orders, families and genera – better described as form-orders, form-families and form-genera – are distinguished by characters based on the structure of the fruiting bodies and of the conidiophores, and on the colour, shape and internal structure (number of cells, presence of septa) of the conidia; the last two characters are particularly important in the classification of the individual species.

Many Deuteromycetes are saprobes; quite a few are parasitic, among them a number of important agents of disease in plants, animals and man.

Form-order

SPHAEROPSIDALES

The members of this form-order produce spherical or flask-shaped pycnidia, shield-shaped conidia resembling those of the Microthyriales, and beak- or disk-shaped conidia that look like apothecia. The pycnidia may open by a pore at the top or by slits; in species where no such apertures are formed, the conidia are not freed until the fruiting body disintegrates. Pycnidia may arise singly or in dense groups from the division of a hypha or of hyphae. The conidia – which may be colourless or pigmented, unicellular or multicellular and of all sorts of

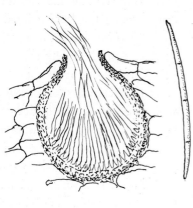

Fig. 246 *Septoria apii*. Left: section through pycnidium (highly magnified); right: conidium (very highly magnified)

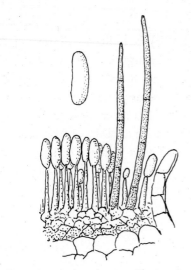

Fig. 247 *Colletotrichum lindemutheanum*. Section through an averculum; top: conidium (both highly magnified)

Fig. 248 *Asterosporium hoffmanni*. Left: section through an averculum; right: conidium (both strongly magnified)

shapes and sizes – arise on short conidiophores lining the entire inner wall of the pycnidia or at least its basal portion; they may also develop directly on the inner wall.

Of the plant parasites in this form-order, the three most important genera are *Phyllosticta*, *Phoma* and *Septoria* – the first two differing merely in that *Phyllosticta* is parasitic on the leaves and *Phoma* on the stems of plants. Both form-genera have rounded pycnidia, embedded in the substrate and provided with ostioles. The conidiophores are very short and colourless, the spores spherical to oval. *Phyllosticta acericola* causes serious leaf spot of maple; *P. hedericola* attacks ivy; *P. solitaria* causes apple blotch. *Phoma oleracea* causes serious damage to cabbages and *P. anthrisci* attacks the stems of chervil (*Anthriscus*). The pycnidia of *Septoria* resemble those of *Phyllosticta/Phoma* except that they have thinner walls; the conidiophores are very short, the conidia themselves long, slender, and often with one or more septa. *S. apii* (Fig. 246), *S. chrysantemella*, *S. lycopersici*, *S. pyricola* and *S. rubi* cause blight in celery, and leaf spot of chrysanthemum, tomato, pear and raspberry; the last two are the imperfect stages of the Ascomycetes *Mycosphaerella pyricola* and *rubi* (see p. 106).

Form-order
MELANCONIALES

Typical of the fungi in this form-order, many of which are parasitic, is the presence of acervuli, which generally develop below the cuticle or epidermis of the host. At maturity, the acervuli erupt and release the conidia in the form of white, creamy, pink,

orange or black droplets. *Gloeosporium fructigenum* causes bitter rot in apples; *Colletotrichum atramentarium* causes black-dot rot in tomato and eggplant. Many taxonomists combine *Gloeosporium* and *Colletotrichum* into a single form-genus. *C. gloeosporioides*, which attacks citrus and other useful plants, is the conidial stage of *Glomerella cingulata* (see p. 118); *C. lindemutheanum* (Fig. 247), the cause of the very common and serious bean anthracnose, is the conidial stage of *Glomerella lindemutheana*. The form-genus *Asterosporium* (Fig. 248) produces star-shaped, multicellular conidia, and lives saprophytically on dead beech branches.

Form-order
MONILIALES

The Moniliales, which comprise some 10,000 form-species and are thus the largest single form-order among the Deuteromycetes, are important because they comprise a large number of fungal pathogens

78 *Cladonia coccifera* (Lichenes)

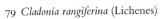

79 *Cladonia rangiferina* (Lichenes)

80 *Cladonia digitata* (Lichenes)

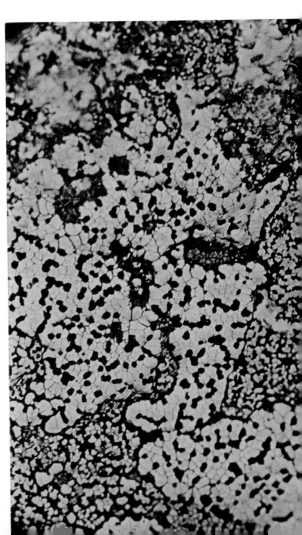

81 *Rhizocarpon geographicum* (Lichenes)

82 *Peltigera canina* (Lichenes)   83 *Solorina crocea* (Lichenes)

84 *Lecidea granulosa* (Lichenes)

85 *Stereocaulon alpinum* (Lichenes),
related to reindeer moss

86 *Umbilicaria arctica* (Lichenes)

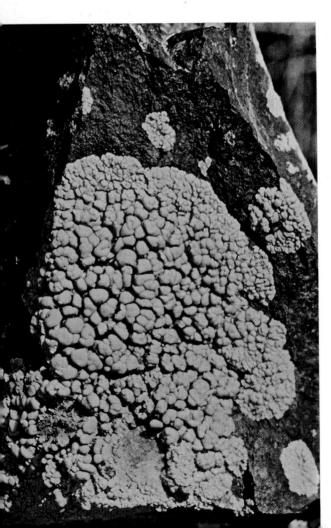

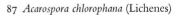

87 *Acarospora chlorophana* (Lichenes)

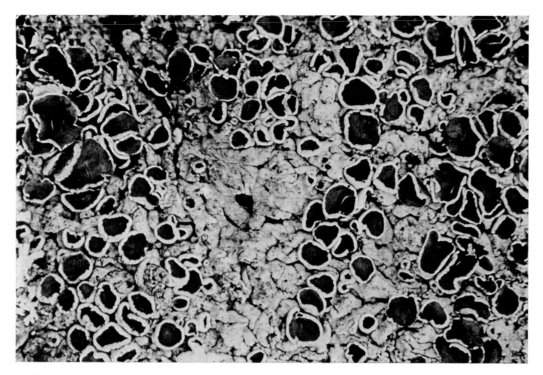

88 *Haematomma ventosum* (Lichenes)

89 *Lecanora subfusca*, a close relative of the manna-lichen

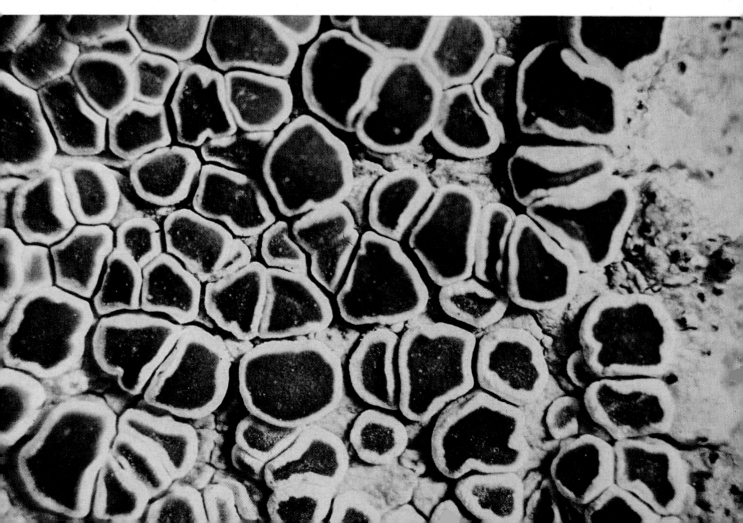

90 *Xanthoria elegans* (Lichenes)

91 *Usnea longissima* (Lichenes)

92 *Parmelia saxatilis* (Lichenes)

93 *Usnea canariensis*, a lichen that grows on cork trees in the Canaries

94 *Parmelia centrifuga* (Lichenes)

95 *Xanthoria parietina* (Lichenes)

97 Two lichens: *Caloplaca bracteata* (with orange apothecia) and *Lecidea decipiens*

96 *Cora pavonia* (Lichenes)

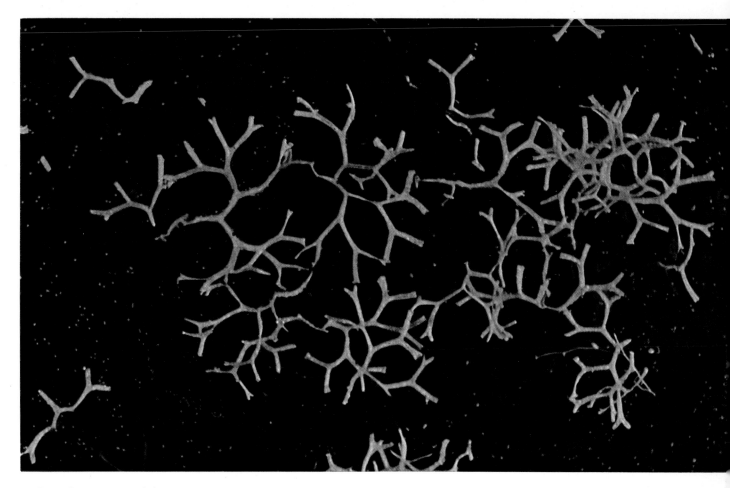

98 *Riccia fluitans*, an aquatic liverwort

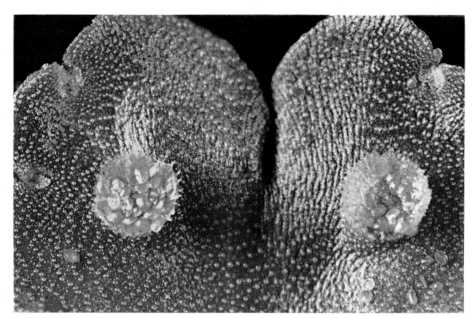

99 The liverwort
Marchantia polymorpha
(magnified)

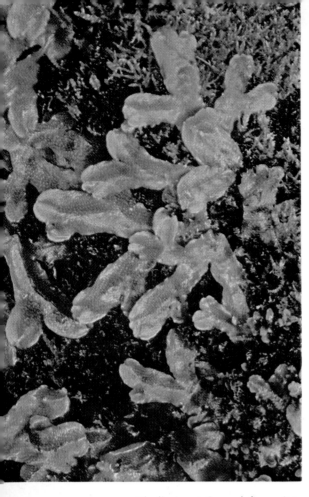

100 The liverwort *Conocephalum conicum*

101 The liverwort *Reboulia hemisphaerica*

102 The liverwort *Plagiochila asplenioides*

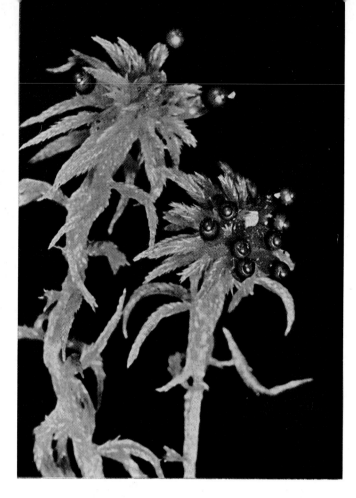

103 *Sphagnum*, bog moss

105 Luminous moss, *Schistostega pennata*

104 The liverwort
Anthoceros punctatus

106 Leafless moss,
    Buxbaumia aphylla

109 Spore capsules of
    Polytrichum commune
    (magnified)

107 *Polytrichum commune*, a moss common on
    damp moorland

108 'Flowers' of *Polytrichum commune*
    (magnified)

110 The moss *Plagiothecium undulatum*

111 The moss *Mnium undulatum*

112 The moss *Diphyscium foliosum*

113 The moss *Leucobryum glaucum*

114 Cushions of *Grimmia trichophylla*

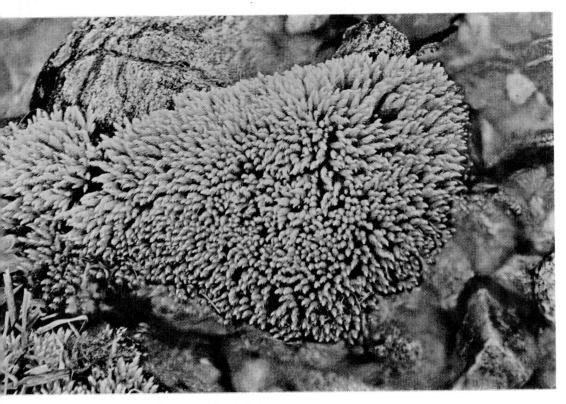

115 The moss *Philonotis fontana*

116 The moss *Hylocomium splendens*

of man, together with many industrially important fungi, such as *Penicillium*, and the so-called false yeasts, which served as food substitutes, particularly in Germany, during the two world wars. The conidia appear on richly branched conidiophores that may arise singly or combined in groups. Most species develop on the surface of the substrate. The order is generally split up into five form-families.

Form-family
Cryptococcaceae

This family comprises a number of false yeasts, i.e. yeasts that are not known to form ascospores. Their elongated cells combine into a pseudomycelium, and more rarely into a mycelium proper. There is an absence of true conidia; instead, the mycelial hyphae break up into single cells, which act as spores. The cells are colourless or contain (e.g. in the form-genus *Rhodotorula*) yellow, orange, or red carotenoids.

Of medical importance are *Candida albicans* and *Trichosporon cutaneum*, both of which produce a true mycelium and a pseudomycelium with thick-walled chlamydospores. *Trichosporon* is the cause of trichosporiasis, or white piedra, a tropical disease of the beard and moustache; *Candida albicans* (*Fig. 249*) causes candidiasis of the mucous membranes, a condition that may prove fatal, particularly when it attacks the mouths of suckling infants. The incidence of this type of candidiasis, and also of bronchopulmonary and pulmonary candidiasis, is on the increase, owing to the ever-increasing use of antibiotics that kill beneficial and harmful bacteria in the human body indiscriminately.

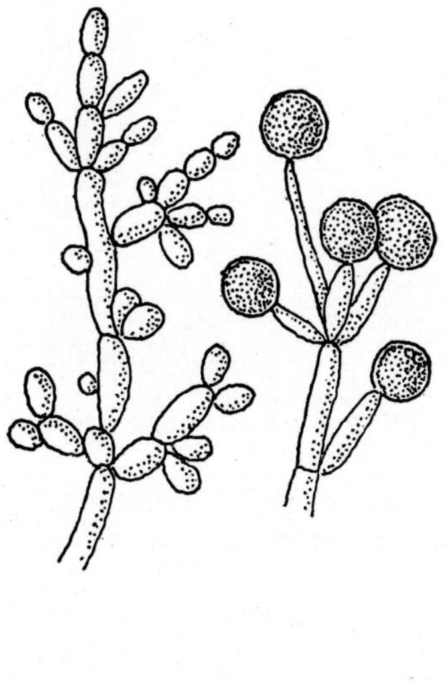

Fig. 249 *Candida albicans*. Left: germinating mycelium; right: formation of chlamydospores (highly magnified)

Other agents of human disease are found in the form-genera *Blastomyces*, which occurs in North and South America, causing skin diseases and a pulmonary condition resembling tuberculosis, and *Histoplasma* which is responsible for the rare but fatal condition known as histoplasmosis, a general infection accompanied by ulceration. *H. capsulatum*, the only known species, undergoes yeast-like budding at body temperature and forms a mycelium with large chlamydospores at room temperature. It occurs chiefly in North and South America, South Africa and, above all, in the Philippines.

A much more pleasant member of this group is *Torulopsis utilis*, which can be used as a food supplement and is commonly sold in health-food shops. *Torulopsis* does not form a mycelium and only occasionally a rudimentary pseudomycelium; it generally takes the form of round or oval cells and multiplies by budding. While the remaining members of this form-genus are all saprobes, growing on all sorts of decaying plant remains, *T. utilis* feeds on sugar alone, and nevertheless produces large quantities of protein and vitamins; in many countries, it is cultivated on a large scale and marketed as a powder or paste for human or animal consumption.

Form-family
Moniliaceae

Most members of this group form a richly branched, colourless mycelium, bearing conidia on unorganized, transparent conidiophores or directly on colourless hyphae. Most species are saprophytic, though quite a few cause damage or diseases to plants, animals and men, among them the form-genus *Penicillium*, which not only provides us with antibiotics, but also forms green or blue 'moulds' on fruit, flour, textiles and leather. We have mentioned *Penicillium* during our discussion of the Eurotiaceae; here we need merely add that most of the 140 or so species of *Penicillium* are imperfect fungi – their perfect stages are mostly unknown. Wherever such stages have been discovered, they were placed in the genera *Carpenteles* and *Talaromyces*. We have also met the form-genus *Aspergillus*, another member of the Moniliaceae (see p. 111); its perfect stages have been placed in the genera *Eurotium*, *Emericella* and

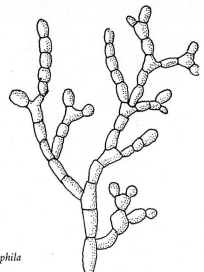

Fig. 250 *Monilia sitophila* (highly magnified)

Sartroya. Thus *Aspergillus* and *Penicillium* provide us with an excellent illustration of just how confusing the nomenclature of partly perfect and partly imperfect fungi may become.

In the Zoopagaceae (p. 102) we have already met a group of fungi capable of trapping small animals. Similar devices are employed by a number of Moniliaceae. Thus the mycelium of the cosmopolitan *Arthrobothrys superba* forms loops or branches capable of capturing nematode worms: as soon as the victim is ensnared, other hyphae immediately invade and digest it. Things are similar in *Dactylella*, where the nematode worm is caught in constricting rings. *Harposporium*, finally, captures its prey by means of sticky conidia; once caught the animal is killed and digested by the internal mycelium.

Some Moniliaceae cause dermatomycoses, skin diseases of man and animals. Thus *Epidermophyton* and *Trichophyton* both cause athlete's foot. Insofar as the perfect stages of these form-genera have been discovered, they have proved to be members of the family Gymnoascaceae (p. 111). (The fact that *Aspergillus* can cause serious mycoses was mentioned on p. 112.)

Form-family
Dematiaceae

This family, most of whose members have a well-developed dark-brown to black, septate mycelium, dark, ramified or unbranched conidiophores and dark conidia (though sometimes the hyphae alone or the conidia only are dark) contains a number of saprophytic species side by side with destructive pests and pathogens.

Thus the genus *Cladosporium* (*Fig. 252*) includes a number of dangerous plant pests: *C. carpophilum* causes peach scab; *C. fulvum* causes serious tomato leaf mould. *Cladosporium* is probably identical with the genus *Hormodendrum*, which includes *H. pedrosoi* and *H. compactum*, both of which cause chromoblastomycosis in man, a predominantly tropical skin disease in which masses of warts are formed over the infected parts of the body, chiefly the legs, feet, arms and hands. This fungus is normally a soil saprobe, and enters the human skin through wounds.

Helminthosporium includes all Dematiaceae with

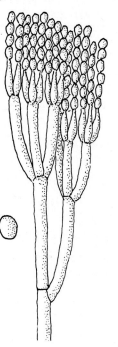

Fig. 251 *Penicillium expansum.* Right: conidiophores (highly magnified); left: conidium (very highly magnified)

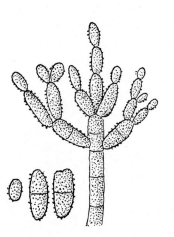

Fig. 252 *Cladosporium herbarum.* Right: conidiophores (highly magnified); left: conidia (highly magnified)

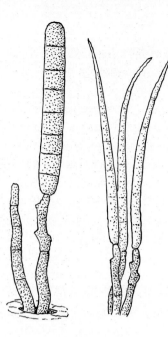

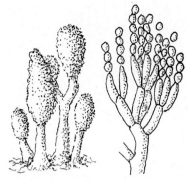

Fig. 254 *Isaria farinosa*; left: coremium (slightly magnified); right: conidiophores (highly magnified)

Fig. 253 *Helminthosporium teres* (highly magnified); right: *Cercospora arachidicola*

dark and multicellular conidia. Of the 175 cosmopolitan species, we can only mention *H. turicum*, which attacks the leaves of maize; *H. iridis* which causes iris leaf spot, and *H. teres* (*Fig. 253*), *H. sativum* and *H. gramineum* which cause net blotch, foot rot, and leaf stripe in barley. The perfect stage of *H. iridis* is *Ophiobolus iridis*, in the order Pleosporales (see p. 107).

All the 3800 or so known form-species in the genus *Cercospora* are parasitic on higher plants throughout the world. Thus *C. apii* causes celery leaf spot, and also attacks tobacco, beet and several other crops. In the tropics, moreover, it may enter the human skin and cause disfiguring lesions. The perfect stages of many species have proved to be members of the genus *Mycosphaerella* (Dothideales; see p. 107).

The form-genus *Alternaria* has a prostrate mycelium, short, unbranched conidiophores, and chains of dark conidia with transverse and longitudinal septa. Several of its species, which live as saprobes in the soil, are picked up by the wind and occur in house dust, causing hay fever. *A. brassica* attacks cabbages; *A. solani* causes early blight of the potato.

Form-family
Stilbellaceae

In this family, the conidiophores may be cemented together to form an elongated and highly branched spore-bearing structure, the synnema, in which the conidia arise at the tips of the branches. In other cases, however, the conidia occupy more than half the 'fruiting body' which is then called a coremium. The hyphae and conidia may be coloured or not. Most Stilbellaceae are saprobes. The form-genus *Isaria* (*Fig. 254*), however, contains species that live partly on plant remains and partly as parasites on insects. The family also includes *Graphium ulmi*, the cause of Dutch elm disease, which has been identified as the conidial stage of *Ceratocystis ulmi* (see p. 112).

Form-family
Tuberculariaceae

The characteristic structure of this form-family is the cushion-shaped sporodochium, built up of hyphae and conidiophores. This group includes saprobes together with such parasites as *Tuberculina*, which attacks the aecidia of rusts (see p. 148). In the form-genus *Volutella*, the spherical sporodochia may have short stalks; their conidiophores are invariably bristly. All the 20 or so species of this form-genus are parasitic on higher plants; *V. fructi* causes dry rot of apples.

Fig. 255 *Tuberculina persicina*. Right: part of sporodochium in the aecidium of a rust (highly magnified); left: conidiophore (very highly magnified)

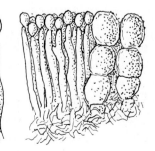

211

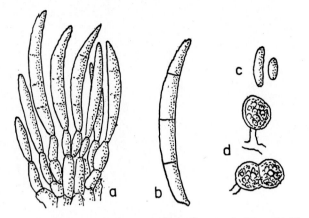

Fig. 256 *Fusarium oxysporum. a:* Part of a sporodochium (highly magnified); *b:* macroconidium (very highly magnified); *c:* microconidia; *d:* chlamydospores (very highly magnified)

Very dangerous parasites are found in the form-genus *Fusaria* (65 species) which produces broad sporodochia of various shapes. The conidiophores are branched and give rise to two types of conidia: unicellular or bicellular, elliptical and colourless microconidia built up of single or branched hyphae, and long, crescent-shaped macroconidia borne on sporodochia. Chlamydospores are also commonly produced. Many species live as saprobes on decaying plant matter; the parasites among them cause wilts of plants by plugging the conducting tissue with their hyphae and also by secreting toxins. Several *Fusariae* have been identified as the conidial stages of Nectriaceae (see pp. 113–114). *F. oxysporum (Fig. 256)* causes potato wilt, *F. oxysporum* var. *cubense* attacks the banana; *F. lycopersici* attacks tomato plants.

Form-order
MYCELIA STERILIA

At the end of the gigantic and multiform world of fungi, taxonomists place a motley group (sometimes treated as a separate form-class) of fungi that cannot be fitted in anywhere else. None of them produces spores under natural conditions; they consist exclusively of mycelia of different shapes and colours; several form sclerotia. Recently, it has been possible to induce spore-production in several species under laboratory conditions, and hence to fit them into known groups, particularly among the Basidiomycetes. However, the great majority refuse to produce spores under any conditions – no doubt because

they have lost this capacity in the course of evolution. All make do with reproduction by hyphal segments or sclerotia.

Species of *Rhizoctonia* are chiefly parasitic on the roots of higher plants – the name means 'root-killer'. The part of the mycelium that grows outside the host is richly ramified, dark, and consists of short cells; the hyphae inside the host are elongated and colourless. The dark mycelium gives rise to small, ray-shaped, black sclerotia. Of the 15 cosmopolitan species, only a few have been identified as imperfect stages. Among these *R. solani*, which causes black scurf of potatoes, was shown to be the imperfect stage of the Basidiomycete *Pellicularia filamentosa* (see p. 156); *R. crocorum* as the imperfect stage of *Helicobasidium purpureum* (a close relative of which is shown in *Fig. 187*), and *R. bataticola*, which attacks tropical crops, as the imperfect stage of *Macrophomina* (Deuteromycetes).

The genus *Orcheomyces* includes all those fungi that go into the endotrophic mycorrhizae of orchids (see p. 88). A few species have been identified as the imperfect stages of Agaricales.

The form-genus *Sclerotium* exists exclusively in the form of small black sclerotia on white, cottony hyphae. In many species, the sclerotia measure no more than a few millimetres; in others, they may attain the size of a child's head. *S. oryzae* attacks rice plants; *S. rolfsii* attacks a number of tropical plants, and *S. cepivorum* causes white rot of onions and garlic.

Loliomyces temulentus, the only species in its form-genus, invariably spreads its mycelium inside the seed of the darnel (*Lolium temulentum*), a close relative of *L. perenne*, rye grass (see *Plants of the World*, Vol. II, p. 260). Darnel seeds contain a poisonous alkaloid which is probably produced by the fungus.

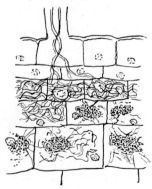

Fig. 257 *Orcheomyces.* Section through orchid root (strongly magnified); note that the fungal hyphae in the lower cell layers of the root are dissolved

6 LICHENES
Lichens

A lichen is an association of a fungus and an alga, in which the two partners are so closely intertwined as to form a single thallus (*Pls. 78–97, pp. 193–200*). Now here, as elsewhere in nature, the whole is more than the sum of its parts: much as a forest is more than a mere collection of trees, shrubs, herbs and animals, so a lichen is more than a mere fungus and alga living together.

Lichens grow over the entire face of the earth and form the outposts of life where other plants are unable to exist – on the storm-swept cliffs of high mountains, on concrete walls, on the rock of the inhospitable tundra, and on barren soil. And wherever they appear, these pioneers of nature create conditions in which other plants can eventually take root. Lichens are able to send their threads into the finest cracks in the substrate and, with the help of water and ice, soften even the hardest rock. When they die, they usually leave a layer, albeit only a few millimetres thick, consisting of their own remains and dust on which mosses followed by higher plants can later establish themselves.

Lichens were formerly considered an independent group of lower plants; it was not, in fact, until the second half of the nineteenth century that Anton de Bary and Simon Schwendener discovered their true nature; de Bary coined the term symbiosis to describe it. Once this great discovery had been made, various taxonomists deemed it necessary to fit the various lichens into those groups of fungi which participate in the association. Though there is much to be said for this approach, the modern view is that lichens must be treated as a systematic category *sui generis*, the more so as by far the majority of fungi in them have become incapable of living independently. In lichens, the symbiotic association of algae and fungi is so intimate that it gives rise to quite specific morphological characters and physiological products (lichen acids); moreover, the fruiting bodies of lichens often have a structure peculiar to themselves.

A microscopic section of a lichen thallus shows that it is composed of a compact tissue of fungal cells (the cortex) at the upper and lower surface, and between, of a system of loosely interwoven and colourless hyphae (the medulla). The algal cells, which are generally green, lie just beneath the upper cortex and are intermixed with the fungal hyphae. The algal symbionts are mostly unicellular green algae, and less often chains of blue-green algae; the fungi are chiefly Ascomycetes and occasionally Basidiomycetes. In some cases, botanists have been able to separate the two symbionts and to grow them in isolation. This is a simple matter with the algal symbionts (phycobionts), which can easily make do without their fungal associates (mycobionts). The isolated mycobionts, on the other hand, remain dormant for a long time, and then produce shapeless colonies consisting of nothing but mycelium. The moment they are introduced to an alga, however, they readily form a new lichen.

Anton de Bary, as we said, applied the term symbiosis to the association of an alga and a fungus. He believed that, while the alga supplies the fungus

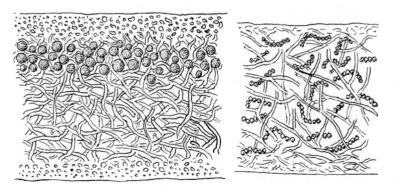

Fig. 258 Left: cross-section of lichen thallus with upper and lower cortex. The algae are confined to a layer near the surface (highly magnified). Right: cross-section through thallus of another lichen species, in which the algae (chains of *Nostoc*) are scattered (highly magnified)

with photosynthetic products which the latter is unable to produce for itself, the fungus supplies the alga with water and salts, absorbed from the substrate, and also with a protective cover. Microscopic examination has, however, shown that far from being symbiotic, i.e. mutually beneficial, the association helps the fungus far more than it does the alga. The fungal hyphae wrap themselves tightly round the algal cells, occasionally penetrating them by means of haustoria, occasionally killing the alga and absorbing its entire substance. In other words, the relationship is anything but an ideal form of symbiosis. Moreover, since the fungus is not viable without 'its' alga, whereas the alga can readily dispense with 'its' fungus, the association is at best a form of 'balanced' parasitism. Modern botanists describe it as 'helotism', to indicate that the alga is enslaved to the fungus much as the helots were to the Spartans.

It must, however, be stressed that when they combine into lichens, the symbionts are capable of

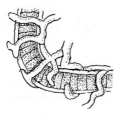

Fig. 259 Top: *Protococcus*; below: *Scytonema*. Two algae, enmeshed in fungal mycelium (highly magnified)

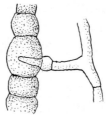

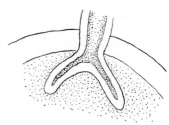

Fig. 260 Top: fungus sending haustorium into a *Nostoc* cell; below: haustorium inside a *Protococcus* cell (both highly magnified)

producing substances that neither fungus nor alga can produce by itself. These are the lichen acids, metabolic products generally secreted by the outer side of the hyphae in the form of small crystals, and to which the thalli of numerous lichens owe their characteristic colour. Moreover, it is the association of algae and fungi that enables lichens to play the part of pioneering plants by preparing the ground for other vegetation – in this process they are even capable of etching glass, as we know from old church windows. We might add that the mycobiont, at least, can only produce its fruiting bodies in the context of the association – we saw that laboratory cultures do not sporulate, which suggests that spore germination is encouraged by the presence of lichen acids.

As we also saw, the fungal hyphae account for the main mass of all lichens; the algae are generally restricted to only one layer near the surface. Very rarely, they may be scattered throughout the thallus. The shape and structure of lichens varies a great deal: their thalli may be *homoiomerous*, i.e. with algal cells uniformly distributed through the thallus (e.g. *Collema*); *heteromerous*, i.e. with algal cells in a definite layer in the thallus (e.g. *Ephebe*); *crustaceous*, i.e. forming a more or less inseparable crust on the substrate (e.g. *Rhizocarpon*); *foliose*, i.e. leaf-like and procumbent and often attached to the substrate by means of root-like hyphal strands, the so-called rhizinae (e.g. *Parmelia*); or *fructicose*, i.e. erect and bush-like and attached to the substrate only at the base (e.g. *Rocella*).

In general, lichens develop very slowly. Thus *Rhizocarpon geographicum* (Pl. *81*, p. *194*) takes 60 years to form a thallus covering one square centimetre. Hence we may take it that the large rock-inhabiting species in the high mountains and in the Arctic live for hundreds if not for thousands of years. And yet precisely those lichens which are so undemanding that they can thrive at the outermost limits of the biosphere are extremely sensitive to air pollution, so much so that they are disappearing from large industrial cities. In fact, the absence of lichens gives us a measure of air pollution; in Zurich, air pollution has been mapped district by district by measuring lichen growth on buildings and trees. The survey incidentally established that certain species of lichens are insensitive to even the smokiest atmosphere.

Reproduction in lichens occurs in various ways. Sexual reproduction as such is invariably delegated to the fungal partner. Vegetative reproduction is common; in the simplest case pieces of the thallus break off and form new lichens. More commonly, reproduction involves the formation of soredia (*Fig. 261*), small groups of algal cells surrounded by fungal hyphae, borne either in extensive patches on the surface of the thallus or else in special structures known as soralia. The soredia are spread by wind, rain or animals, and form new thalli when they land in suitable places. Sexual reproduction is chiefly by asci – the reader will remember that most mycobionts are Ascomycetes – generally in the form of apothecia and more rarely in the form of perithecia (see p. 105). The mature ascospores are expelled and can only participate in the formation of new lichens if they chance upon the right algal partner – which is not, however, too difficult in species living on walls, the bark of trees, or on stones. Some lichens, moreover, make special 'provision' for such meetings: thus in the order Lecanorales, the edges of the asci are studded with algal cells, which help to provide the spores with the 'right' partners from the start. Some lichens dispense with sexual reproduction altogether – possibly because they 'lost' the sexual capacity in the course of evolution. Finally, quite a few species produce pycnidia lined with fungal hyphae from which tiny colourless spores, the pycnoconidia, are budded off. It has not yet been established whether such conidia represent male sexual cells that have lost their function; it has, however, been found that hyphae occasionally germinate from them.

As we saw, a small number of Basidiomycetes also enter into lichen-forming associations, generally with filiform blue-green algae. The resulting lichens are treated as a separate class.

Occasionally two distinct algae, one green and one blue-green, may go into a lichen; when that happens, the colony of blue-green algae is either restricted to small wart-like outgrowths on the surface, known as cephalodia, or else, as in *Solorina crocea* (*Pl. 83, p. 195*), to a special cephalodial zone beneath a layer of green algae. Conversely, a lichen

Fig. 261 Soredia
(highly magnified)

may consist of one alga and two fungi, each of which is capable of producing fruiting bodies (e.g. in *Cetraria* and *Usnea*). The second fungus, or parasymbiont, may compete for the available algal substances or else may be a pure parasite and finally kill the lichen. We also know of lichens that attack other lichens and parasitize their algae, so much so that some of these parasitic species have been able to dispense with algal partners of their own.

There are some 16,000 species of lichens all over the earth. We said that they advance further and higher than any other plants. Thus, close to the South Pole, rock protruding from the ice is inhabited by 7 known species, and lichens have been found in mountains up to an altitude of 18,000 ft. and more. They grow on the soil, on bare rock, on bark and wood, and, particularly in the tropics, on the leaves of various plants. European species include no real pests; but lichens can cause indirect damage to trees by covering the bark so densely that they deprive the host of moisture. Some tropical species living on mosses can, moreover, kill the host by proliferating in its thallus. Species of *Strigula* cause severe damage to coffee, tea, rubber and citrus by sending their algal hyphae into the leaf tissue, thus opening the way to fungal parasites which cause the plant to shed its leaves prematurely.

Useful lichens include *Lecanora esculenta*, which many people believe was the manna eaten by the Israelites in the wilderness. This crustaceous lichen, which generally lives on the ground, is one of the few quick-growing species in the division, often covering large areas with its small-lobed, knobbly thalli; dried plants are carried over vast distances by the wind, to rain down as bread from heaven (Exodus *xvi*, 4–15). In the East, *L. esculenta* serves as a foodstuff to this day, as does *Gyrophora esculenta* in Japan. In times of famine, Europeans, too, used to bake bread from lichens. *Cladonia rangiferina*, reindeer moss, which abounds in the Arctic tundra, serves as fodder for deer; other species of *Cladonia*, all of which are rich in starch, are used in Scandinavia to prepare alcohol and sugar. Some lichen acids yield pigments in reaction with various chemical substances; the best-known of these is litmus (obtained from *Roccella* species in North Africa and the Canary Islands), a chemical indicator which turns red in acid and blue in alkaline solutions. *Evernia prunastri* yields the perfume known as *mousse de chênes*; *Cetraria islandica*, Iceland moss, contains a form of starch that has been eaten by man and is used in cough mixtures. More recently, antibiotics have been prepared from several lichens, including *Usnea hirta*, which yields usnic acid, a bacteriostatic substance used in the treatment of tuberculosis. The only poisonous European lichen is *Letharia vulpina*.

By their fungal component, lichens are divided into two large classes: the Ascolichenes and the far less common Basidiolichenes. Some taxonomists treat as Deuterolichenes all those species that reproduce exclusively by means of soredia – among them the family Leprariaceae, which includes the very common *Lepraria aeruginosa*. This lichen has a powdery thallus and grows in damp shady places on rocks and trees.

Sometimes alga-like fungi (Phycomycetes; see p. 94), harbouring symbiotic blue-green algae in their cells, are also treated as a separate taxonomic category, the Phycolichenes.

Class

ASCOLICHENES

The Ascolichenes are divided into two sub-classes, the Pyrenocarpeae and the Gymnocarpeae.

Sub-class

PYRENOCARPEAE

Characteristic of this small sub-class is the presence of flask-shaped perithecia. The phycobionts in the crustaceous, foliose or fructicose thalli may be green or blue-green algae.

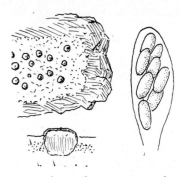

Fig. 262 *Verrucaria muralis*. Top left: thallus attached to a stone (slightly magnified); bottom left: cross-section of perithecium (highly magnified); right: ascus (highly magnified)

The crustaceous lichens in the order Verrucariales live mostly on and in limestone; their phycobionts belong to the genera *Protococcus* and *Palmella*. The thallus is often so deeply embedded in the rock that it appears as a coloured spot on the surface. The perithecia are hidden inside the thallus with only their mouths protruding. The asci have 8 spores each. Of the 220 species distributed throughout the world, but particularly in temperate zones, *Verrucaria dolomitica* and *V. muralis* are two of the most common (*Fig. 262*).

Foliose thalli, usually attached at a central point, are typical of the order Dermatocarpales, whose phycobionts also belong to the genera *Palmella* and *Protococcus*. Their perithecia are embedded in the thallus, and each of the asci bears 8 unicellular spores. The 70 or so species of the cosmopolitan genus *Dermatocarpon* live on the ground or on rock, and more rarely on the bark of trees. *D. miniatum*, whose thallus may be a simple, rounded, leaf-like structure or else dissected into a number of lobes, is attached to the substrate by means of a central pad.

The order Pyrenulales includes species with crustaceous thalli lacking rhizinae or a cortex. The phycobionts are algae of the genus *Trentepohlia*. The perithecia are mostly single; each ascus bears 6–8 colourless or brown, unicellular or bicellular spores. The 400 or so cosmopolitan species constituting this order inhabit rocks and the bark of trees. The genus *Porina* includes *P. faginea*, which forms a greyish-green crust at the base of dead trees. *Pyrenula*, a predominantly tropical species, lives chiefly on the bark of trees; the only common British species, *P. nitida*, prefers smooth bark; its thallus is olivebrown.

The order Strigulales was mentioned in connection with the leaves of tropical trees; its algal partners belong to the genera *Cephaleuros* and *Phycopeltis*.

Two further orders in this sub-class are the green

Pyrenidiales whose phycobionts are neither spherical (like *Protococcus*) nor filamentous (like *Trentepohlia*), and the Dermatinales, whose perithecia are septate.

Sub-class
GYMNOCARPEAE

The members of this sub-class account for the great majority of lichens in general; all of them produce apothecia of various forms. Compared to the apothecia of fungi, those of lichens are tough and durable, with relatively thick-walled asci. In what follows we shall only consider the most important orders, families and genera.

Order
CALICIALES

The lichens in this order form diffuse horizontal crusts; their algal partners belong to the genus *Protococcus* and its near relatives. The apothecia are generally stalked, the 8-spored asci short-lived; the bicellular spores combine with paraphyses to form a loose, powdery mass. The 80 or so species of the universally distributed genus *Calicium* grow on bark, on dead plant remains, and on stones. *C. viride*, which has a bright-green, powdery thallus, is widespread on the bark of old trees in Britain.

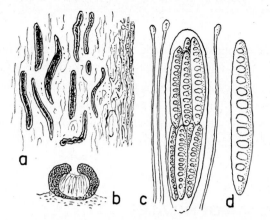

Fig. 264 *Graphis scripta. a:* thallus (slightly magnified); *b:* cross-section of apothecium (more highly magnified); *c:* ascus and paraphyses (highly magnified); *d:* spore (very highly magnified)

layer of the thallus or scattered throughout it. The genus *Graphis*, which comprises some 280 predominantly tropical species, includes *G. scripta* (*Fig. 264*), which is common on the bark of young ash, beech, hazel and other trees.

Order
ROCCELLALES

This order of fructicose lichens grows chiefly on rock; its phycobionts belong to the genus *Trentepohlia*. The apothecia (with 8-spored asci) of *Roccella*, comprising 20 species in temperate and sub-tropical zones, often on the coast, are rounded and attached laterally to the thallus. *R. fuciformis* (*Fig. 265*) and *R. tinctoria* from the Mediterranean region and

Fig. 263 *Calicium hyperellum.* Right: stalked apothecia (magnified); left: spore (very highly magnified)

Order
GRAPHIDIALES

This order forms thin, crustaceous thalli and characteristically elongated apothecia resembling commas or other punctuation marks – whence their name. Their phycobionts are various species of *Palmella*, *Trentepohlia* and *Chroolepus*, arranged in a single

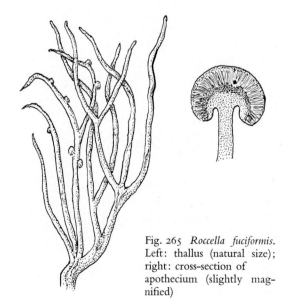

Fig. 265 *Roccella fuciformis.* Left: thallus (natural size); right: cross-section of apothecium (slightly magnified)

Africa yield litmus and orsellic acid, from which a reddish-violet dye can be prepared. Because of their elongated apothecia the Graphidiales and Roccellales are combined into the series Graphidiidae; all the other Gymnocarpae, which have round apothecia, are combined as Cyclocarpiidae.

Order
CYANOPHILALES

This order contains all lichens having blue-green algae as their phycobionts. The family Ephebaceae, whose small, filiform, densely ramified thalli are inhabited by algae in the genera *Scytonema* and *Stigonema*, includes *Ephebe lanata*, which spreads its blackish-green filaments on sunny, moist rocks in primary formations and sandstone. The tiny apothecia with their 8-spored asci are embedded in thickened regions of the filaments. Three further species occur in Europe and North America.

In the family Collemaceae, the thallus, which is firmly attached to the substrate, scaly and foliaceous, becomes gelatinous when wet. The phycobionts, species of *Nostoc*, are arranged in chains scattered throughout the thallus. The apothecia are either embedded in, or placed on top of, the thallus; the asci form 8 colourless spherical or conical spores with

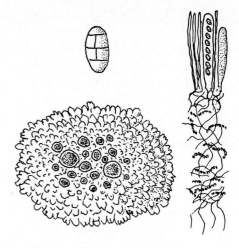

Fig. 267 *Collema pulposum*. Left: thallus (natural size); right: partial cross-section of apothecium and thallus (magnified); top left: spore (highly magnified)

one, two or more cells. *Collema pulposum*, one of the 80 species in a universally distributed genus, forms thick, blackish-green deposits on clay and limestone. This genus lacks a cortex; not so the 100 or so species constituting the genus *Leptogium*, in which the surface of the thallus has a layer of compact fungal cells. *Fig. 268* depicts the tropical *L. saturninum*. Its British counterpart, *L. tremelloides*, usually grows on mossy rocks in the west. Its thallus-lobes are rounded and translucent when wet.

Members of the family Stictaceae have large-lobed, partly erect and sometimes stalked thalli. The phycobionts (Palmellaceae or Nostocaceae) occupy

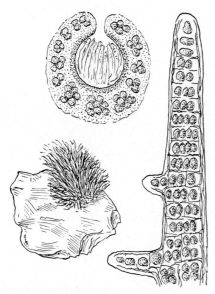

Fig. 266 *Ephebe lanata*. Lower left: thallus growing on a stone (natural size); upper left: cross-section of apothecium (magnified); right: branching thallus (magnified)

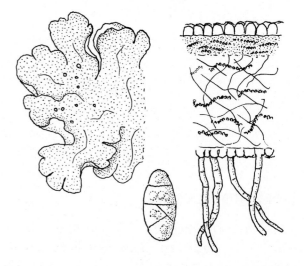

Fig. 268 *Leptogium saturninum*. Left: thallus (natural size); right: cross-section of thallus (magnified); centre: spore (highly magnified)

218

a layer immediately beneath the upper cortex. The shield-shaped apothecia are found on the surface or the edge of the thallus, and the brown or colourless bicellular or multicellular spores are spindly or needle-shaped. In the 70 species of the predominantly sub-tropical genus *Lobaria*, the thallus lobes may be more than 4 ins. wide; the phycobionts are various species of *Cystococcus*, *Protococcus* and *Nostoc*. *L. pulmonaria*, sometimes called the tree lungwort, one of the most striking of all British lichens, has lobes more than 4 ins. in length, bright-green when wet, and yellowish-brown when dry.

The genus *Sticta* includes some 200 chiefly sub-tropical species, most of which grow on bark. Their large, semi-erect or stalked thalli have a well-developed cortex, and harbour phycobionts of the genus *Nostoc* or the family Palmellaceae in a layer directly beneath the surface. The lower cortex is often densely matted and studded with white spots. *S. sylvatica* is a common species on mossy trees in the west and north of Britain. It exudes a strong smell of urine; the thallus is generally rounded and deeply divided into numerous crisped lobes, each up to $\frac{1}{2}$ in. wide.

Members of the family Peltigeraceae have large foliose thalli, anchored to the substrate by means of rhizinae; the thalli invariably have an upper cortex and often a lower cortex as well. The downy lower surface bears prominent veins. The phycobionts are again Palmellaceae or species of *Nostoc*. The round to kidney-shaped apothecia may appear on the edge,

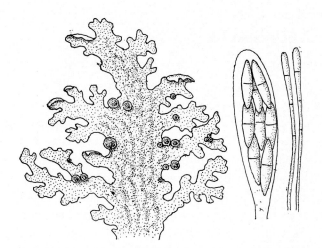

Fig. 270 *Lobaria pulmonaria*. Left: thallus (natural size); right: ascus and paraphyses (highly magnified)

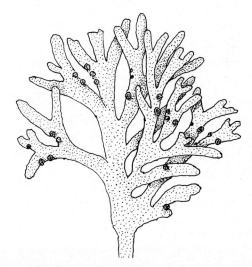

Fig. 271 *Sticta dichotomoides* (approx. natural size)

Fig. 269 *Peltigera sp.*

on the lower, or on the upper surface of the thallus; the asci bear 2 to 4 bicellular or multicellular spores, colourless to brown, ranging in form from spindle- to needle-shaped. *Fig. 269* depicts the large thalli of *Peltigera*, whose lower surface bears prominent white, brown or black veins; of the 20 or so cosmopolitan species constituting this genus, *P. canina*, the dog lichen (*Pl. 82, p. 195*), is common on sand dunes in Britain. Its large, thin lobes are bluish-brown when wet and pale-grey when dry. The genus *Solorina* (10 species) has large apothecia sunk in the surface of the thallus, lobes that are bright-green on top when wet and, in some species, orange beneath. *S. canina*, with lobes up to 2 ins. across, grows on shady rocks.

219

Order
LECIDEALES

Members of this order have crustaceous thalli with a smooth or lobed edge, often scaly or cracked. The phycobionts are spherical green algae of the *Protococcus* or *Trebouxia* type; the edge of the apothecia is invariably devoid of algae. The asci bear from one to eight unicellular or multicellular spores.

Species of Lecideaceae have a rudimentary cortex or none at all. The genus *Lecidea* comprises more than 500 species, chiefly in cold or temperate zones; each of the asci contains 8 spores. *L. parasema*, with whitish to greenish-grey thalli, is common on the bark of trees; *L. granulosa* (Pl. *84*, p. *195*) grows on peaty soil and rotten wood; *L. lapicida* on primary rocks in the Alps; *L. decipiens* (Pl. *97*, p. *200*) on limestone and calcareous soil. *Rhizocarpon* (90 species in cold and temperate zones) is one of the most striking genera of all: here the thalli are divided into fields of bright colour intersected by black lines. *R. geographicum* forms large, black-edged patches of bright-green on siliceous rocks in upland areas; *R. concentricum*, which also grows on siliceous rocks and on walls, has white to greyish-brown thalli, and apothecia arranged in circles.

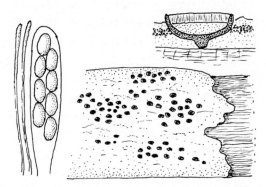

Fig. 273 *Lecidea parasema*. Lower right: thallus (slightly magnified); top right: section through apothecium (magnified); left ascus and paraphyses (highly magnified)

Family
Cladoniaceae

This family has flat thalli, consisting of a basal crust of small scales and an erect system of bushy stems (podetia) bearing the apothecia. Their phycobionts belong the genera *Protococcus* and *Trebouxia*. Once the podetia are formed, the basal crust often disappears. The apothecia are rounded, often arched, and brightly coloured. The spores, 6–8 to each ascus, are colourless and may be unicellular or multicellular.

In the genus *Baeomyces*, the brown to flesh-coloured apothecia are borne on short, columnar podetia; this genus comprises some 25 species on the ground or on rock, mainly in temperate zones. *B. rufus* and *B. roseus* (*Fig. 272*) grow on peaty soil or damp rock in Britain; the first species is fairly frequent, the second is rare.

The genus *Cladonia* comprises some 280 species, mostly growing on the ground, and more rarely on wood or stone, throughout the world. The podetia may be columnar and unbranched, flask-shaped, or bushy. The asci, bearing 6–8 spores each, may be club-shaped or cylindrical; the spores are colourless, oval, straight or spindle-shaped, and mostly unicellular. Pl. *79*, p. *194*, depicts *C. rangiferina* which, with its relatives, *C. sylvatica* and *C. alpestris*, covers wide stretches of the tundra with a green carpet, supplying reindeer herds with their winter fodder. *C. coccifera* (Pl. *78*, p. *193*) has glorious scarlet apothecia at the edge of the flask-shaped podetia. *C. digitata* (Pl. *80*, p. *194*) is a cosmopolitan species with prominent

Fig. 272 *Baeomyces roseus*

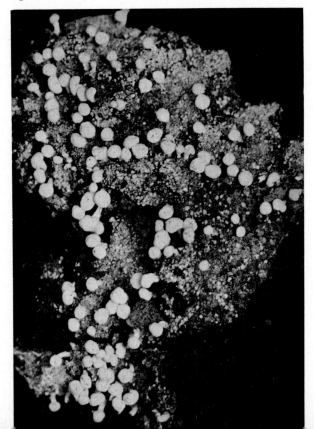

Fig. 274 *Cladonia pyxidata*

shaped spores, built up of 4 or more cells. *S. alpinum* forms whitish to reddish-grey matted cushions on mountain rocks.

Order

LECANORALES

The Lecanorales, like the Lecideales, are inhabited by *Protococcus* algae, though, in their case, the algae also occur at the edge of the apothecia.

The family Umbilicariaceae includes species with leaf-like and bushy thalli, attached to the substrate by their middle. The apothecia are borne on the surface of the thalli; each ascus produces 1–8 colourless or dark, unicellular or multicellular spores. The genus *Umbilicaria* (6 species) ranges from temperate latitudes to the Arctic. *Pl. 87, p. 196*, depicts the leathery thalli of *U. arctica*; it resembles *U. cylindrica*, which is abundant on mountains in Wales and Scotland. This family also includes the genus *Gyrophora* with some 35 species on rocks in cold and temperate zones. *G. esculenta*, iwatake-lichen, is eaten in Japan.

Members of the family Acarosporaceae have poorly developed, crust-shaped, scaly or leaf-like thalli devoid of rhizinae; their cortex is missing or rudimentary. The apothecia are borne on the surface of the thallus or else embedded in warts within it. The asci produce numerous very small, unicellular spores. *Pl. 85, p. 196*, depicts *Acarospora chlorophana*.

The Pertusariaceae are a family of lichens with crust-like thalli firmly attached to the substrate. They have a very thin cortex (or no cortex at all); the apothecia are embedded singly or in groups in warts in the thallus; the asci produce one to eight generally

scales. *C. pyxidata* (*Fig. 274*) has a finely serrated cup, and grows in limy places.

In the genus *Stereocaulon*, whose 80 species grow on rock and on the ground throughout the world, both the flat, crust-like base of the thalli and the bushy podetia may be grainy, warty or scaly; the brown or black apothecia contain club-shaped asci, each bearing 6–8 colourless, spindle- or needle-

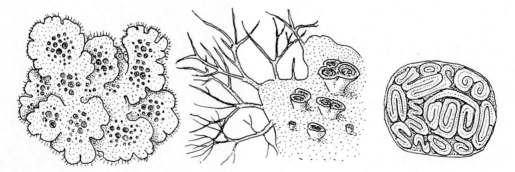

Fig. 275 *Gyrophora cylindrica*. Left: thallus (natural size); centre: part of thallus margin (slightly magnified); right: apothecium, seen from the top (more highly magnified)

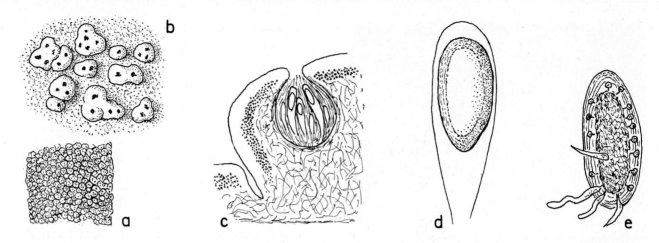

Fig. 276 *Pertusaria communis. a:* Thallus (natural size); *b:* part of thallus (slightly magnified); *c:* section of apothecium (magnified); *d:* ascus (highly magnified); *e:* germinating spore (highly magnified)

large, colourless, less often brownish, thick-walled spores. The cosmopolitan genus *Pertusaria* (200 species) is found on bark, rock or moss. *P. communis* (*Fig. 276*) occurs throughout Europe; *P. bryontha* causes damage to moss.

More than 1000 cosmopolitan species, growing on every possible substrate available to lichens, are included in the genus *Lecanora* to which the whole order owes its name. Their thalli are mostly crustaceous, generally without marginal lobes or scales, and devoid of rhizinae. A cortex may or may not be present. The round apothecia are embedded in the thallus or sessile upon it; the asci bear 8–32 colourless, rarely brown spores. *L. subfusca* (*Pl. 89, p. 197*), which is common on the bark of deciduous trees, has brown apothecia with a white margin. *L. esculenta*, and its relatives *L. fruticulosa* and *L. affinis*, have already been mentioned in connection with manna (see p. 215). Some 20 species are included in the genus *Haematomma*, which has scarlet to brown apothecia. *H. coccineum*, with blood-red fruiting bodies on a yellow thallus, lives on the bark of deciduous trees or on granite; *Pl. 88, p. 197*, depicts *H. venosum*, which has brown apothecia.

Foliose and fruticose, procumbent or erect thalli are found in the family Parmeliaceae, whose thalli are generally provided with rhizinae. A cortex is invariably present on the upper, and sometimes on the lower surface as well. The round apothecia are sessile or have a short stalk; each ascus gives rise to 6–8, more rarely to 16–32, colourless and unicellular

spores. Some 400 species growing on all sorts of substrates make up the cosmopolitan genus *Parmelia*. *P. physodes* (*Fig. 277*) is one of the commonest lichens of Europe (and of a large part of the rest of the world as well); it occurs in a variety of forms, but is readily identified by its glistening, somewhat crinkled, brown under-surface and its somewhat swollen lobe margins. *P. saxatilis* (*Pl. 92, p. 199*), whose lobes are cross-ribbed, grows on bark, wood and rock; in *P. centrifuga* (*Pl. 94, p. 199*), the centre of the thallus

Fig. 277 *Parmelia physodes*

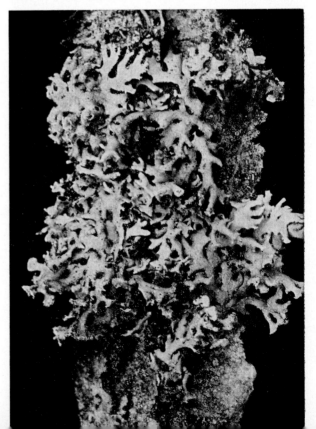

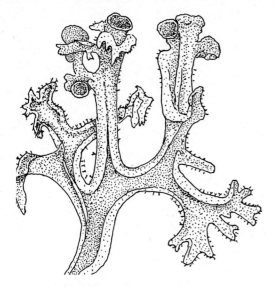

Fig. 278 *Cetraria islandica*, Iceland moss (approx. natural size)

commonly dies off. We saw that *Cetraria islandica*, Iceland moss, whose bushy and erect thalli, up to 2 ins. high, are common in dry woods, on heaths, on the tundra and in high mountains, is the source of a cough medicine. The same genus includes another 50 or so species, mainly in cold and temperate zones; they generally grow on the ground, wood or bark and more rarely on rock. Their shield-shaped apothecia are marginal; each ascus produces 6–8 colourless, unicellular, elliptical to spherical spores.

Family

Usneaceae

Anyone who walks observantly through a pine forest will notice the many pendant beards, thongs and bushes representing the thalli of members of this family – on the ground, on rock, or on the bark of trees. In addition, the family also includes a number of erect and shrubby species. All are attached to the substrate by rhizinae or by adhesive disks. A cortex is invariably present. The phycobionts (*Protococcus*) are scattered or organized into a closed layer beneath the cortex. The disk-like apothecia are sessile or have a very short stalk; the asci form 1–8 colourless, rarely brown, uni- or multicellular spores.

In the genus *Evernia*, the pendant thalli are 1–4 ins. long, flattened and narrow. Of the two species common in temperate zones, *E. prunastri*, which grows on the bark of trees and shrubs, yields the French perfume known as *mousse des chênes*.

In the genus *Ramalina*, the 3-in. thalli are narrow, tufted, and generally flaccid and pendant. The 100 cosmopolitan species constituting this genus live on coniferous and deciduous trees and shrubs. *R. farinacea*, whose forked branches may be up to 1 in. wide, lives on all kinds of wood; *R. fraxinea* is found on deciduous trees.

Fine, hair-like thalli are found in the genus *Alectoria* (= *Bryopogon*). One of its 20 species, *A. jubata*, is common in Britain, forming tangled masses of hair-like strands up to 8 ins. in length on trees and posts, and less commonly on the ground, in mountainous areas.

The genus *Usnea*, beard lichens, is easily recognized by its richly branched filamentous, bluish-green, grey or yellow, erect or drooping thalli. The large, oval apothecia, which generally bear bristles at the margin, arise from the forks of the branches. The 100 or so cosmopolitan species comprising this genus grow mainly on the bark of trees and very rarely on rock. *U. florida*, which is common in Britain, has a fairly rigid thallus; *U. longissima* (*Pl. 91, p. 198*), which prefers cold and temperate zones, may form beards many feet long. *U. canariensis* (*Pl. 93, p. 199*) grows on the bark of cork-trees in the Canaries. *U. hirta* is the source of the bacteriostatic substance mentioned

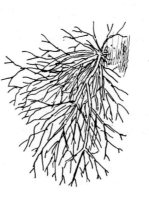

Fig. 279 *Evernia prunastri*. Bottom: thallus (natural size); top: branches (slightly magnified)

223

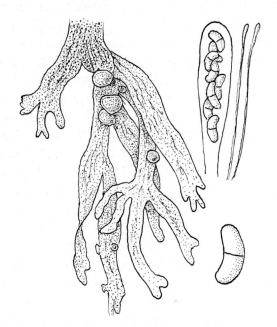

Fig. 280 *Ramalina fraxinea*. Left: thallus branch (approx. natural size); top right: ascus and paraphyses (highly magnified); lower right: spore (very highly magnified)

on p. 216. This family also includes the thong-shaped genus *Letharia*. *L. divaricata* has grey to greenish-white tangled beards up to 10 ins. in length that hang down from the crowns of coniferous trees. *L. vulpina*, the only poisonous species in Europe, grows in coniferous woods in the Arctic and High Alps.

Order
CALOPLACALES

This order has a characteristic spore structure: the 2 (sometimes 4) cells of the thick-walled spores are not squashed together, as they are in other orders, but move towards the poles, either leaving an empty space between them (*Xanthoria*-type) or else joined together by a thin isthmus (*Caloplaca*-type). The phycobionts are *Protococcus* algae.

In the family Theloschistaceae, the bright-yellow, lobed or bushy thalli are attached to the substrate by means of an adhesive pad or by rhizinae. A cortex is invariably present. The round, sessile apothecia appear on the surface of the thallus or on the margin on its lobes. Each ascus forms 8 colourless spores, their 2–6 cells joined by an isthmus. In the genus *Theloschistes*, with 12 species throughout the

world, the bushy thalli have flat branches. *Xanthoria parietina* (*Pl. 95, p. 200*) is one of the commonest lichens in Britain; its yellow, rosette-like thalli have distinct foliose lobes, procumbent or erect, 1–4 ins. wide, and are attached to the substrate by rhizinae. This lichen grows on rocks, roof-tops, trees and fences. The coarsely notched, orange apothecia, measuring 1–5 mm. across, appear near the centre of the thalli.

The family Buelliaceae has crustaceous or scaly thalli, sometimes with a lobate margin, and generally without a cortex. The round apothecia are embedded or sessile; the asci contain 8 spores each. The cosmopolitan genus *Buellia* comprises some 200 crustaceous species on wood, bark, rock, moss and dead plant remains. *Fig. 281 (top)* depicts *B. pulchella*; the British *B. canescens*, which grows on trees and walls throughout the country, has small, black apothecia. The genus *Caloplaca*, with some 100 species throughout the world, is sometimes treated as a separate family, the Caloplacaceae. Their procumbent, generally yellow thalli have a lobate or notched margin. *C. murorum* is lemon to yolk-coloured and its thalli have a cracked centre. This species is nitrogen-loving, and grows on walls and plaster; for the same reason, the bright orange, star-shaped thalli of *C. elegans* are often found on the nests of birds and mammals in the mountains. *Pl. 97, p. 200*, depicts *C. bracteata*, which grows on weathered limestone, calcareous soils and gypsum in temperate latitudes.

The family Physciaceae includes a number of leaf-shaped or shrubby forms attached to or raised up from the substrate by means of rhizinae. The apothecia appear on the thallus and contain 8-spored asci. The genus *Physcia*, with more than 50 species on various substrates throughout the world, generally forms rosette-shaped thalli close to the substrate. The apothecia are brown to black, the bicellular spores brown and elongated to elliptical. *P. aipolia* is greyish on top and dark underneath; it grows on deciduous trees at all altitudes. *P. caesia*, which is abundant on a wide range of substrates, is lead-grey in colour. The genus *Anaptychia* (10 species) has leaf-shaped or shrubby, richly lobed or branched, procumbent or slightly erect thalli, growing mostly on bark, and less commonly on rock throughout the world. The lobes have long, marginal, hair-like processes; the notched apothecia are borne on the surface of the thalli or in the forks of the branches. Each ascus produces 8 bicellular, elliptical to straight, brown spores. *A. ciliaris*, which is easily identified by its black marginal hairs, grows on rocks and trees by the sea in Britain. It does not creep close to the substrate, but has an ascending habit.

Class

BASIDIOLICHENES

This class differs from the preceding in that its mycobionts are no longer Ascomycetes but Basidiomycetes in the family Corticiaceae (see p. 155), and the phycobionts blue-green algae in the genera *Chroococcus* and *Scytonema*. The algae occupy a layer beneath the surface of the foliose, scaly or crustaceous thallus. The lower surface is lined with hymenium consisting of basidia and paraphyses. Each basidium bears 4 spores on short sterigmata. This class, which comprises only a very few species, is entirely restricted to the tropics.

The best-known genus, *Cora*, includes *C. pavonia*, the peacock lichen, shown in *Pl. 96, p. 200*. All the 8 known species of *Cora* have kidney-shaped to circular, rosette-like and foliose thalli, which generally grow on trees but occasionally on the ground. They are attached to the substrate by bundles of marginal rhizinae so that they generally stick out like so many brackets. The upper surface of the thallus is marked with concentric grooves. The hymenium is found on the lower surface of the lobes and takes the form of cracked, brightly-coloured layers or of separate islands. The unicellular spores are colourless. Bracket-shaped thalli are also found in the genus *Dictyonema*, which grows on trees or between mosses.

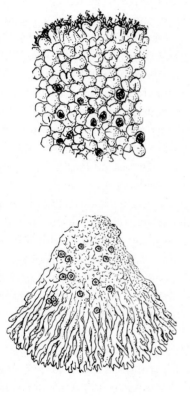

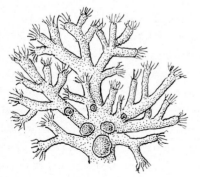

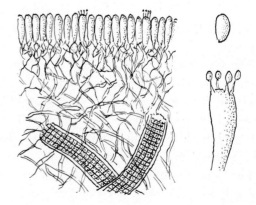

Fig. 281 *Buellia pulchella* (slightly magnified); *Physica caesia* (natural size); and *Anaptychia ciliaris* (natural size)

Fig. 282 *Dictyonema sericeum*. Section through thallus undersurface (magnified); right: basidium (highly magnified), and above it a spore (very highly magnified)

225

7 BRYOPHYTA
Liverworts and Mosses

With the liverworts and mosses, we leave that large group of plants known as the Thallophyta. True, the Bryophyta, too, include a number of forms whose plant bodies are constructed on the thallus pattern, but the more highly developed types bear some resemblance to flowering plants: their plant body generally consists of a slender stem and delicate leaves, generally no more than one cell-layer in thickness. However, they differ from plants in being devoid of roots. Instead they form rootlike organs in the shape of small filaments, the so-called rhizoids. These have a very simple structure and, unlike true roots, merely serve to anchor the plant to its substrate. (In mosses, the main function of roots, i.e. the absorption of water and salts from the soil, is taken over by the entire plant surface.) The evolutionary progress of the Bryophyta towards the higher plants is also reflected in a number of other characteristics. Thus cellulose is invariably present in their cell walls, and their chlorophyll has the same chemical composition as that of higher plants.

The most important innovation, however, is in the reproductive sphere. With the Bryophyta, we meet our first plants having multicellular sex cells: their archegonium is a multicellular flask-shaped organ; it consists of an enlarged basal portion, the venter, and a slender elongated portion, the neck. The cavity of the neck and venter contains a single row of cells, the lowest and largest of which is the egg cell.

The male organs, or antheridia, also differ from those of Thallophyta. Their walls, one cell thick, enclose the tissue from which the spermatozoids arise. These, discharged from the antheridia on reaching maturity, are filamentous and have two long flagella, which help them to swim in the water.

The formation of a zygote by the fusion of sperm and egg cell gives rise to a sporophyte plant. The life cycle of Bryophyta thus involves the alternation of a sexual generation and an asexual generation. However, whereas each of these generations is an independent plant in most algae, the asexually produced form of Bryophyta develops on the sexual form and remains associated with it throughout its life.

The life cycle of every Bryophyte begins with a spore. It is unicellular, contains chlorophyll grains in its protoplasm, and is enclosed in a double wall. The inner wall, or endosporium, is thin and contains no pigments; the outer wall, or exosporium, is tough and brown. On germination, the spore absorbs water and swells, whereupon the exosporium bursts and the endosporium protrudes in the form of a short tube. The spore then germinates into a filamentous and highly branched little green plant with a thallose structure, greatly resembling a filamentous alga. This is the so-called protonema.

The protonema, which grows by division of its apical cells, slowly creeps across the substrate, to which it clings by means of rhizoids, threads of elongated cells devoid of chlorophyll. The septa inside each protonema are diagonal to the long axis of the filament, a characteristic that is extremely rare in the plant kingdom and that helps in the identification of Bryophyta. Protonemata may multiply vegetatively; each of their filaments is capable of producing a complete thallus. In addition, the ends of the threads occasionally bear small rounded 'buds', which may break free and germinate into new protonemata.

The protonema concludes its history with the formation of lateral buds, from which the leafy moss plants develop. These may grow in loose bunches or squashed together into cushions, and represent the sexual or gametophyte generation. The sexual organs are borne separately on the tip of their leafy shoots or, in the case of some thallose Bryophyta, they are combined into special organs. Some mosses are dioecious; in others the male and female reproductive organs are borne on separate plants.

Once the sexual cells are mature, fertilization can take place, but only on condition that the plants have

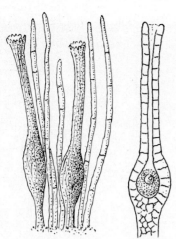

Fig. 283 *Mnium*. Left: archegonia and paraphyses (magnified); right: longitudinal section through archegonium (more highly magnified)

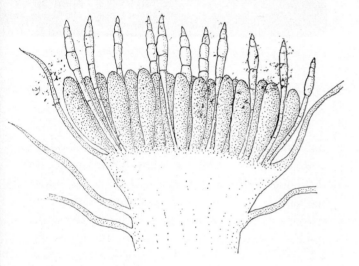

Fig. 284 Tip of *Mnium hornum* with antheridia and paraphyses (magnified)

Fig. 286 *Dawsonia polytrichoides*. Left: plant with spore capsules (natural size); right: leaf (slightly magnified)

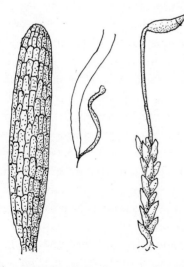

Fig. 285 Right: moss plant with spore capsule; left: antheridium (magnified); centre: spermatozoid (highly magnified)

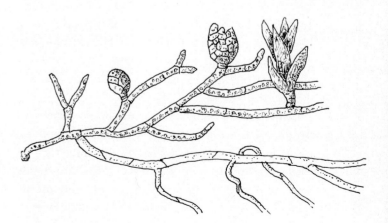

Fig. 287 Protonema of moss with buds and young plants (magnified)

227

been moistened by rain or dew – the spermatozoids can only move in water.

During fertilization, the mouth of the archegonium widens, the neck cells degenerate into mucilaginous material and release chemical substances that attract the spermatozoids. Once one of these (haploid) swarmers comes close enough to the (haploid) archegonium, it enters through the neck and fuses with the egg cell. The diploid zygote immediately undergoes repeated divisions that finally lead to the formation of the embryo.

The embryo, in its turn, gives rise to the spore-forming organ or sporogonium. It is diploid and represents the asexual or sporophyte generation of the Bryophyta. The basal part of the embryo pushes through the venter of the archegonium into the underlying tissue of the gametophyte, to which it becomes anchored by its foot. This is not only an organ of attachment but also acts as a sucker through which the sporophyte, which is unable to fend for itself, can derive nourishment from the green moss plant. The sporophyte may therefore be called a parasite, albeit one that does not cause its 'host' any serious damage.

The upper part of the embryo bears the sporogonium which, in its mature stage, is divided into a stalk or seta, and a cylindrical spore-producing capsule. During their formation, the spores undergo reduction division, with the result that they have the haploid number of chromosomes. As soon as they are ripe, they leave the capsule, eventually germinate, and found a new, haploid gametophyte generation by way of protonemata. Usually, the adult gametophytes are only a few centimetres or even millimetres in height, but in a small number of tropical species, they may grow very much taller. The extreme case is the Australasian genus *Dawsonia* (order Polytrichales, family Dawsoniaceae) which can attain a height of up to 18 ins.

Although Bryophyta occur in almost every part of the earth, hardly any of them are cosmopolitan: most species are restricted to very definite regions. Moreover, the sites on which they grow are highly specific as well. With the exception of a few mosses that occur on swamps, in bogs, on water or even under water, mosses generally prefer dry land, albeit they require a certain degree of moisture. At the

Fig. 288 Spore capsules of *Polytrichum formosum*

other extreme are a few species that have become adapted to surviving prolonged periods of drought.

Although mosses grow in fairly large concentrations, they play a relatively small part in the earth's vegetative cover. Only in a few isolated places do they outweigh other plants enough to dominate the landscape. Thus *Sphagnum* forms dense spongy masses on bogs; other genera help to carpet the tundra; others again grow in profusion in the so-called mist forests, where they not only cover the ground but hang down from trees and branches in the form of thick veils or garlands. Moreover, though mosses do not play a predominant role in the vegetation of most of the world, they are nevertheless essential agents of natural equilibrium, preventing desiccation of the forest floor by retaining rain water in their thick, far-flung cushions of green.

The phylogenetic history of Bryophyta is still largely unknown. It seems likely that the ancestors of modern mosses were various groups of primitive plants; in any case, there is no evidence that they are descended from any specific group. On the other hand, the geological age of mosses is known with some degree of accuracy: fossil forms go back to the Carboniferous.

Taxonomists divide the Bryophyta into two distinct classes: the Hepaticae or Liverworts, and the Musci or Mosses.

HEPATICAE

Liverworts

The liverworts are considered to be the more 'primitive', i.e. the more original, class of the two. This view is corroborated by a number of characteristics, chief among them the relatively simple structure of their gametophyte generation. The gametophyte, which develops from a small and fairly undifferentiated protonema, takes a thallose form in a few species, and is more or less procumbent. In the great majority, however, the plant body is leaf-like, and bears an external resemblance to true mosses. The leaves, which are built up of a single layer of cells, are normally quite flat; only in a small number of species do they have a midrib, which, by contrast, is present in most mosses. The leaves grow by division of an apical cell; the division takes place in one direction only. The rhizoids consist of a single elongated cell. Many liverworts are capable of storing water for long periods. Most of them have oil bodies in their cells; these contain droplets of aromatic oil of a kind not found in any other groups of plants.

The sexual organs of thallose liverworts are embedded in the tissue of the gametophyte, those of foliose species are more or less free-standing. The antheridia are spherical or oval structures with a small stalk. The mature spermatozoids are provided with two flagella each. They respond to proteins released during the disintegration of the neck cells, and are thus led to the mature egg cells in the venters of the archegonia.

The sporogonium, which develops from the fertilized egg cell, remains inside the growing archegonium during much of its development; only when the spore capsule is nearly full-grown does the stalk begin to elongate, whereupon the sporogonium pierces the wall of the archegonium and breaks out. However, the archegonium does not shrivel up, but continues to act as a sheath round the base of the sporogonium stalk. In a few liverworts, the capsule remains inside the archegonium throughout its life.

In general, the sporophyte of liverworts is considerably smaller than the gametophyte. The spore capsule is filled with a multicellular tissue that gives rise to spore mother cells and associated structures that develop into elaters, elongated structures with spiral thickenings on their walls; they are capable of executing hygroscopic movements and thus facilitate the dissemination of the spores. At maturity, the spore capsules split longitudinally, and generally open by 4 valves. Some liverworts are capable of vegetative reproduction: on the upper side of their thalli there arise small cups, which give rise to small disk-shaped bodies, known as gemmae, each consisting of a number of cells, mostly green. The gemmae separate readily from the base of the cup and each of them may grow into a gametophyte.

Liverworts enjoy a world-wide distribution, but generally prefer moist sites. Their role in the flora of past geological periods cannot be determined – fossil finds are few and far between. However, we do know that liverworts resembling modern species were in existence as far back as the Carboniferous.

Thallose liverworts are divided into three orders: the Sphaerocarpales, Marchantiales and Metzgeriales.

Order

SPHAEROCARPALES

This order comprises two families of minute plants. In the Sphaerocarpaceae, the gametophyte occurs in two forms, one bearing the archegonia, and the other the antheridia. The second family, the Riellaceae, consists of aquatic plants. The most striking features of Sphaerocarpales are their sexual organs; these are invariably surrounded by large, flask-shaped involucres.

Family

Sphaerocarpaceae

The Sphaerocarpaceae consist of only the one genus, *Sphaerocarpus*, with a few species in Europe and America. The sexual generation appears in the form of small, flat, and sometimes forking, thalli. With the exception of the broad midrib, built up of several superposed layers of cells, the thalli have an extremely simple structure and are in no way differentiated. They lie flat on the substrate, to which they are attached by means of unicellular rhizoids, devoid of chlorophyll. Male and female thalli are easily distinguished. The male are considerably smaller, and, moreover, have a purple sheen. Antheridia and archegonia alike are enclosed in large involucres. The sporophyte takes the form of an unstalked spore capsule which develops within the archegonium. The tissue of the spore capsule becomes differentiated into spore mother cells and a second type of cell, carrying chlorophyll, and supplying the maturing spores with food. Of the 4 spores to which each mother cell gives rise, two germinate into male and two into female thalli.

Family
Riellaceae

This family, too, is represented by only one genus, *Riella*, which, however, comprises a relatively large number of species. Riellaceae are typical water plants, and occur at the bottom of ponds, pools, etc. The gametophyte, which bears both archegonia and antheridia, has an erect axis that is flattened into a wing-like structure on one side. The axis is covered with small scales, often interspersed with gemmae. The wing of the thallus bears the sexual organs. The antheridia lie close to notches near the edge; the archegonia are found in a row along the point of attachment of the wing. The sporophyte resembles that of *Sphaerocarpus*. The genus *Riella* (17 species) occurs in Europe, Asia, South Africa and North America.

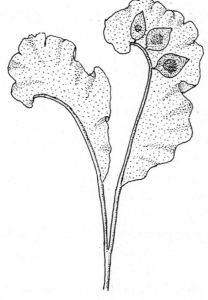

Fig. 289 *Riella americana* (slightly magnified)

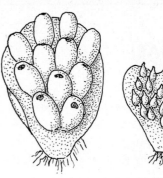

Fig. 290 *Sphaerocarpus californicus*. Left: female plant; right: male plant (both slightly magnified)

Order
MARCHANTIALES

This order includes a number of fairly common liverworts. Marchantiales are largely terrestrial plants, but prefer moist habitats. The gametophyte has a band-shaped thallus, regularly forked, and closely attached to the substrate. The under-surface is covered in scales and rhizoids. The thallus is composed of several tiers of cells, whose structure differs markedly. The surface is riddled with air chambers, each opening by means of a pore. The sexual organs are devoid of involucres. In some species, they are combined into special structures borne on a vertical stalk. The sporophyte generation is far less conspicuous than the gametophyte – in some species they even lack a stalk.

Family
Ricciaceae

The only genus in this family, *Riccia*, comprises close on 130 species throughout the world. All Ricciaceae are moisture-loving plants. Some species, including the common *R. fluitans* (*Pl. 98, p. 201*), occur in two forms, one free-floating, the other submerged on the bottom of ponds. The gametophyte of *Riccia* is a flat, regularly forking thallus. In most species, the thallus lobes form an extensive rosette, for instance in *R. glauca*, perhaps the commonest British species. The various thallus segments are more or less band-shaped and have a prominent midrib. The layer nearest the substrate consists of colourless cells. On top of it lies a spongy tissue of chlorophyll-bearing cells studded with elongated air chambers. The surface layer, one cell thick, is broken by pores. The lower surface is covered in scales and rhizoids. The edges of the thallus lobes curl upwards to form a fold in which the sexual organs can safely develop. In most species of *Riccia*, the archegonia and antheridia occur on one and the same thallus; in a few others the gametophyte generation is divided into distinct male and female plants.

The fertilized egg cell develops into an unstalked spore capsule within the archegonium. As in Sphaerocarpales, the spores of Ricciaceae are associated with nutritive cells. Each mother cell produces 4 spores which remain together until they are nearly mature (tetrads); even at maturity, they are not immediately released from their capsule, but must wait until the surrounding tissue has decomposed, a process that may take a whole year.

Family

Marchantiaceae

The Marchantiaceae, a family of 4 genera, is represented in Britain by *Marchantia polymorpha* (*Fig. 291*). All Marchantiaceae have flat, richly-branching

thalli, divided into band-shaped lobes. The lobes are densely studded with scales and attached to the substrate by means of smooth or tuberculate rhizoids.

The upper surface of the thallus is divided into diamond-shaped fields, caused by the presence of air chambers, which are sometimes several layers thick. Every air chamber opens by means of an aperture. A transverse section through the thallus will show that these apertures are not simple pores, but barrel-shaped channels lined by regular tiers of cells. From the bottom of the air chambers numerous branched or unbranched filaments rise up, their cells filled with chloroplasts. These represent the assimilation tissue of the thallus, and are called assimilators. Beneath the air chambers lies the colourless tissue constituting the under-surface of the thallus; some of its cells contain oil bodies; others are filled with mucus.

The thallus, which is procumbent, bears umbrella-shaped organs divided into small lobes and supported on erect stalks; their lower surface is covered with archegonia. These 'umbrellas' are the most characteristic feature of the entire family. In the genus *Marchantia*, the antheridia, too, are borne on

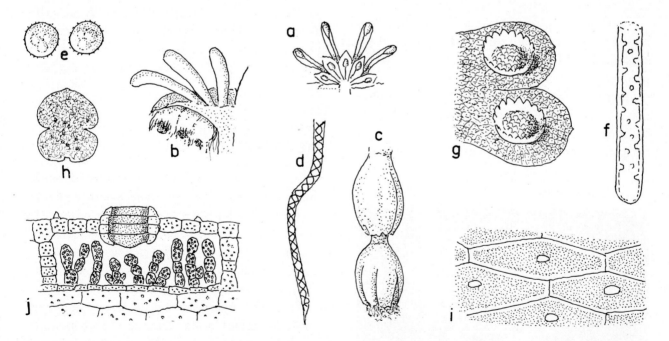

Fig. 291 *Marchantia polymorpha. a:* Part of female 'umbrella' seen from below (slightly magnified); *b:* section of female umbrella with spore capsules (more highly magnified); *c:* expanding spore capsule (more highly magnified); *d:* fragment of elater (highly magnified); *e:* spores (highly magnified); *f:* tip of rhizoid (highly magnified); *g:* thallus lobes with two cups and gemmae (slightly magnified); *h:* individual gemma (highly magnified); *i:* surface of thallus showing diamond-shaped fields and central pores; *j:* cross-section of air chamber (highly magnified)

231

Fig. 292 *Marchantia polymorpha*. Centre: thallus bearing antheridial receptacle; left: longitudinal section through antheridial receptacle (slightly magnified); right: thallus bearing archegonial receptacles (slightly magnified)

stalked structures, the so-called antheridial receptacles. They resemble the archegonical receptacles, but have a broader 'umbrella' with shorter lobes. In all other Marchantiaceae, the antheridia are embedded in the surface tissue of the thallus, often in groups and in sharply defined zones only.

Some species are monoecious; in the majority, however, both sexes are combined on one and the same thallus. After fertilization of the egg cell, the sporogonium grows in step with the basal part of the archegonium, which provides it with a protective cover. The spore capsule is anchored to the umbrella tissue with a short stalk; at maturity, the stalk elongates and the capsule is pushed out. The sporo-

Fig. 293 *Marchantia paleacea*

genous tissue inside the capsule gives rise to spores together with elaters (see p. 229). Marchantiaceae also reproduce vegetatively by means of gemmae.

The most important genus in this family, *Marchantia*, is represented by some 60 species throughout the world; their discoid gemmae arise at the bottom of flat cups with a serrated edge. *M. paleacea* (Fig. 293) occurs in Italy; *M. polymorpha* (Pl. 99, p. 201) is common on moist brickwork, on damp moorland, and by streams.

Very similar in habit is *Conocephalum*, which owes its Latin name to its conical archegonial receptacles. Its thallus differs from that of *Marchantia* in that the channels of its large air chambers protrude a fair way above the surface. In Britain, this genus is represented by *C. conicum* (Fig. 294), which is common on wet rocks in a large variety of habitats.

In the genus *Lunularia*, the gemmae are crescent-shaped and not discoid as in *Marchantia*. The archegonial 'umbrellas' generally have four lobes. *L. cruciata* is often a troublesome weed on flowerpots and moist brickwork in gardens.

In the genus *Reboulia*, the thallus is honeycombed with air spaces. Moreover, assimilation is not by assimilators but by the cells forming the walls of the air chambers. The archegonial 'umbrellas' generally have 5 lobes; the antheridia lie embedded in crescent-shaped thallus processes. *R. hemisphaerica* is very common in limestone crevices in the west Yorkshire hills.

Order
METZGERIALES

The gametophytes of this order generally resemble those of the Marchantiales. The thallus is divided into individual lobes which cling to the substrate by means of rhizoids. The inner tissue is undifferentiated, except in *Metzgeria*, whose thallus lobes have a prominent midrib which probably conducts water, and consists of thick-walled cells.

The sexual organs arise on the side or upper surface of the thallus. A number of species are monoecious. The sporophytes of Metzgeriales are much more conspicuous than those of Marchantiales, because the spore capsules are borne on relatively long seta. They produce spores as well as elaters, some of

Fig. 294 *Conocephalum conicum* (slightly magnified)

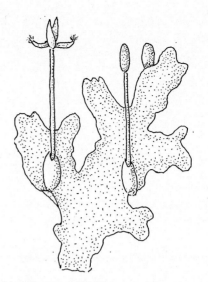

Fig. 295 *Riccardia pinguis* (slightly magnified)

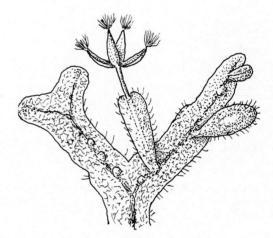

Fig. 296 *Metzgeria conjugata* (slightly magnified)

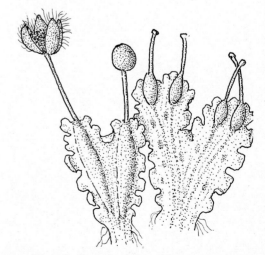

Fig. 297 *Blasia pusilla.* Left: thallus with spore capsule (slightly magnified); right: thallus with flask-shaped organs containing gemmae (slightly magnified)

which remain attached to the tip of the capsule. At maturity, the capsule opens by 4 valves, each crowned with a tuft of elaters. This arrangement is typical of all Metzgeriales, with the exception of the genus *Pellia* (Family: Haplolaenaceae) where the remaining elaters are attached to the base and not to the top of the capsule.

The Metzgeriales are found throughout the world, and three of its four families are at home in Britain.

The Aneuraceae include the genus *Riccardia*, comprising altogether some 250 species. Their thalli are completely flat. Another characteristic feature is the presence of a calyptra, which develops from the archegonium and acts as a fleshy cover for the young sporophyte and remains as a collar round the foot of the elongated seta. *R. pinguis* grows on a wide range of habitats with moist surfaces throughout Britain.

The Metzgeriaceae form band-shaped, irregularly forked thalli, covered with bristles along the edge and also along the prominent midrib. The spore capsules bear dense bunches of elaters. The best-known British species, *M. furcata* and *M. conjugata*, live on rock, and on the bark and trunk of deciduous trees respectively.

The family Haplolaenaceae comprises the genera

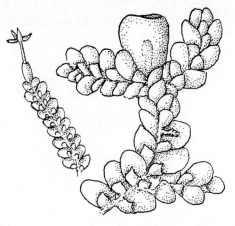

Fig. 298 *Radula complanata*. Left: part of plant with spore capsule (natural size); right: part of plant with 'perianth' (slightly magnified)

Fig. 299 *Trichocolea tomentella*; thallus (slightly magnified)

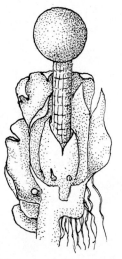

Fig. 300 *Nardia geoscypha*; top of stem with anterior leaf removed (slightly magnified)

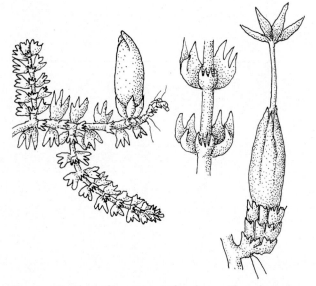

Fig. 301 *Lepidozia filamentosa*. Left: plant with archegonium surrounded by perianth (slightly magnified); right: spore capsule emerging from perianth (more highly magnified); centre: part of stem

Blasia and *Pellia*, both with broad thalli and prominent lateral lobes. Those of *Blasia* often bear flask-shaped organs enclosing gemmae. In *Pellia*, the archegonia are surrounded by a protective sheath which is pierced by the growing sporophytes. Since the sheath as well as the archegonial wall persists, the foot of the elongated seta becomes enveloped in a double collar.

Order
JUNGERMANNIALES

The liverworts in this order are very easily mistaken for mosses, chiefly because their gametophyte has a foliose plant body, divided into a stem-like axis and leaf-like appendages. The stems, which are often richly branching, but rarely of the forking type, are densely covered in leaves, generally arranged in three ranks, two of which grow laterally on either side of the stem. In many species they are so closely crowded together that their upper and lower margins overlap. They are mostly divided into two lobes, whose shape and size may differ considerably. The most marked differences in the size of the lobes are found in the genera *Radula*, *Porella*, *Frullania* and *Lejeunea*, where the larger lobes are so folded as to cover the smaller completely. In some other genera, the lateral leaves are split up into more than two lobes or into numerous threads (e.g. in *Trichocolea*). The third rank consists of amphigastria or underleaves, and can only be seen if the surface of the thallus nearest the substrate is turned over: they are generally much smaller than the lateral leaves and often differ from them in shape. Amphigastria are not equally well developed in all Jungermanniales, and are completely missing in the genera *Jungermannia* and *Scapania*, and in the family Radulaceae. Their place is taken by rhizoids, which are lacking in most other Jungermanniales. The lateral leaves as well as amphigastria are flat and generally have a simple structure. The stem, too, is generally undifferentiated, except that the surface cells, which form a kind of cortex, are larger and more thick-walled than the rest. Like other liverworts, many Jungermanniales have oil bodies in several cells of their thalli.

Differences in the shape and size of the leaves apart, Jungermanniales exhibit a marked morphological

Fig. 302 *Ptilidium ciliare*

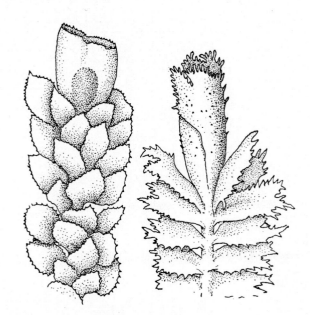

Fig. 303 Left: *Lophocolea liebmannia*, branch and perianth (slightly magnified); right: *Scapania nemorosa*, branch with perianth (slightly magnified)

unity, not only in the structure of their thalli, but particularly in that of their reproductive organs. The archegonia, and hence the sporophytes, are typically borne at the tips of the main stem or of the lateral branches. In most Jungermanniales, the uppermost leaves are fused into a sheath round the archegonium. This sheath, which is large and conspicuous, is sometimes referred to as a perianth. Its base is often surrounded by a wreath of ordinary leaves or bracts. This wreath persists and helps to protect the young sporophyte; it later swells up to form a collar round the lower part of the seta. The antheridia, too, are restricted to certain parts of the thallus; they are relatively inconspicuous and arise, singly or in groups, from the axils of certain leaves. Every antheridium is borne on a long stalk.

The gametophytes of Jungermanniales may be monoecious or dioecious. The sporophytes, which, as we saw, arise at the tip of the main stem or of the lateral branches, consist of an oval or spherical capsule and a long stalk. The capsule has a tough wall, built up of 2–6 layers of cells. It opens by means of 4 valves, and releases a large number of spores and elaters.

Many Jungermanniales multiply by means of gemmae; these are generally unicellular and borne on the leaves. In *Scapania* (*Fig. 303, right*) they occupy

the tips of the leaves; in other genera, including *Radula*, they occupy the leaf margin.

Vegetative reproduction is not, however, invariably bound up with the presence of gemmae, as witness the genus *Gymnocolea* (Family: Lophoziaceae) in which the perianth may break free and grow into a new plant.

Jungermanniales are terrestrial plants which, like all liverworts, prefer moist, shady habitats. Some species are, however, adapted to life under all sorts of conditions. Thus *Gymnocolea inflata* can live on very moist as well as on very arid spots.

The Jungermanniales are divided into more than 10 families, few of which comprise more than a few genera.

Though Jungermanniales are common in Britain, their thalli are so small and grow so close to the substrate that they are often overlooked. The most attractive forms are found among the Ptilidiaceae, a family which includes the genera *Ptilidium* and *Trichocolea*. *P. ciliare*, which is fairly common in Britain, has a much-branched leafy shoot; the lobes of each leaf are fringed with cilia, to which the genus owes its name. In *Trichocolea*, the leaves are divided into fine threads, so that the stem appears densely covered in hair.

Relatively large forms are found in the mainly

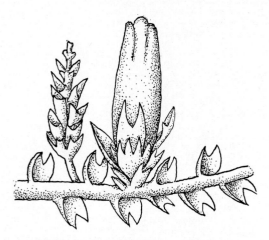

Fig. 304 *Cephalozia pleniceps* (slightly magnified)

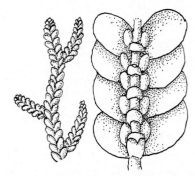

Fig. 305 *Porella platyphylla*. Left: partial view of plant (slightly magnified); right: part of branch seen from below (more highly magnified)

tropical family Lepidoziaceae, which comprises the genera *Lepidozia* and *Bazzania*. A characteristic feature of this family is the presence of flagella – whip-like lateral branches of unusual length.

In the genus *Lophocolea*, we find another peculiarity: here the lateral branches arise in the axils of the amphigastria.

As we mentioned earlier, some Jungermanniales have greatly reduced amphigastria. A case in point is the family Jungermanniaceae. Of its two constituent genera, *Jungermannia* and *Nardia*, only the second is provided with underleaves.

Even the Plagiochilaceae, the family with the largest number of species, has strongly reduced amphigastria. Its only genus, *Plagiochila*, includes the largest Jungermanniales of all. One tropical species has a thallus up to 1 ft. long and may thus be called a giant among liverworts. In Britain, *P. asplenioides* (*Pl. 102, p. 202*), one of 1200 species in its genus, is

one of the most widespread liverworts; it grows in moist places, including loamy banks in woods.

One of the strangest of all liverworts is *Cephalozia*, whose small, prostrate thallus is crowned by a gigantic perianth. The most robust of the three fairly common British species is *C. byssacea*; in *C. pleniceps* (*Fig. 304*) the perianths are borne on short lateral branches.

One group of families – the Radulaceae, Porellaceae, Frullaniaceae and Lejeuneaceae – is characterized by the presence of leaves of a most unusual kind. Seen from the top, these leaves seem entirely devoid of lobes; as we saw on p. 234, their two lobes differ very considerably in size and are, moreover, so folded that the smaller are hidden beneath the larger, which may be rounded (Porellaceae) or pointed (Frullaniaceae and Lejeuneaceae). The smaller lobes are scaly in the families Radulaceae and

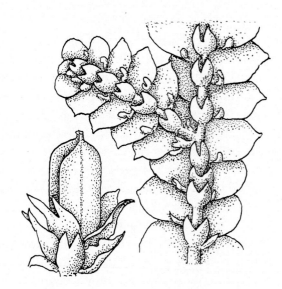

Fig. 306 *Frullania apiculata*. Right: part of plant seen from below (slightly magnified); left: perianth (slightly magnified)

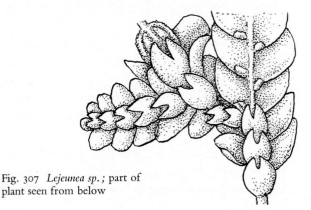

Fig. 307 *Lejeunea sp.*; part of plant seen from below

Porellaceae, and swollen up to form kidney-shaped water-sacs in the Lejeuneaceae and the Frullaniaceae, a chiefly tropical family with 4 species in Britain. The water-sacs of *Frullania* often contain colonies of wheel animalcules (Rotatoria).

Order
ANTHOCEROTALES

The Anthocerotales, which closely resemble other liverworts in habit, occupy a very special position among Bryophyta. To begin with, their cells contain chloroplasts provided not only with chlorophyll but also with pyrenoids, or starch-forming bodies, which we met among the green algae. Moreover, Anthocerotales differ from all other Bryophyta in that the sporophyte does not live as a 'parasite' on the gametophyte: the spore capsules contain chlorophyll and are therefore able to synthesize their own food.

The thallus of Anthocerotales tends to form a rosette, and is anchored to the substrate by a dense mat of rhizoids. Though built up of several cell layers, the thallus is in no way differentiated, except for the fact that cells in different layers have different numbers of chloroplasts: the surface cells contain a single large chloroplast each, the underlying cells 2–8 chloroplasts each. The tissue facing the substrate is, moreover, studded with mucilage cavities which are often filled with colonies of the blue-green alga, *Nostoc*.

The sexual organs are embedded in the upper surface of the thallus. The antheridia develop, singly or occasionally in groups, inside special cavities. The archegonia, on the other hand, show their necks above the thallus. Most Anthocerotales are dioecious.

The fertilized egg cell grows into a pod-shaped, sessile spore capsule. Its foot is surrounded by a small involucre, built up partly from the wall of the archegonium and partly from thallus tissue. At the base of the capsule, new cells are continuously split off, with the result that the capsule keeps growing in length. The capsule wall is several cells thick. In most Anthocerotales, the epidermis is broken by stomata at regular intervals; these small apertures are framed by two crescent-shaped cells whose structure corresponds to that of the guard cells of higher plants. The cells of the capsule wall contain two chloroplasts

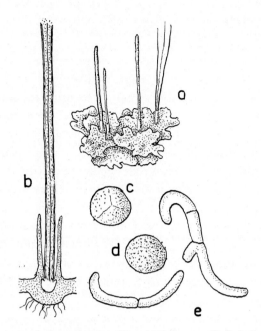

Fig. 308 *Anthoceros laevis. a*: Plant (slightly magnified); *b*: longitudinal section of spore capsule (more highly magnified); *c*: spore seen from above (highly magnified); *d*: side view of spore (highly magnified); *e*: pseudo-elaters (highly magnified)

each. From the tip to the base of the capsule runs a thin strand of sterile tissue, the columella. It is surrounded by sporogenous tissue which develops into spore mother cells together with sterile pseudo-elaters. The spores mature from the tip of the capsule downwards. The capsule opens by means of two small valves through which the persistent columella can be seen to protrude.

Anthocerotales also reproduce vegetatively, especially during unfavourable conditions. Certain marginal lobes of the thalli can swell up and surround themselves with a corky 'shell'. Even if the thallus should die, which can easily happen if the substrate dries out, the marginal lobes are able to survive within their tough wall. As soon as there is enough moisture again, they readily develop into new thalli.

The Anthocerotales form a tightly closed group among the Bryophyta, so much so that they are sometimes treated as a separate class, the Anthocerotae. Their only family, the Anthocerotaceae, consists of the one genus, *Anthoceros*. Among its few species, chiefly restricted to Europe and America, *A. laevis* and *A. punctatus* (*Pl. 104, p. 203*) flourish on damp clay banks and fallow fields in Britain.

MUSCI

Mosses

The Musci include a large number of variously shaped plants that form dense cushions on the forest floor, on rocks, walls and tree trunks, often dominating the vegetative picture of moors and mountain heaths. Though mosses are relatively small plants, they are generally crowded together so closely, often in habitats that other plants eschew, that they become highly conspicuous.

As in liverworts, the gametophyte generation is the dominant one; it represents what we commonly call the moss plant. Its foliose stems are reminiscent of those of higher plants, unlike which, however, mosses, too, are devoid of roots.

The gametophyte develops from a sizeable protonema that generally covers the ground with a web of green threads and is anchored to the substrate by means of colourless filaments. Each protonema gives rise to a large number of young moss plants whose pyramid-shaped apical cell divides in three directions. The resulting leaves are arranged in three rows along the stem, though occasionally we meet forms whose apical cell divides in two directions only; in that case the plants become pinnate.

The leaves of mosses have a thin-skinned blade and a more or less prominent midrib. While the blade is generally no more than one cell layer thick, the midrib consists of a multicellular strand with thick walls. In numerous mosses the leaf upper surface (and sometimes the leaf under-surface as well) bears countless 'assimilators', thin ridges whose cells are packed with chlorophyll grains. The stems of many mosses bear more than one type of leaf, arranged in 'storeys': the leaves nearest the base are scaly and almost completely devoid of pigment; next come the leaves proper which are responsible for assimilation and occupy the major part of the stem; at the tip, finally, there often appears a crown of leaves of a much more conspicuous colour than the rest.

While the leaves of mosses still have a very simple structure – they are known as microphylls, or small leaves – the stem suggests much greater progress in the direction of the higher plants. It is clearly divided into individual tissue complexes, each with a distinct structure and function. The periphery is made up of cells with thickened walls, and helps to support the plant. The centre generally contains a strand of elongated cells in which water and food-conducting elements can often be distinguished. True vascular bundles, as they occur in higher plants, are lacking in mosses, but mosses nevertheless provide us with our first example of plants having a water-conducting system.

The sexual organs also incorporate a number of innovations. They are arranged in groups, partly unisexual and partly bisexual, at the tip of the stem or of its lateral branches. They are always associated with the presence of sterile filaments, or paraphyses. Every group of sexual organs and paraphyses is surrounded by a ring of bracts. These may differ considerably in form and colour from ordinary leaves, and in many respects are reminiscent of the perianth of higher plants. For the rest, the sexual organs of mosses correspond largely with those of liverworts, both in structure and also in external appearance. The spermatozoids consist of a spiral cell body bearing two flagella. While their vegetative development has taken mosses out of the water – some species are adapted to life in very dry habitats – reproduction is still bound up with the presence of moisture. The spermatozoids are unable to move in dry media, hence fertilization generally takes place after rain or in the dew. In the film of moisture which then covers the plants, the spermatozoids, attracted by chemical substances (chiefly saccharose) released by the necks of the archegonia, swim towards the female receptacles. Those mosses in which the sexes are borne on separate plants release their spermatozoids in heavy rain; the splashing drops carry the male cells to the female plants. Although several archegonia of one and the same group are often fertilized, only one of them normally gives rise to a sporogonium.

The sporogonium is a more or less elongated capsule, anchored in the tissue of the gametophyte by means of a well-developed haustorium. The capsule has a very tough multicellular wall, and its centre is traversed by a columella of the kind we met in liverworts. The columella is surrounded by a closed spore sac in which the spores are produced. Below the spore sac and next to the seta lies a swelling, the apophysis, whose surface is covered in stomata; this organ is present in all mosses.

The growing spore capsule is often capped with a calyptra, a protective covering formed from the enlarged wall of the archegonium, which usually remains on the capsule until it is nearly ripe. The basal part of the archegonium is generally preserved as well and forms a torn sheath round the foot of the seta. The mature spore capsule of most mosses opens by means of a circular lid; beneath it lies the so-called peristome, a ring of sharp teeth that protrudes over the edge of the capsule mouth. The teeth consist of thick-walled cells, and are strongly hygroscopic: in dry weather they bend outwards, thus allowing the spores to pass out, and in moist weather they fold inwards and close over the mouth.

Mosses very often reproduce vegetatively by means of gemmae on the stem or leaves, which eventually break off to give rise to new moss plants. Broken branches and individual leaves, too, are capable of producing new plants. In addition, the stalk of the spore capsule and even fragments of it can develop into protonemata. The protonemata often bear gemmae in their turn. This great reproductive versatility helps to compensate mosses for the restrictive conditions governing their sexual behaviour.

Mosses are found throughout the world – from the tropics to the Arctic and Antarctic. They are divided into three sub-classes, the Andreaeidae, the Sphagnidae and the Bryidae.

Sub-class
ANDREAEIDAE

This sub-class includes only one genus, *Andreaea* (Order: Andreaeales; Family: Andreaeaceae) comprising some 120 species, all of which form dense cushions, mainly on primary rock and on erratic boulders. Their generally band-shaped protonemata cling close to the substrate to which they are anchored by means of marginal rhizoids. Under unfavourable conditions, a protonema may enter a resting stage, in which it remains until the situation improves.

The gametophyte of *Andreaea* is a much-branching stem, bearing leaves on three sides. Stem and leaves

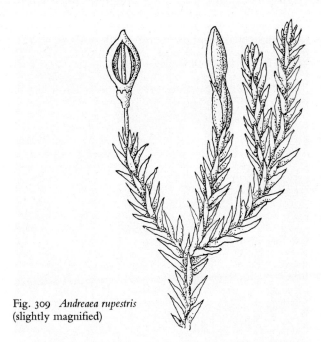

Fig. 309 *Andreaea rupestris* (slightly magnified)

have a very simple structure; the stem, in particular, lacks the central strand of cells so typical of other mosses. Each plant bears both antheridia and archegonia, though on separate branches. After fertilization, the archegonium-bearing branches elongate at the tip to form a short stalk for the spore capsule. This development alone ensures the Andreaeidae a special position among the mosses – the normal moss spore capsule and stalk are derived from the fertilized egg cell.

The capsule, moreover, has neither a lid nor a peristome. It opens by means of longitudinal slits which gape widely apart during dry weather and close in moist. The columella is attached at the base of the capsule only. Over it the sporogenous tissue is turned back much like a sack.

Andreaeidae are cold-loving plants, and occur chiefly in Arctic and high mountainous regions. The best-known British species, *A. rupestris* (Fig. 309), forms characteristic blackish or red-brown patches on hard siliceous rocks at altitudes of more than 1200 ft.

Sub-class
SPHAGNIDAE

This sub-class, too, consists of only one genus (*Sphagnum*), one family (Sphagnaceae) and one order (Sphagnales). These plants are popularly known as bog mosses and, like the Andreaeidae, constitute a

Fig. 310 *Sphagnum*, bog moss

cells are, moreover, capable of absorbing water and retaining it for a considerable time. In the stem, they fuse to produce a relatively thick cortical layer. Another unusual feature of bog mosses is the complete absence of rhizoids, except in the protonemal form.

Bog mosses may be monoecious or dioecious; in the second case the sexual organs are borne on separate branches surrounded by a rosette of sterile ones. The antheridia develop on spindle-shaped branches, often with a reddish tinge; the archegonia are combined in groups of three at the tips of very short shoots. The fertilized egg cell develops into a tiny, spherical spore capsule with a short stalk (*Pl. 103, p. 203*). As in Andreaeidae, the stalk is derived from the gametophyte and not from the egg cell itself. *Sphagnum* also corresponds to *Andreaea* in the internal structure of its spore capsule: the cone-shaped columella is attached to the base of the capsule only, and covered by a bell-shaped spore sac. There is no peristome. The capsule, which is enclosed in a tough wall, opens by means of a lid which bursts open at maturity.

closed group differing radically from the main body of mosses, the Bryidae, both in the vegetative and also in the generative sphere. The protonema of *Sphagnum* is a flat structure divided into lobes. Each protonema gives rise to only a single plant of characteristic shape and structure: the erect stem bears numerous lateral branches, arranged in whorls. These are pendent near the base of the stem but straighten out more and more as they occur higher up on the stem, with the uppermost whorl forming a horizontal rosette. The branches are densely crowded with small, overlapping leaves, of a type characteristic of bog mosses. Their blade, one cell thick, is built up of patterns of live and dead cells; the former, which include numerous chlorophyll grains, are narrow and form a green meshwork; the latter, which are colourless, fill the interstices. Their walls are reinforced with annular or spiral fibrils, and they all have large pores. Since the dead cells occupy a far larger surface than the live, they influence the colour of the plants very considerably: Sphagnum is an unusually pale green, often whitish moss. The dead

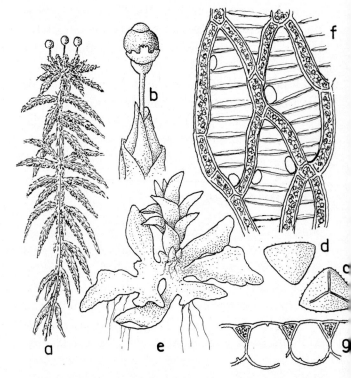

Fig. 311 *Sphagnum. a:* Plant with spore capsules (natural size); *b:* spore capsule (slightly magnified); *c:* spore seen from above; *d:* spore seen from the side (both highly magnified); *e:* protonema with young plant (magnified); *f:* leaf segment seen from above (highly magnified); *g:* cross-section of leaf

240

Sphagnidae are highly specialized to aquatic life, particularly to life in acid waters. As a result, they favour moorland lakes and various types of bog, which they often cover with dense cushions. The transformation of moorland lakes into peat bogs can be clearly observed in Alpine moraines. From the banks, small colonies of bog moss, floating on the water surface, gradually spread out to form a layer of turf. The layer gradually increases in thickness, as individual moss plants keep growing upwards, while their basal part dies off; the high acidity of the water prevents the decomposition of the dead material, with the result that it forms a compact mass beneath the 'lawn'. It is subjected to increasing pressure and transformed into peat, at a rate of approximately 0.5 mm. per year. The peat we use today is therefore of considerable age. Peat bogs can tell us a great deal about the flora of moorlands and forests hundreds and thousands of years ago because the pollen of many other plants is preserved in them.

Peat used to be of great importance as a fuel; today it is chiefly used in horticulture.

The 320 species in this order are distributed throughout the world, particularly in the moorlands of Europe and America. In Britain, *S. palustre* is widespread but avoids the wettest places; *S. cuspidatum* is found in little pools in moorland; and *S. plumulosum* occurs over vast areas of moorland and in blanket bog.

Sub-class
BRYIDAE

This sub-class includes all those forms that the lay-man normally calls 'moss'. Although they come in a host of different forms and may differ considerably in their choice of habitat, they nevertheless constitute a homogeneous group with strong similarities in the structure of both their gametophyte and also their sporophyte.

The protonema of Bryidae is typically filamentous; it is relatively long-lived and gives rise to a large number of moss plants; this great productivity is the reason why mosses so often form dense cushions.

All moss plants are foliose and often have highly-branched stems. They may differ considerably in size and form, particularly in the shape and arrange-ment of their leaves. Normally, mosses do not rise more than a few centimetres or even millimetres above the substrate, but some may attain quite considerable heights, including the tropical genus *Dawsonia* (*Fig. 286*), which may grow to more than 18 ins. in height, and *Fontinalis antipyretica*, which occurs in Britain and whose leafy branches may grow to a length of more than 2 ft.

The stems are generally traversed by a central strand of cells, round which the remaining tissue is arranged in concentric layers. The leaves usually have a central vein which rises slightly above the thin-skinned epidermis. They vary in shape from lanceolate to obovate, may have smooth or finely serrated margins, and often come to a sharp point, spiralling up the stem in three rows, and less often in two.

The reproductive organs, combined or separate, are associated with paraphyses into structures resembling inflorescences. They invariably arise at the tip of the main or of certain lateral stems. The fertilized egg cell gives rise to a sporogonium divided into a capsule and a long stalk. Its foot acts as a haustorium by which the capsule is anchored in the tissue of the parent plant. The spore capsule is generally oval to pear-shaped and has a pointed lid, and often a calyptra as well. The columella runs from the base to the tip of the capsule, and is surrounded by a cylindrical spore sac. An air space, between the sac and the multicellular wall of the capsule, is generally divided into chambers by rigid cell filaments. The spore capsules usually bear peristomes.

Mosses range throughout the world – from the tropics to the polar regions, and in a great many different habitats. Tropical species often live on the leaves of evergreen plants; polar mosses form a dense carpet on the tundra, which they share with certain lichens but with no other plants. Relatively few mosses are aquatic; quite a few can exist in very dry habitats, exposed to continuous periods of sunlight (walls, rocks and roofs); others again live in the cracks of rocks and at the mouths of caves where they are protected from the sun. However, the greatest number are found on the forest floor, often forming a dense carpet. Mosses play an essential role in the water economy of woods – they retain moisture and, lacking roots, cannot, in any case, withdraw much water.

Fig. 312 *Schistostega pennata*

Order
SCHISTOSTEGALES

This order is represented by only a single species, *Schistostega pennata* (Family: Schistostegaceae) and is one of the exceptional mosses in which the leaves are arranged in two ranks (except at the tip of female plants, where 5 leaves combine to form a rosette). The leaves are completely flat and almost translucent. Each leaf is attached to the stem by a broad base which is more or less confluent with the bases of the adjacent leaves above and below it (*Pl. 105, p. 203*). *S. pennata* (Fig. 312) lives in fissures among rocks and in shallow caves, and is so small that it is often overlooked. The protonema, however, is capable of emitting a bluish-green glow. Instead of the weft of branching filaments that constitutes the protonema of most mosses, *Schistostega* has a plate of almost lens-shaped cells. Their convex outer walls focus the light on the green chloroplasts concentrated in the rear wall of each cell, and reflection from these produces the green sheen.

Order
BUXBAUMIALES

This order includes the genera *Diphyscium* and *Buxbaumia*, both in the family Buxbaumiaceae and characterized by a marked reduction in the size of their gametophytes. Male plants consist of a tiny scale enclosing a single antheridium; female plants, too, are tiny but, in *Diphyscium* at least, still look like foliose plants, divided into a tiny stem, 1 mm. high, and bristle-like leaves. In *Buxbaumia*, the female plant disappears almost completely as the spore capsule develops. The sporophyte, which is sizeable in most mosses though generally smaller than the gametophyte, is the dominant generation in Buxbaumiales. *Diphyscium* forms pear-shaped spore capsules surrounded by a ring of stiff bristles (*Pl. 112, p. 206*). The capsules of *Buxbaumia* have stouter stalks, and look like so many grains of wheat, except that they bear a pointed lid and are reddish-brown in colour.

While *Diphyscium*, which generally grows on rocks, can synthesize its own food, *Buxbaumia* lives as a saprobe on decaying plants on the forest floor.

Order
POLYTRICHALES

This order includes the two families Polytrichaceae and Dawsoniaciae, the second of which is exclusively tropical but deserves special mention because it is made up of the largest mosses of all (the Australasian genus *Dawsonia*; see *Fig. 288*).

The very much wider family Polytrichaceae comprises the 3 genera *Polytrichum*, *Pogonatum* and *Atrichum*, which play an important part in the flora of Central Europe. In all Polytrichales, the stem has become modified into a kind of underground rhizome that sends up leafy shoots year after year. The little shoots are densely covered with narrow, generally serrated, leaves on top; in *Polytrichum* and *Pogonatum* the leaves have a broad sheathing base. *Atrichum* can be identified by its narrow, undulate blades.

The reproductive organs are borne at the tip of the leafy shoots. In *Polytrichum*, the antheridia are surrounded by reddish bracts that combine to form a

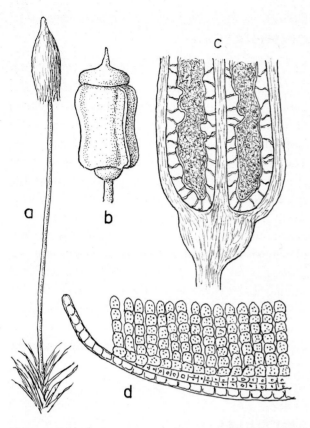

Fig. 313 *Polytrichum commune. a:* Spore capsule with calyptra (slightly magnified); *b:* spore capsule after shedding calyptra (more highly magnified); *c:* longitudinal section through spore capsule (magnified); *d:* part of leaf in longitudinal section (highly magnified)

conspicuous 'flower' (*Pl. 109, p. 205*). The spore capsules are borne on long stalks; in *Pogonatum* and *Atrichum* they are more or less cylindrical; in *Polytrichum* they have 4 to 6 edges and resemble dice. A calyptra is always present and, in *Pogonatum*, it is densely covered with hair.

The 3 genera enjoy a world-wide distribution. *Polytrichum commune* (*Pls. 107–109, pp. 204–205*) stands out among British wood-growing mosses because of its large size and luxuriant growth. Very similar in habit is *P. formosum*, which can be identified by its 5- to 6-edged spore capsules. *Atrichum undulatum* is commonly found in British woods and on heaths and open wasteland.

Order
FISSIDENTALES

In this order, the leaves are typically arranged in two ranks, and fused to the stem by one of their edges. Their dorsal side bears a central vein prolonged into a wing that is often larger than the leaf itself. The order comprises the genus *Fissidens* (Family: Fissidentaceae) with some 700 species, predominantly in the tropics. *F. bryoides*, the commonest British species, forms dense colonies on shady banks.

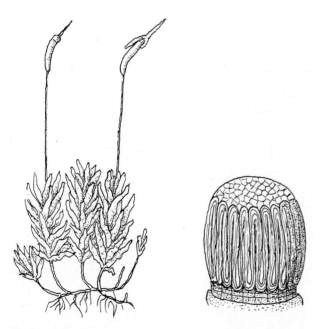

Fig. 314 *Atrichum undulatum*. Left: plant with spore capsules (slightly magnified); right: peristome (more highly magnified)

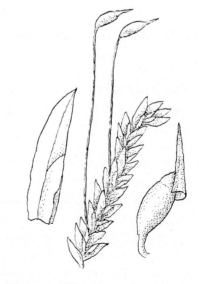

Fig. 315 *Fissidens taxifolius*. Centre: branch with spore capsules (slightly magnified); right: capsule (more highly magnified); left: leaf (magnified)

243

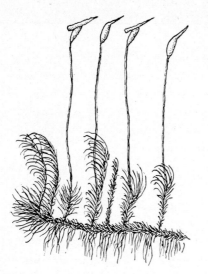

Fig. 316 *Dicranum scoparium*; plant and spore capsules (slightly magnified)

Order
DICRANALES

In this order, which comprises the families Dicranaceae and Leucobryaceae, the leaves are wrapped tightly round the stem and branches. They are narrowly lanceolate in shape and often curved at the tip. Another distinguishing mark is the angle of the spore capsules: they are inclined to the stalk at angles of up to 90 degrees. The genus *Ceratodon* includes *C. purpureus*, one of the commonest mosses in Britain; it is readily identified by its red setae. In the genera *Dicranum* and *Dicranella*, the leaves appear to be attached to one side of the stem only – half of them curl round the stem. *Dicranum* species are much larger than *Dicranella*; their lateral branches are covered in a whitish fur. All Dicranaceae prefer acid soils and, under favourable conditions, form dense mats on the substrate.

The family Leucobryaceae – which consists of only the one genus, *Leucobryum* – forms wide, hemispherical, whitish-green cushions or mats on the woodland floor, and is very common in Britain. The pale colour is produced by leaves which, their vein apart, consist entirely of colourless, dead cells with porose walls – in structure and function alike these cells resemble the water-storing cells of bog-mosses. *Leucobryum glaucum* (*Pl. 113, p. 207*) grows under beech, oak or conifers in woods, on wet moorland and in bogs; in wet districts it is, moreover, common on the trees themselves. It is not found on calcareous soil.

Order
GRIMMIALES

This order of small, highly branching mosses grows on stones, rocks, walls and often on roofs. The family Grimmiaceae is made up of the two genera, *Grimmia* and *Rhacomitrium*; the first forms large cushions (*Pl. 114, p. 207*), the second dense mats. The cushions and mats of many species are covered in grey felt. When fruiting, the plants bear countless spherical or cylindrical spore capsules on delicate stalks. The water-retaining ability of their cushions enables these mosses to live on relatively dry soil and to survive fairly prolonged periods of drought. *G. maritima* is unusual in that it lives on rocks by the sea and is therefore one of the few mosses that can survive in a saline environment.

This order, which is common in temperate regions, is widely represented in Britain by a number of other species as well.

Order
POTTIALES

This order, which includes only the one family, Pottiaceae, consists of small, mostly soil-dwelling, mosses that generally combine into mats. Of the several genera, *Phascum* is remarkable because its oval,

Fig. 317 *Leucobryum glaucum*. Top left: branch with spore capsule (slightly magnified); top right: leaf (more highly magnified); below: cross-section of leaf fragment (highly magnified)

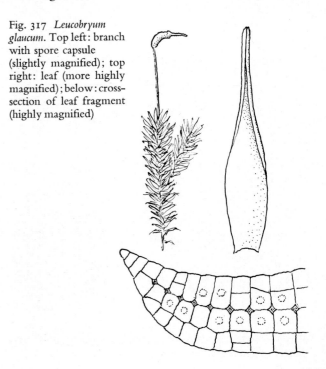

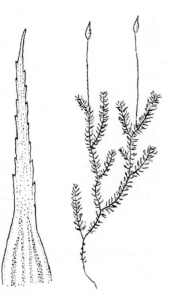

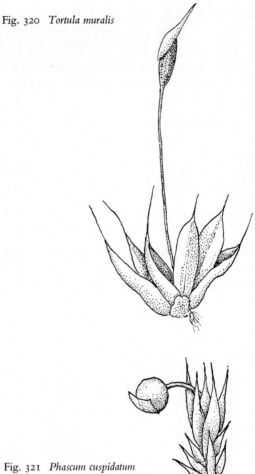

Fig. 320 *Tortula muralis*

Fig. 318 *Rhacomitrium canescens*. Right: plant with spore capsules (natural size); left: leaf tip (slightly magnified)

sessile or stalked capsules do not open by means of a lid but by dissolution of the entire wall. In *Pottia*, we meet another rare genus of mosses adapted to a saline habitat. The genus *Tortula* includes *T. muralis* (*Fig. 320*), one of the commonest mosses on walls throughout Britain, including towns. It often grows in association with species of Grimmiales, from which it is, however, easily distinguished by its relatively broad leaves.

Fig. 319 *Splachnum luteum*

Fig. 321 *Phascum cuspidatum* (slightly magnified)

Order
FUNARIALES

This order includes another extremely common moss, *Funaria hygrometrica*, which colonizes bare soil and burnt land in a wide range of habitats. Its stems are surrounded by broad leaves, and rarely grow to more than $\frac{3}{4}$ in. in length. By contrast, the sporogonium is very conspicuous: the pear-shaped capsule is borne on a long, pliable stalk that curls down under moist conditions. The genera *Funaria* and *Physcomitrium* make up the family Funariaceae.

The second family, the Splachnaceae, a small group of mat-forming mosses consisting of the one genus, *Splachnum*, is mainly restricted to polar regions. It is easily identified by the bright-yellow or red umbrella which, as *Fig. 319* shows, spreads from the base of the spore capsule and represents the apophysis. It is believed that the bright colour, and also the strong aroma, of this moss serve to attract

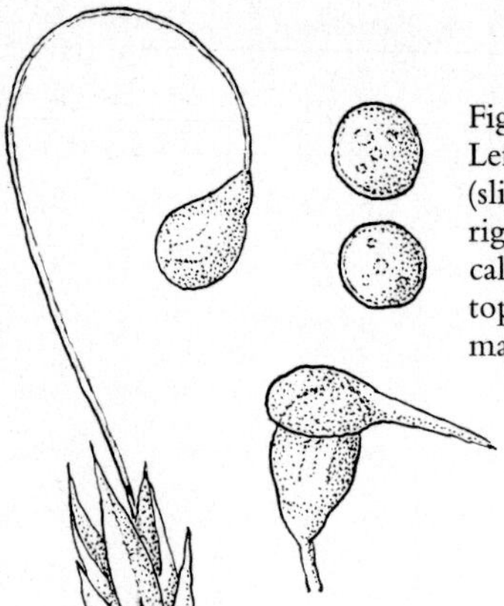

Fig. 322 *Funaria hygrometrica.* Left: plant with spore capsule (slightly magnified); bottom right: spore capsule with calyptra (slightly magnified); top right: spores (highly magnified)

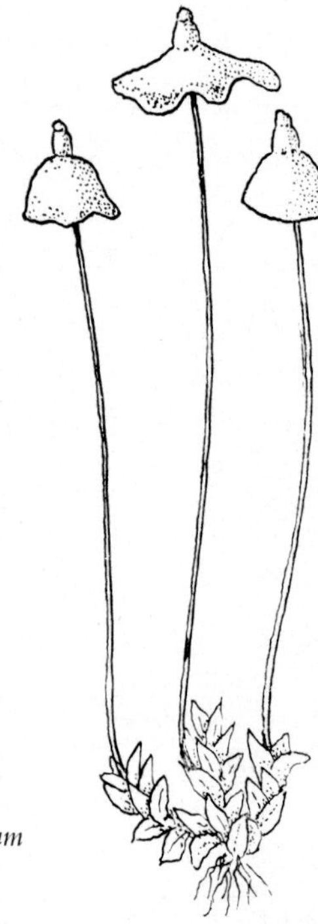

Fig. 323 *Splachnum luteum* (natural size)

flies which help to disseminate the spores – an interesting parallel to the colourful scented flowers of many higher plants.

The Splachnaceae are also unusual in their choice of substrate: they live on animal excrement and on decaying plant matter.

Order
ORTHOTRICHALES

This order, which includes the very large genus *Orthotrichum* (Family: Orthotrichaceae) forms dense cushions, reminiscent of those of the Grimmiaceae. However, only a few species occur on rock; the great majority live on the bark of trees. They owe their scientific name (*orthos*, straight; *trichos*, hair) to the presence of erect hairs on the calyptra of their short-stalked spore capsules.

Order
BRYALES

This order comprises a number of large mosses, all of which form dense mats on the forest floor, on rocks and in bogs. The most typical representatives, the families Bryaceae and Mniaceae, may be identified by their horizontal or pendulous spore capsules. This peculiar feature results from the fact that the long seta curls downwards at the tip.

The Bryaceae, which include the genera *Pohlia* and *Bryum*, form one of the largest of moss-families – the genus *Bryum* alone includes more than 600 species, many of them indigenous to Britain. *B. argenteum*, which is often found at the edge of pavements in towns, has a silvery-grey colour produced by the tips of the broad, overlapping leaves.

The family Mniaceae, with the genus *Mnium*, represents the unique case of a moss in which several of the archegonia in one and the same 'flower' are capable of producing sporogonia. As a result, each female plant is usually crowned with several spore capsules. For the rest, these mosses are easily identified by their unusually large leaves, loosely arranged on the lower part of the stem but combined into dense rosettes at the tip; the reproductive organs arise in the centre of the rosette. A widespread and conspicuous British representative is *Mnium undulatum* (*Pl. 111, p. 206*), which forms extensive, bright-green patches on grassy banks, woodlands and shaded rocks, and is easily identified by its filmy, tongue-shaped leaves. It often grows in association with *M. affine*, which has a rather round leaf.

Another family of Bryales represented in Britain, the Aulacomniaceae, comprises the two genera *Aulacomnium* and *Philonotis*. Aulacomniaceae differ from other Bryales in having erect capsules, and in many other respects as well. A special feature of *Aulacomnium* is the presence of gemmae combined into dense spherical clusters at the ends of distinct terminal stalks. All Aulacomniaceae have a marked preference for moist habitats. In *A. palustre*, which is common on wet moorland and bogs in Britain, the lower stems bear a dense felt of rhizoids (tomatum). The genus *Philonotis*, represented in Britain by *P. fontana* (*Pl. 115, p. 208*) and *P. calcarea*, grows in marshy spots, bogs and springs.

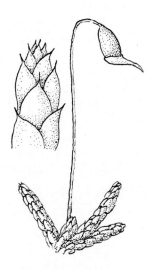

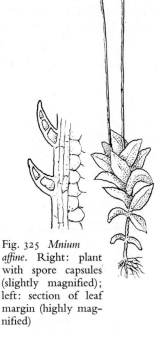

Fig. 325 *Mnium affine*. Right: plant with spore capsules (slightly magnified); left: section of leaf margin (highly magnified)

With the Bryales we have come to the end of the largest group among the mosses, namely those in which the sexual organs are borne at the tips of the stem or branch. Such mosses are said to be acrocarpous; in the rest, called pleurocarpous, the archegonia are borne on a short lateral branch. Pleurocarpous mosses are divided into three orders: Leucodontales, Hookeriales and Hypnales. All three correspond largely in the structure of their vegetative plant bodies: the main stem is richly branched, and evenly covered in leaves. Differences in appearance are largely due to differences in the growth of the lateral branches, which may be erect, pendent or prostrate and have the leaves inserted in a variety of ways.

Order

LEUCODONTALES

Probably the best-known member of this order is *Fontinalis antipyretica* (Family: Fontinalaceae), a widespread species in rivers and at the edge of lakes throughout Britain. Its richly branched, leafy shoots may attain a length of up to 1 ft. and are covered in dark-green leaves. Bundles of rhizoids from the base of the branches anchor the plant to rocks at the bottom of the water. The antheridia appear on the side of long branches; the archegonia develop on the tips of very short, bud-like lateral shoots; they are hidden in a sheath of bracts from which only their cap-shaped calyptra protrudes.

The Neckeraceae, which are common on rocks and trees, have a sessile and more rarely a short-stalked spore capsule. Here the main stem is prostrate and bears leafy side shoots at relatively large intervals. These are erect in rock-inhabiting species and pendent in tree-dwellers. The side shoots are densely covered in small leaves, forming 8 ranks along the axis. In *Neckera crispa*, which is found on trees and rocks throughout Britain, the leaves are wrinkled and have marked transverse undulations, which greatly facilitate its identification.

Order

HOOKERIALES

This almost exclusively tropical order includes the family Hookeriaceae, the only one to grow in temperate latitudes. The Javanese *Ephemeropsis tjibodensis* (*Fig. 329*) deserves special mention because its plant body consists of filamentous organs of assimilation. These tiny plants form colonies on the stems and leaves of higher plants, to which they cling by means

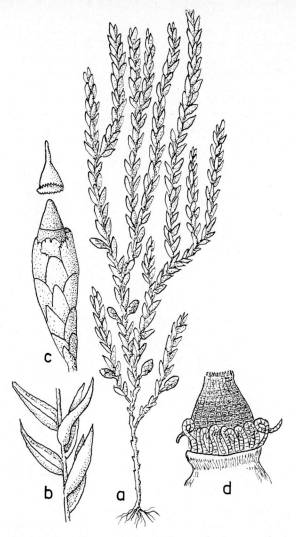

Fig. 327 *Fontinalis antipyretica. a:* plant with spore capsules (natural size); *b:* fragment of stem with leaves (slightly magnified); *c:* spore capsule with discarded calyptra (slightly magnified); *d:* peristome (more highly magnified)

of finely branching protonemal threads modified into haustoria. Their epiphyllous habitat is unique among Bryophytes, so much so that *E. tjibodensis* is generally treated as an independent family, the Nemataceae.

Order

HYPNALES

Most species in this order have prostrate stems and numerous, highly branched side shoots.

The genus *Thuidium* (Family: Thuidiaceae) has unusually stout, rigid side shoots which branch at regular intervals. *T. tamariscinum*, which is common in woods and on hedge banks especially in western and northern Britain, is readily identified by its bright-green colour and frond-like tripinnate branches, which are reminiscent of *Thuja*, the arbor-vitae. The long-stalked, curved spore capsules grow at the tip of short lateral shoots.

The family Brachytheciaceae is widely represented in Britain. Here, too, the main stem is generally procumbent and sends up numerous ascending or upright secondary stems covered densely in silky leaves. The rounded spore capsules are borne on slender stalks between the lateral shoots. This family includes the genus *Brachythecium* (189 species), the largest in the entire order, and distributed throughout

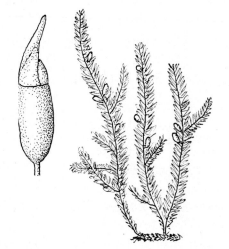

Fig. 328 *Neckera pennata.* Right: plant with spore capsules (natural size); left: spore capsules (slightly magnified)

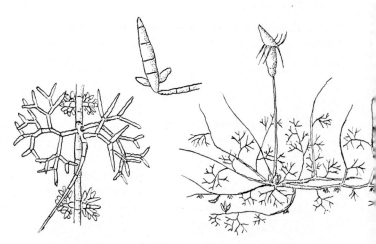

Fig. 329 *Ephemeropsis tjibodensis.* Right: plant with spore capsules (slightly magnified); left: fragment of filamentous plant body with organs of photosynthesis and of attachment (more highly magnified); centre: gemma (highly magnified)

the world. *B. rutabulum* is extremely robust in habit and grows profusely on stones, tree stumps and decaying branches in woodland throughout Britain.

The family Hypnaceae, which includes some of the most beautiful of all mosses, is chiefly represented in Britain by the genera *Hypnum*, *Plagiothecium*, and *Hylocomium*. The secondary shoots are pinnately branched in *Hypnum*, and unevenly branched in *Plagiothecium*. In both genera, the shoots look unusually flat; this is because the leaves of mature species seem to lie in a single plane. This arrangement is particularly striking in *P. undulatum*, whose flat, almost vitreous leaves may be seen in woods in northern and western Britain. In *Hypnum*, the leaves have a relatively long, needle-shaped, inrolled tip; one British species, *H. cupressiforme* (*Fig. 331*), is common on grassy heathland. *Hylocomium splendens* (*Pl. 116, p. 208*), a robust and common plant on heaths, has an erect stem, almost bare at the top, where numerous branches spread out horizontally in different directions. At the beginning of each new vegetative period, a bare shoot starts growing upwards at the base of one of the horizontal branches, with the result that the plant develops a new 'storey' each year.

The Hypnaceae are chiefly distributed in temperate and cold regions. Many species grow on trees; others form dense mats on rocks or on the forest floor.

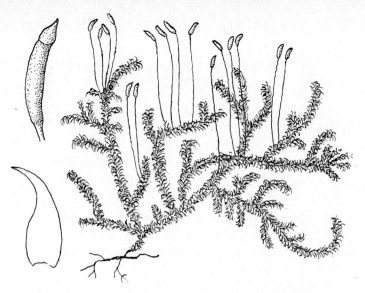

Fig. 331 *Hypnum cupressiforme*. Right: plant with spore capsules (natural size); lower left: leaf (slightly magnified); top left: spore capsule (slightly magnified)

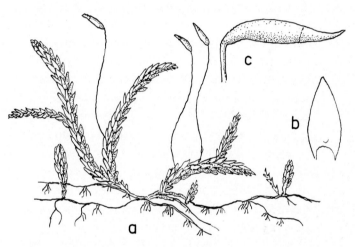

Fig. 332 *Plagiothecium sylvaticum*. *a:* Plant with spore capsules (natural size); *b:* leaf (slightly magnified); *c:* spore capsule (slightly magnified)

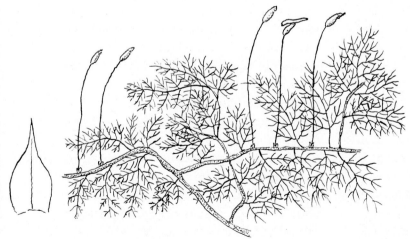

Fig. 330 *Thuidium tamariscinum*. Right: plant with spore capsules (natural size); left: leaf (slightly magnified)

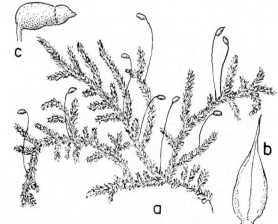

Fig. 333 *Brachythecium salebrosum*. *a:* Plant with spore capsules (natural size); *b:* leaf (slightly magnified); *c:* spore capsule (slightly magnified)

8 PTERIDOPHYTA
Ferns and Fern Allies

With the Pteridophyta, which include the club mosses, horsetails and true ferns, we come to the most highly developed cryptogamia, having characters – internal as well as external – normally associated with flowering plants. At the same time, however, the Pteridophyta still have enough primitive characters to justify our comparing them with the Bryophyta, even though this treatment must not be thought to have any phylogenetic implications.

In the Bryophyta, we first met plant bodies divided into stem and leaves; numerous species, moreover, were seen to have a central strand of tissue through which the entire plant was supplied with dissolved food substances. As we also saw, Bryophyta are devoid of true roots. Pteridophyta, most of which are typical land forms, have gone a considerable step further in the differentiation of their plant body: in addition to a distinct stem and leaves, they also have true roots. Now the presence of a stem, leaves and roots is the structural hallmark of higher plants.

In many Pteridophyta, the differentiation of the plant body goes hand in hand with an increase in size. As a result, there is a need for an extensive water and food conducting system. In Pteridophyta, this takes the form of true vascular bundles (*Pl. 120, p. 258*), built up from two distinct types of cells. Water absorbed by the roots, and dissolved salts, rise up through a system of elongated, dead cells whose walls are rigid and impregnated with lignin. The lignin reinforcement is broken in certain places by pits through which the water can pass. The water-conducting part of the vascular system is known as the xylem. The second system consists of living, thin-walled cells of different lengths; they are joined together by cytoplasmic strands which run through minute perforations in the cell wall. The perforations are restricted to the so-called sieve plates; cells with such plates are called sieve cells; they combine with others to form the phloem of the vascular bundles. The phloem helps to conduct organic substances produced in the plant. Unlike water, these substances are usually, but not invariably, conducted downwards. The distribution of xylem and phloem is not uniform, though in most Pteridophyta it takes the form of concentric vascular bundles, in which the xylem forms the core and the phloem the sheath.

Three types of tissue are involved in the construction of the stem: an outer epidermis, a cortical layer and a central cylinder mainly of vascular bundles.

Pteridophyta differ markedly in the size and structure of their plant bodies. Thus while some are richly branching, others produce no branches at all. Again, while some attain heights of less than $\frac{1}{2}$ in., others grow to 60 ft. and even more. The differences are particularly marked in the shape of the leaves – these range from undivided with smooth margins to lobate and multi-pinnate forms. For the rest, most Pteridophyta are herbaceous in habit.

Like higher plants, Pteridophyta have their stems and leaves covered with a cork-like cuticle, whose function it is to prevent excessive water loss.

Their leaves enable us to divide Pteridophyta into two main groups. In the first (the club mosses and horsetails), the leaves are extremely small (microphyllous), and have a single, central vein. The vascular bundles in it merge smoothly with the vascular system of the stem. In the second group (the true ferns), the leaves are large (macrophyllous) fronds, and have a richly branching vein structure. Moreover, at the point where these vessels communicate with those of the stem, there is a clear break in the conducting tissue. These breaks are a characteristic of all macrophyllous Pteridophyta, i.e. of all true ferns.

The plant body, as we have described it above, represents the diploid sporophyte of Pteridophyta. The life cycle of these plants, like that of mosses, involves an alternation of generations. Pteridophyta, however, differ from mosses in that the sporophyte is the dominant generation – the haploid gametophyte is so small and inconspicuous that it is often extremely difficult to find. The sporangia of Pteridophyta are usually attached to the leaves; in a few species, however, they also arise in the leaf axils and, very exceptionally, directly on the stem.

Certain Pteridophyta produce two types of spores: very small microspores, from which the male gametophytes eventually develop, and macrospores that give rise to female plants. Pteridophytes of this type are said to be heterosporous.

The mature spore germinates into a small thallus, less than $\frac{1}{2}$ in. in diameter. This is the so-called prothallus or prothallium, and represents the gametophyte generation. On it are borne the archegonia and antheridia. In some Pteridophyta, the prothallus takes the form of a small, colourless tubercle growing underground; in most cases, however, particularly in the true ferns, the prothallus is a small, green, often heart-shaped structure that grows on the surface and is anchored to it by means of rhizoids. The archegonia and antheridia are attached to its under-side. These organs resemble those of Bryophyta but have a simpler structure; they are, moreover, partly embedded in the tissue of the prothallus. In wet weather, the flagellate spermatozoids escape from the antheridia, swim towards the archegonia and fertilize the mature egg cells. The neck of each archegonium secretes certain substances – malic acid in ferns, citric acid in club mosses – that help to attract the male cells.

In heterosporous species, each microspore gives rise to a tiny prothallus bearing a small number of strongly reduced antheridia. The macrospores develop into female prothalli with a few archegonia each. When the spermatozoids and egg cells are mature, the archegonia open and the eggs can be fertilized. The entire development of the sexual generation is often concluded within a matter of hours. In all cases, the fertilized egg cell develops into a tiny prothallus, divided into root, stem and leaf. The prothallus takes up water and nourishment from the ground and grows into a new sporophyte.

Pteridophyta used to play a crucial part in the vegetation of the earth – their mighty ancestors can be traced back to the Silurian, some 450 million years ago. The extensive forests that carpeted the earth in the Carboniferous were dominated particularly by the family Lepidodendraceae and the genus *Sigillaria*, tree-like club mosses that often attained heights of up to 135 ft. The horsetails, too, reached their peak in the Carboniferous, with various species of *Calamites* attaining heights of up to 100 ft.

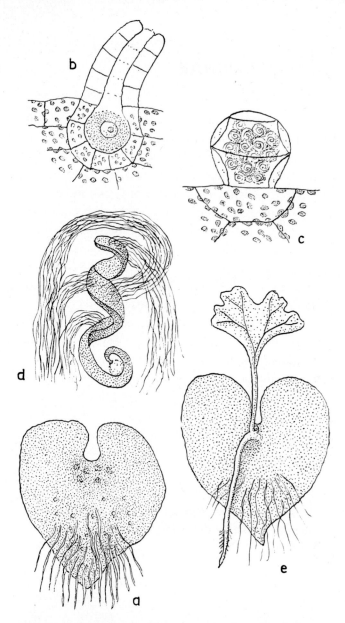

Fig. 334 *a*: Fern prothallus (Leptosporangiatae) seen from below. The archegonia are concentrated near the invagination; the antheridia are more loosely scattered. *b*: Longitudinal section of archegonium (highly magnified). *c*: Antheridium (highly magnified). *d*: Spermatozoid (very highly magnified). *e*: Embryo with rhizoid and leaf (slightly magnified)

Though numerous fossil finds enable us to form a fairly accurate picture of the history of Pteridophyta, their origins remain largely unexplained. It is believed that all Pteridophyta are descended from algae. Fern plants have no phylogenetic affinities with mosses, which are probably descended from algae as well, but must have developed independently of Pteridophyta.

Modern Pteridophyta are found throughout the world, but prefer the tropics and sub-tropics.

Class

LYCOPODIINAE

Club Mosses

The living representatives of this group give no hint that they are descended from mighty ancestors; all are tiny plants that cling close to the substrate. The forking stems bear scaly or needle-shaped microphylls, crowded close together and, in some species, overlapping like tiles. The sporangia are borne singly on special leaves known as sporophylls. Usually, sporophylls are combined into strobili, club-shaped spikes of fructification at the tips of the branches. While some club mosses produce only one kind of spore, others develop both macrospores and microspores. The spermatozoids are provided with single pairs of flagella. Most species, and the most imposing among them, have become extinct long ago; only two orders, with one family each, have survived to this day.

Order

LYCOPODIALES

This order includes only the one family, Lycopodiaceae, with one large genus, *Lycopodium*, and the small Australasian genus *Phyloglossum* of which only one species is known. *Lycopodium* is distributed throughout the earth, but avoids the most arid zones. All species are herbaceous and most have procumbent, richly forking stems. Many species, however, look as if they had two rows of lateral branches; this is because one 'prong' of each fork is longer than the other and because the shorter is erect while the longer continues the creeping habit. The forks are, however, quite plain to see in such tropical species as *Lycopodium phlegmaria* (Fig. 336), which grows epiphytically on trees, from which its branches droop down. The leaves of all club mosses are small, mostly needle-shaped and sometimes scale-like, as, for instance, in *L. complanatum*, which is common in Central Europe.

Only certain regions of the stem, generally at the tip, bear strobili, which branch out in a number of species. The sporophylls are usually smaller than the normal leaves. An exception is *L. selago*, fir club moss (Pl. 119, p. 258), whose sporophylls, moreover, do not combine into strobili.

The kidney-shaped sporangia release the spores through a central slit; the spores are all of the same size and pyramidal in shape. The prothalli into which the spores develop are of two types. One contains chlorophyll, grows on the ground and attains a diameter of 2–3 mm.; its full development never

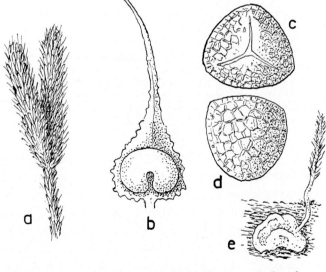

Fig. 335 *Lycopodium clavatum*, common club-moss. *a*: Spike of fructification (natural size); *b*: sporophyll with sporangium (slightly magnified); *d*: spore seen from the side (strongly magnified); *e*: underground prothallus with young plant (slightly magnified)

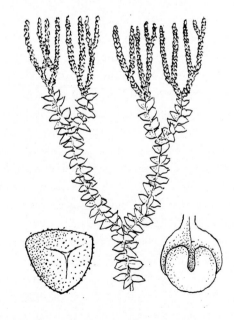

Fig. 336 *Lycopodium phlegmaria*. Centre: section of stem with spikes of fructification (slightly reduced); right: sporophyll

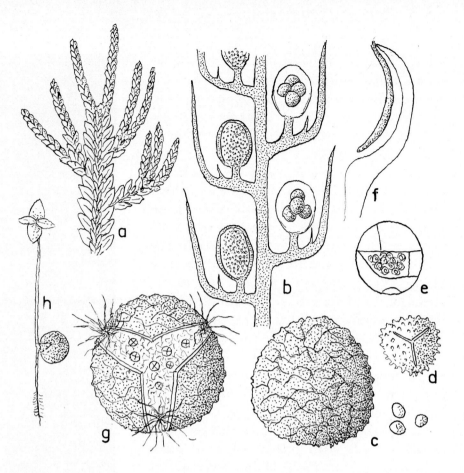

Fig. 337 *Selaginella sp.*, prickly club moss. *a*: Section of stem with spikes (natural size); *b*: longitudinal section of spike of fructification (cone) with microsporangia and macrosporangia (slightly magnified); *c*: macrospore and three microspores (same magnification); *d*: microspore (highly magnified); *e*: microspore containing antheridium (highly magnified); *f*: spermatozoid (very highly magnified); *g*: expanded macrospore showing prothallus and several archegonia (magnified); *h*: macrospore and embryo (slightly magnified)

takes longer than one vegetative period. The second type of prothallus is a colourless tubercle 1–2 mm. across, and develops underground. Here, the formation of antheridia and archegonia may take up to 15 years. In many cases, the prothallus persists to provide the growing embryo with food, until such time as it can fend for itself.

British species of *Lycopodium* include *L. annotinum*, interrupted club moss (*Pl. 118, p. 258*), which is chiefly restricted to the Scottish Highlands; *L. clavatum*, common club moss (*Pl. 117, p. 257*), in which the strobili are often combined in groups of 2 or 3 at the tip of a long, erect stem. The spores are used in the manufacture of waterproof coatings for pills. Most British species live on relatively dry ground; the exception is *L. inundatum*, marsh club moss, which occurs chiefly on swampy heaths and the margins of bogs.

Order
SELAGINELLALES

This order, too, comprises a single family, the Selaginellaceae, with a single genus *Selaginella* (700

species). It is found throughout the world, but is most widespread in the tropics.

Selaginellales are herbaceous plants with thin forking branches. Some species are of the type we have already described: one 'prong' is longer than the other and grows in the direction of the 'handle', so that the plants appear to bear two ranks of lateral branches (*Fig. 337*). All Selaginellales are microphyllous. The base of the leaf upper surface bears a small scale, the so-called ligule, which is believed to act as a water regulator. In many species, the leaves are all of one size; others produce microphylls of two distinct sizes. In some species, moreover, the cells of the leaves may contain only a single, key-shaped chloroplast of unusually large size.

Like the Lycopodiales, the Selaginellales have their sporophylls combined into strobili. The sporangia are either borne singly on the sporophyll or else on its axils; in some species, however, they are attached to the central axis of the strobilus. All Selaginellales are heterosporous, but unlike heterosporous Lycopodiales, they have their microspores and macrospores combined into special structures, the so-called microsporangia and macrosporangia (*Pl. 121, p. 259*).

253

Usually, both types of sporangium participate in the construction of a strobilus, with the macrosporangia occupying the basal part and the microsporangia the top section. The brown to orange-coloured microsporangia are much smaller than the green or whitish macrosporangia.

Every microsporangium contains a considerable number of very small microspores, each of which gives rise to a prothallus. The prothallus remains inside the microspore throughout its development, during which its 1 or 2 reduced antheridia develop into biflagellate spermatozoids. Only when these are mature does the microspore rupture. Each macrosporangium produces 4 relatively large macrospores, which eventually split at the tip to reveal a small prothallus. The protruding part bears the archegonia. The fertilized egg cell begins its development inside the macrospore, which continues to enfold the base of the embryo for some considerable time.

Though quite a few exotic *Selaginella* are grown in our greenhouses, the only species indigenous to Britain is *S. selaginoides*, prickly club moss, which grows in boggy and marshy places, particularly on mountains.

S. lepidophylla, Rose of Jericho, is indigenous to the deserts of South America; its leaves are arranged in rosettes, except under dry conditions, when the stems roll up, and the plant looks like a desiccated and quite lifeless ball. In this state it can survive for many years; the moment it rains, however, it opens its dark green rosettes with astonishing speed. In the past, this plant was often grown indoors, not only because of its spectacular powers of revival, but also as a kind of barometer-cum-hygrometer.

Class
PSILOTINAE

This class comprises one order, the Psilotales, with only one family, the Psilotaceae. Though it used to be rich in species, only two small genera, *Psilotum* and *Tmesipteris*, have survived.

The Psilotinae occupy a special position among the Pteridophyta: all of them lack roots. The stem is divided into two distinct parts: an underground rhizome covered in rhizoids, supplying the plant with water and, moreover, harbouring mycorrhizal fungi,

Fig. 338 *Psilotum triquetrum*

and a surface stem bearing a varying number of branches. In *Psilotum*, the branching system is well-developed, and the plant may attain a height of up to 3 ft. *Tmesipteris tannensis*, on the other hand, the only member of the second genus, forms only a few branches. In both genera the branching is of the forking type.

Apart from their lack of roots, Psilotinae also display a number of other peculiarities: the place of leaves is taken by foliose processes. In *Tmesipteris tannensis* these cling more or less closely to the stem, which often terminates in a special, leaf-like appendage. In the two species constituting the genus *Psilotum*, the processes may look like scales, or be completely absent, in which case the stem itself acts as an organ of assimilation – the requisite increase in surface area is provided by flattening of the stem or by means of special crossribs.

The forks of the branches give rise to loosely arranged humps bearing the sporangia. Each sporangium is associated with a fork-shaped sporophyll

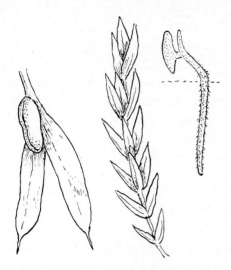

Fig. 339 *Tmesipteris tannensis*. Centre: part of stem (natural size); left: sporophyll with sporangia (slightly magnified); right: underground prothallus with emerging embryo (slightly magnified)

which, in *Psilotum*, is reduced to two tiny flaps, and in *Tmesipteris* resembles the leaf-like appendages. The sporangia of *Psilotum* are divided into two near-spherical compartments (*Pl. 123, p. 259*); those of *Tmesipteris* into two elongated compartments.

The spores of both genera germinate into bisexual prothalli—cylindrical, colourless tubercles that develop underground. Their surface is studded with antheridia, which produce numerous multiflagellate spermatozoids. The archegonia are embedded in the tissue of the prothallus.

Psilotum is found in all tropical regions; *P. triquetrum* (*Fig. 338*) mainly under palm trees. *Tmesipteris* ranges from Australia through Malaysia to the Philippines. It flourishes as an epiphyte, but also grows on the ground.

Class

ISOETINAE

The Isoetinae, too, comprise only a single order, the Isoetales, and only a single family, Isoetaceae, the quillworts, with the single genus *Isoetes*. All species are perennial herbs and generally grow on the bottom of shallow ponds and lakes. Some species make do with moist soil, and some are even able to survive on ground that regularly dries out for prolonged periods.

The most characteristic feature of quillworts is the apparent absence of a stem (*Fig. 340*). It has been suppressed into a tuber-like, underground corm which increases in thickness rather than in height, and is underpinned by countless forking roots. The corm also sends up a large number of quill-shaped leaves, mostly combined into dense rosettes. Although the leaves can grow to a length of 3 ft., they have only a single, undivided vein. Internally, they are split into 4 air chambers by transverse septa. The leaves have greatly dilated bases, each bearing a small membranous ligule, together with a small pit, the fovea. While the innermost leaves of each rosette are sterile, each of the others bears a sporangium, which develops in the protection of the fovea. The sporophylls nearest the sterile leaves bear microsporangia, the peripheral sporophylls bear macrosporangia (*Pl. 122, p. 259*).

Every macrospore germinates into a small prothallus carrying a small number of archegonia,

Fig. 340 *Isoetes lacustris*, common quillwort, *a*: Entire plant (slightly reduced); *b*: internal view of leaf base with microsporangium and ligula; *c*: longitudinal section of leaf base (*b* and *c* slightly magnified); *d*: macrospore and 4 microspores (same magnification); *e*: spermatozoid (highly magnified)

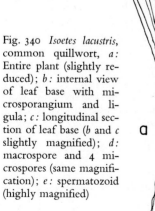
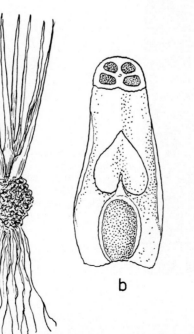
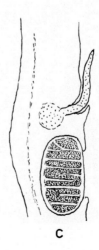

and sometimes only a single one. When the wall of the macrospore bursts, part of the prothallus begins to protrude. The microspores give rise to much smaller prothalli, reduced to 2 cells and a single antheridium which eventually releases 4 multiflagellate spermatozoids.

The genus *Isoetes* comprises more than 60 species in all but tropical regions. Seventeen species occur in Europe, mostly in the Mediterranean region. *I. lacustris*, common quillwort or Merlin's grass (*Pl. 130, p. 262*), grows on the bottom of mountain lakes in the northern half of Britain; *I. hystrix* is restricted to Guernsey, Alderney, and the Lizard in Cornwall.

Class
ARTICULATAE

This class used to play an important part in the vegetation of past geological epochs, particularly during the Carboniferous. Today, it is represented by the single order Equisetales, horsetail. There is only one family, the Equisetaceae, and only one genus, *Equisetum*.

Horsetails, all of them herbaceous plants, have an underground rootstock. In some species, including *E.*

arvense, field horsetail, the underground rootstock splits up into lateral branches that thicken into tubers, break off, and grow into new plants. The rootstock also sends up upright stems, which grow by the division of a single apical cell. The stems are tubular, with a central cavity, and consist of elongated joints, the so-called internodes. The tip of each internode is crowned by a sheath ending in long pointed teeth, into which the lower end of the next joint fits tightly (see *Fig. 341*).

The central cavity is quite hollow except for septa at the nodes. It is surrounded by two further, concentric cavities: an inner one formed by a ring of small circular tubes, and an outer one, which is embedded in the cortex and consists of broader tubes. Many of the cells in the cortex contain chlorophyll – the stem clearly acts as an organ of assimilation. The surface of the stem is thickly coated with silica.

Horsetails develop two types of stems: sterile ones with chlorophyll-containing cells, and fertile ones bearing sporangia. In some species, this functional difference goes hand in hand with a difference in shape. Thus in the field horsetail, the fertile stems, which appear in the spring, are straight and crowned with sporangia, while the infertile stems, which

Fig. 341 *Equisetum sp.*, horsetail; whorl of lateral branches seen from above

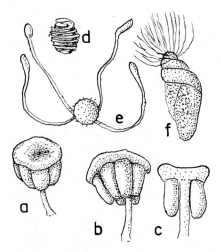

Fig. 342 *Equisetum arvense*, field horsetail. *a:* Sporophyll seen from above; *b:* sporophyll seen from below; *c:* longitudinal section of sporophyll (*a*, *b* and *c* slightly magnified); *d:* moist spore (slightly magnified); *e:* dry spore (slightly magnified); *f:* spermatozoid (very highly magnified)

117 *Lycopodium clavatum*, common club moss

118 Sprouting *Lycopodium annotinum*, interrupted club moss

119 *Lycopodium selago*, fir club moss

120 Section through stem of a club moss to show
    vascular bundles (magnified)

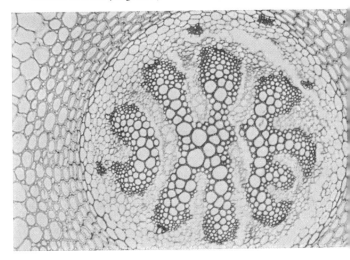

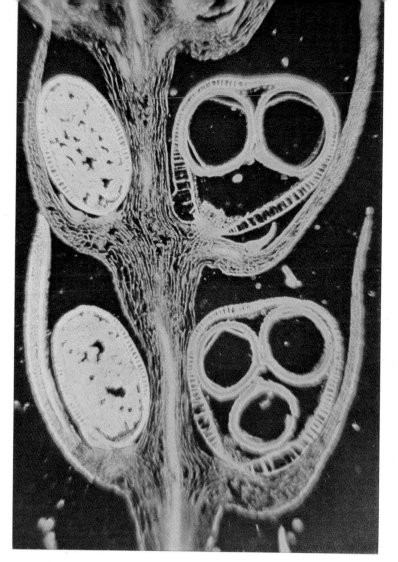

121 *Selaginella*, prickly club moss, showing microsporangia (left) and macrosporangia (right); magnified

123 *Psilotum triquetrum* with trilocular sporangia

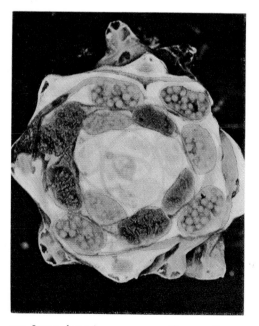

122 *Isoetes lacustris*, common quillwort. Cross-section of sheathing base with macrosporangia (outer circle) and microsporangia (inner circle)

124 *Equisetum sylvaticum*, wood horsetail

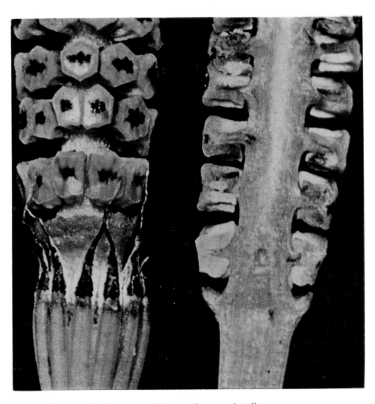

128 *Equisetum sylvaticum*;
sterile and fertile stems

125 *Equisetum sylvaticum*, wood horsetail; central stalk
bearing sporophylls (right in longitudinal-section),
magnified

126 *Equisetum palustre*, marsh horsetail;
young fertile stem (magnified)

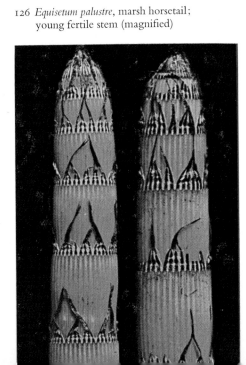

127 *Equisetum palustre*,
marsh horsetail;
cross-section of fer-
tile stem (magnified)

129 *Ophioglossum vulgatum*, adder's tongue fern

130 *Isoetes lacustris*, common quillwort, leaf rosette

131 *Allosurus crispus*

132 Fern prothallus (magnified)

133 *Botrychium lunaria*, moonwort

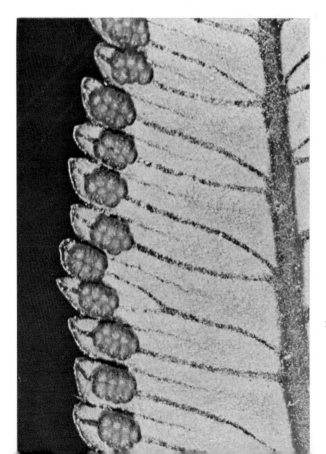

134 *Angiopteris evecta* (Marattiales); leaf under-surface with sori

135 *Osmunda regalis*, royal fern

136 *Adiantum reniforme*, a relative of the maidenhair fern (*A. capillus-veneris*) from the Canaries

137 *Notholaena marantae*, Mediterranean region to Himalayas

138 *Polystichum braunii*, a prickly shield fern growing on mountains in the northern hemisphere

139 *Cyathea sp.*, a tropical tree fern

140 *Alsophila* (= *Cyathea*), a tree fern of
S.E. Asia and Australia

142 *Aspidium (Phegopteris) vulgaris*, a shield fern

141 *Dryopteris filix-mas*,
male fern; young leaves

143 *Aspidium (Phegopteris) vulgaris*; leaf
under-surface with sori

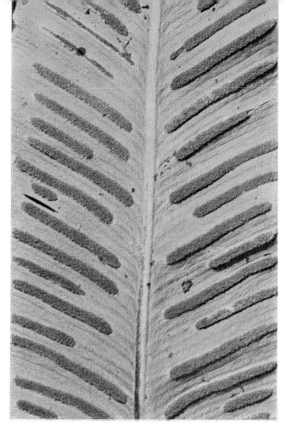

144 *Asplenium (Phyllitis) scolopendrium*, hart's tongue; leaf under-surface with sori

145 *Asplenium (Phyllitis) scolopendrium*, hart's tongue

146 *Blechnum spicant*, hard fern

147 *Asplenium nidus*

148 *Platycerium angolense* from tropical Africa

149 *Platycerium bifurcatum* from tropical Asia

150 *Asplenium nidus*; leaf under-
surface with sori

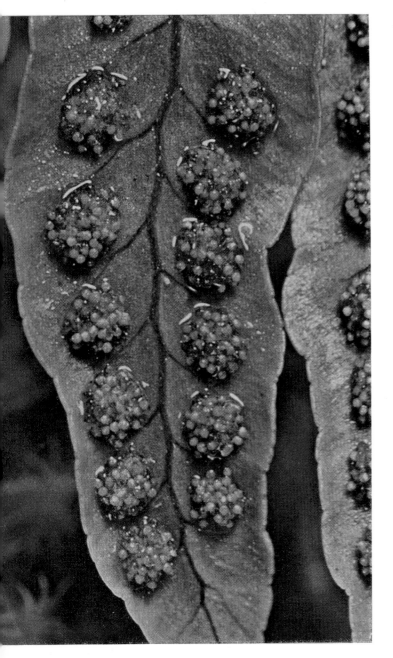

151 *Polypodium vulgare*, common polypody; leaf under-surface with sori

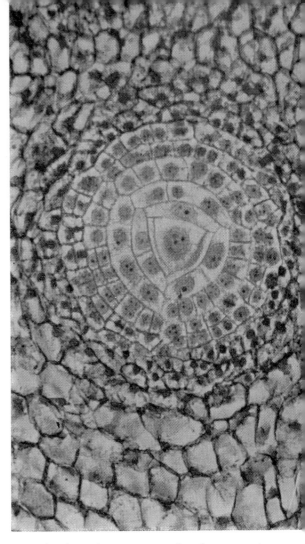

152 *Polypodium vulgare*, common polypody; cross-section of rootstock (magnified)

153 *Polypodium (Phymatodes) bifrons* from Ecuador

154 *Pilularia globulifera*, pillwort

155 *Marsilea quadrifolia*

156 The water fern *Salvinia natans*

157 *Azolla filiculoides*, American water fern

appear much later, are richly branched. In most horsetails, however, both fertile and infertile stems divide into branches. The lateral branches arise in the same spots as the leaves, like which they are arranged in whorls. They are not, however, borne in the leaf axils, but alternate with them.

The fertile stems bear a large number of sporophylls at their tips; the sporophylls are combined into a cylindrical cone which is often called a 'flower' (Pls. 125, 127, p. 260). In their appearance, sporophylls differ radically from the other leaves: each resembles a six-sided table with a central leg. On its lower surface, every sporophyll bears 5–10 elongated sporangia. All of these are identical in shape and contain only one type of spore in which chlorophyll is invariably present. The outer layer of the sporangial wall is divided into 4 narrow bands, spatular at the tip, and with much the same function as the elaters of liverworts. They are attached to the spores and very sensitive to variations in the humidity of the atmosphere: when the air is moist, they spiral round the spore, but in dry weather they fan out, and fling the spores out in groups.

The spores germinate into thallose, strongly lobed, green prothalli that cling to the ground by means of rhizoids, and bear archegonia and antheridia in special pits. The spermatozoids are spiral and multi-flagellate.

The genus Equisetum (25 species) is distributed throughout the world, with the exception of Australasia. Various species are common in Britain, including the imposing E. telmateia (Fig. 343), giant horsetail, which grows in wet places; its infertile stems rise to a height of more than 6 ft. and are clothed with whorls of long, pale green branches. E. sylvaticum, wood horsetail (Pls. 124, 128, pp. 260, 261), ranges in woods from the Shetlands to Kent and Devonshire. It is readily identified by its delicate barren stems and relatively long, down-curving lateral branches. E. palustre, marsh horsetail (Pls. 125, 126, 127, p. 260), grows on all sorts of swampy ground; its stems, barren and fertile alike, are branched.

The most widespread British species, E. arvense, field horsetail, often grows in such abundance and with its creeping and deep-lying rhizomes so deeply embedded in the soil, that it constitutes a serious pest,

and one, moreover, that is exceedingly difficult to eradicate. Another widespread British species is E. pratense, blunt-topped horsetail. Its fertile and barren stems, though different in shape, appear simultaneously and not at intervals as in E. arvense.

E. giganteum, from the tropics of America, is the tallest of all horsetails: its thin stems grow to heights of more than 40 ft. and wind themselves round the stems of trees.

Class
FILICINAE
Ferns

This class comprises the true ferns, plants whose living representatives can trace their ancestry back to the Devonian. Though most of their ancestors are extinct, ferns continue to play an important part in carpeting the earth. With 9000 species, moreover,

Fig. 343 *Equisetum telmateia*, giant horsetail

they account for the great majority of Pteridophyta.

Ferns like to settle in habitats that provide them with shade as well as with moisture, for only a few species can stand direct sunlight. This explains why tropical forests are their main centre of distribution. Most ferns have large, often pinnate, leaves or fronds – typical macrophylls with a richly branching vein system. In the great majority of species, the leaves curl over at the tips in youth (*Pl. 141, p. 266*).

Ferns do not produce sporophylls – their sporangia develop on the edge or under-surface of ordinary leaves. In certain species, however, the leaf is divided into a sterile and a spore-bearing section.

Most ferns are homosporous, i.e. they produce but a single type of spore. Every spore germinates into a small, green, and generally more or less heart-shaped prothallus bearing archegonia and antheridia on its lower surface (*Pl. 132, p. 263*). The class Filicinae is divided into two sub-classes, differing in spore structure.

Sub-class
EUSPORANGIATAE

In members of this sub-class, the mature sporangia are derived from more than one leaf cell, and have a multi-layered wall. In some species individual sporangia are combined into spikes; more often, however, they occur in loose or fused groups on the lower surface of the fronds.

Order
OPHIOGLOSSALES

The order Ophioglossales, which comprises only one family, the Ophioglossaceae, and only two genera, is represented in Britain by two species. Ferns in this order form a deeply buried and generally simple rootstock that gives off fleshy roots. From it rises a (usually) solitary frond, with a barren and a fertile section. The sterile part is an organ of assimilation and consists of a flat blade, whose margin may be smooth or pinnately divided. The fertile part is more or less cylindrical, and in some species, pinnate. Unlike those of all other ferns, Ophioglossales fronds do not curl at the tips when young.

The spores of Ophioglossaceae germinate into tuber-like or cylindrical prothalli devoid of chlorophyll. They develop in the soil with the help of mycorrhizal fungi, and may persist for up to 20 years.

Ophioglossum vulgatum, adder's tongue fern (*Pl. 129, p. 262*), grows on loamy soil throughout Britain. The fertile part of its frond consists of a spike bearing two longitudinal rows of sporangia; the sterile part is oval. *Botrychium lunaria*, moonwort (*Pl. 133, p. 263*), one of 23 species in its genus, is widely distributed in Great Britain, ascending to 3350 ft. in the Highlands. This species is readily identified by its barren leaves, which have a stout midrib with a set of half-moon-shaped pinnae on either side. The fertile portion, too, is bipinnate.

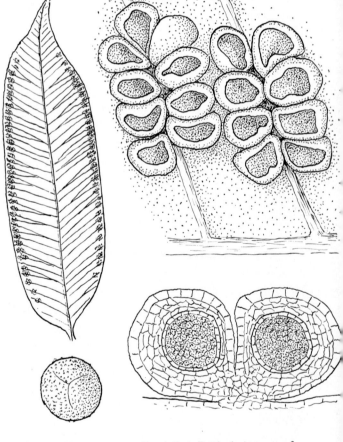

Fig. 344 *Angiopteris erecta*. Top left: individual pinna seen from below (natural size); top right: sporangia, open except for one (slightly magnified); bottom right: two young sporangia in cross-section (more highly magnified); bottom left: spore (highly magnified)

274

Order
MARATTIALES

This order, with one family, the Marattiaceae, reached the peak of its development in the Carboniferous. Today, it is represented by 4 genera, all of them restricted to the tropics.

Marattiaceae may have a swollen surface stem (*Angiopteris* and *Marattia*) or an underground, creeping rootstock. All genera have conspicuous fronds; in *Angiopteris* these may grow to a length of up to 20 ft. The fronds are usually pinnate. At the base of each one are found two large 'bracts', reminiscent of the stipules of higher plants; this characteristic distinguishes Marattiaceae from other ferns. On their under-surface, the fronds bear a large number of tough-walled sporangia, generally at the margins and combined into groups, known as sori. The sporangia in each sorus are generally joined side by side to form what is known as a synangium (*Figs. 345–347*). The genus *Angiopteris* forms the exception, for most of its sporangia are uncombined.

All Marattiaceae are homosporous. Each spore gives rise to a flattened, relatively thick, and generally pinnate prothallus. It contains chlorophyll and grows on the ground. Antheridia are present both on its upper and lower surface; archegonia on its lower surface only.

In *Angiopteris*, the gigantic pinnate fronds are borne on a tuberous stem. The bracts are fleshy and persist on the stem after the frond has dropped off. This genus comprises some 50 species, which some taxonomists treat as mere varieties. *A. evecta* (*Pl. 134, p. 263*) is widespread in tropical Asia.

The genus *Marattia* is not only the largest but also the most widely distributed: one of its 60 species, *M. fraxinea*, is common throughout the tropics. Like *Angiopteris*, *Marattia* has a tuberous stem, with a dense crown of large fronds. The sporangia are fused into elongated synangia, which open by means of two valves.

The genera *Christensenia* and *Danaea* both have a creeping rootstock. The only known species of *Christensenia*, *C. aesculifolia*, occurs in India, Indonesia and the Philippines. Its fronds have a most unusual shape: the blade is palmately divided into 3–5 lobes, of which the central one is larger than the

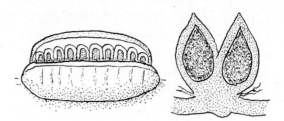

Fig. 345 *Marattia fraxinea*. Left: synangium seen from the side (slightly magnified); right: synangium in cross-section (slightly magnified)

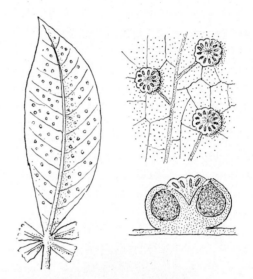

Fig. 346 *Christensenia aesculifolia*, pinna (after removal of the remaining four) seen from below (reduced); upper right: synangia (slightly magnified); lower right: synangium in cross-section (slightly magnified)

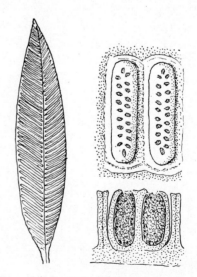

Fig. 347 *Danaea elliptica*. Left: pinna seen from below (reduced); top right: two synangia (slightly magnified); bottom right: synangium in cross-section (slightly magnified)

rest and is borne on a short stalk. The frond resembles the leaf of the horse chestnut – whence the specific name of *aesculifolia*, 'chestnut leaf'. The sporangia are borne on the lower surface of the leaves and are fused into circular synangia, measuring 3 mm. across. They open by means of radial slits.

The genus *Danaea* comprises 32 genera in tropical America, all with pinnate fronds; here the fertile leaves are much narrower than the barren ones. The sporangia are combined into elongated synangia, each built up of 2 rows of sporangia spreading from the central vein to the edge of the pinna. They are embedded in pits in the leaf upper surface and surrounded by folds.

Sub-class
LEPTOSPORANGIATAE

This sub-class accounts for by far the greatest number of ferns. Here, the sporangia are invariably derived from only a single cell in the leaf epidermis. Their wall is built up of only one layer of cells, and they

Fig. 348   Cross-section through rootstock of a tree fern

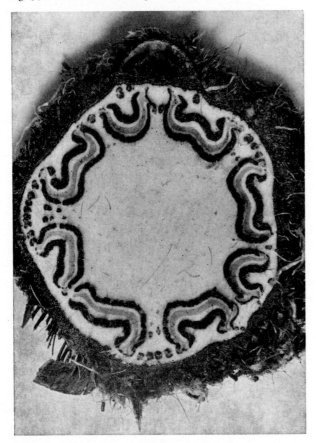

contain a fixed number of spores. The sporangia are combined into sori, but do not fuse together. The sori, which are restricted to the leaf under-surface, and mostly to the margins, are protected by a membranous fold, the indusium, or else by the curled-up leaf edge.

Most ferns in this sub-class are homosporous. The spores germinate on the surface into small, green prothalli, bearing the reproductive organs on their under-surface. The protruding antheridia give rise to a relatively small number of multiflagellate spermatozoids.

Unlike most Leptosporangiatae, the small order Hydropteridales produces two types of spores. Its sexual generation, too, differs from the usual Leptosporangiate type.

Order
FILICALES

This order comprises an extraordinarily large number of species and hence of plants differing greatly in shape and size. It includes tiny moss-like forms, together with herbaceous plants, creepers, epiphytes and large tree ferns.

Most Filicales, including the majority of British ferns, have their stem system underground, with the vascular bundles forming characteristic patterns (see *Fig. 348*).

Some species, however, have erect woody stems which, in the case of tropical tree ferns, may attain a considerable height. While the erect stems are invariably unbranched, the underground rhizomes may give rise to lateral branches. A large number of thin roots arise directly from the stem; remarkably enough, the root formation is most pronounced near the stem apex, no matter whether the stem grows above or below the ground. This is best seen in tree ferns, where the stems are enveloped in a dense web of roots.

The leaves vary considerably in size and shape. In some species, they are only a few millimetres long, in others they may attain lengths of several yards. The fronds generally consist of a stalk or stipe which is prolonged to form the rachis, from which a large number of pinnae arise laterally. In the bud, the fronds are characteristically curled up.

Many ferns form sterile and fertile leaves of different shapes; in others, all the fronds act as combined organs of assimilation and reproduction.

The sporangia, which are always produced in large numbers, are found at the margins of the leaf underside, and are usually combined into sori whose shape may be spherical to linear. The sporangia themselves are usually borne on short stalks. In the majority of Filicales, the sporangial wall contains a number of special cells forming a ring or annulus either round the top of the sporangium (e.g. in *Lygodium, Fig. 350*), or else running from the stalk over the top and part way down the other side (as in *Dryopteris, Fig. 368*). The inner and radial walls of the cells composing the ring are much thickened, the outer walls relatively thin. Both types of cell are dead and filled with water, which evaporates when the sporangia are ripe. As the sporangium gradually dries up, the ring begins to straighten out, and the thin walls of the sporangium are torn. Finally, when all the water is gone and the cohesive pull on the cell wall ceases, the ring returns to its original position, at the same time dispersing the spores.

Some Filicales are able to reproduce their kind vegetatively: bulbils on their leaves germinate into new plants that eventually drop off.

Family

Osmundaceae

This family is considered as the most 'primitive' of all Filicales, occupying an intermediate position between the Eusporangiatae and the Leptosporangiatae. It comprises two genera, *Osmunda* and *Todea*, of which the latter consists of only one species, *T. barbata*, distributed in South Africa and Australasia.

Osmundaceae have relatively thick, but short and erect stems. In many species the surface of the stem is enmeshed in a dense web of tough roots, which invariably arise in pairs from the base of the fronds.

All species are profusely covered in fronds; in some *Osmunda* these may attain lengths of up to 10 ft. The fronds may have a thick and leathery or a thin epidermis. *Osmunda* has pinnate or bipinnate fronds; *Todea* bipinnate fronds only. For the rest, the fronds of the two genera differ characteristically. In *Todea* they are of one type and combine the functions

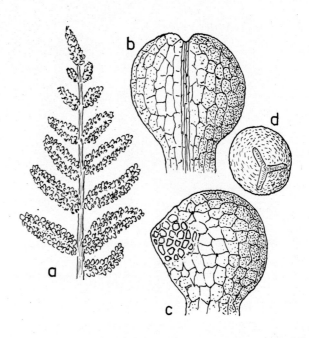

Fig. 349 *Osmunda regalis*, royal fern. *a*: Tip of fertile frond (natural size); *b*: sporangium (front view, slightly magnified); *c*: sporangium seen from the side (slightly magnified); *d*: spore (highly magnified)

of photosynthesis with spore production; the sporangia form a dense row along the lateral veins. The fronds of *Osmunda*, on the other hand, are generally divided into fertile and barren sections. The former usually occupy the tip of the fronds (e.g. in *O. regalis*, royal fern, which grows in bogs and riversides throughout the British Isles) or fit between two sterile sections. Some species go a step further, and produce separate fertile and barren fronds. The fertile sections or fronds are pinnately divided like the rest, but the blade of each leaflet is reduced to the veins, round which the sporangia are crowded in large numbers (*Fig. 349*).

The sporangia of Osmundaceae are relatively large and pear-shaped. Just beneath the top is found a group of thick-walled cells that cannot, however, be called a true annulus. All the sporangia mature simultaneously. The spores germinate into large prothalli of unusual thickness, and are provided with a midrib.

The genus *Osmunda* (14 species) enjoys a worldwide distribution. The only British species, *O. regalis* (*Pl. 135, p. 264*), has become so rare that it has had to be placed under protection.

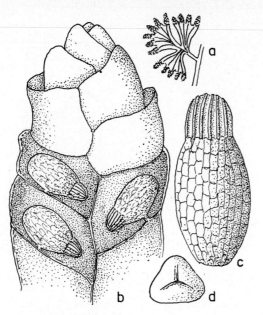

Fig. 350 *Lygodium japonicum*. *a*: Part of fertile frond (natural size); *b*: section through frond to reveal sporangia (slightly magnified); *c*: sporangium (more highly magnified); *d*: spore (highly magnified)

Family
Schizaceae

This family has its main centre of distribution in the tropics, and comprises 3 fairly large genera: *Schizaea*, *Lygodium* and *Anemia*. The stem may be prostrate or erect and bears pinnate fronds, which are richly branched in many species.

In *Lygodium*, the fronds keep growing throughout the plant's entire life, often attaining lengths of up to 100 ft. For support, they wind their stipes round

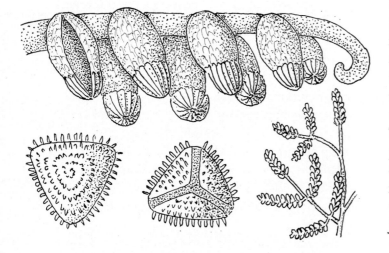

Fig. 351 *Anemia phyllitidis*. Lower right: part of fertile frond (natural size); top: pinna (slightly magnified); lower left: spore seen from above (highly magnified); centre: spore seen from the side (highly magnified)

other plants. Each frond is usually divided into a sterile and a fertile section. The pinnae of the fertile sections are considerably narrower than the sterile.

In the genera *Schizaea* and *Lygodium*, the fertile sections occupy the tip of the fronds. In *Anemia*, the two pinnae nearest the base of the frond are transformed into long stalks and bear terminal pinnules with two rows of sporangia each. Certain species of *Schizaea* have separate fertile and sterile fronds. The sporangia develop on the upper surface of the fertile pinnae. In *Lygodium*, every sporangium lies embedded in a fold. The sporangia, which generally have a short stalk, are oval in all species. Their top is crowned by a ring of thick-walled cells.

Schizaea is unusual in that its prothallus is a branched filament bearing its antheridia and archegonia on the upper surface.

Family
Gleicheniaceae

Like the Schizaceae, the Gleicheniaceae are a predominantly tropical family. Though they comprise only the two genera, *Gleichenia* and *Sticherus*, they play an important part in the flora of the tropics – the genus *Sticherus*, in particular, is made up of a very large number of species.

Gleicheniaceae fronds have a very distinct structure: their branching appears to be of the forking type (see *Fig. 353*). In fact, the leaf axis gives rise to two rows of opposite branches and then ceases to grow. The branches themselves continue to develop in the direction of the axis, produce further branches, and cease to grow in their turn. In some species, the fronds may attain lengths of more than 165 ft. From the base of each 'fork' there arise two fronds which, unlike the bare, lateral branches, bear pinnate leaves. The peripheral frond sections are also covered in pinnae. The pinnae, which have a leathery consistency, bear a small number of sporangia combined into small sori. The number of sporangia per sorus varies from 2 to 6. The sporangia have an annulus just above their centre.

The Gleicheniaceae are among the few ferns that can live in direct sunlight. In their tropical habitat, they quickly transform bright clearings into an almost impenetrable jungle.

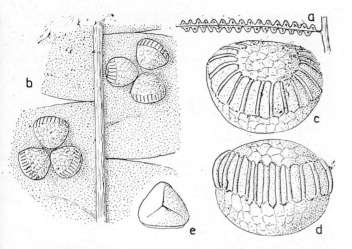

Fig. 352 *Gleichenia sp. a:* Pinna (natural size); *b:* part of pinna with two sori (slightly magnified); *c:* sporangium seen from top (more highly magnified); *d:* lateral view of sporangium (magnified); *e:* spore (highly magnified)

Fig. 353 *Gleichenia sp.*

Family

Hymenophyllaceae

The Hymenophyllaceae are small ferns that flourish in tropical rain forests, where numerous species (e.g. in the genus *Mecodium*) live as epiphytes, their roots anchored to the accumulated humus layer on the stems or branches of trees. Other species live on the ground, among them many members of the genera *Hymenophyllum* and *Trichomanes*. A few Hymenophyllaceae make do without roots altogether, among them species of *Didymoglossum* from the tropics of America. Here, the place of the roots is taken by root hairs which originate in the stipe and rachis.

All members of this family have extremely thin fronds: the blade (with the exception of the veins which, moreover, are missing in many species) is built up of a single layer of cells.

The fronds are usually pinnately lobed. In some species, the leaf blade has been reduced to a small band on either side of the vein; the fronds of such ferns look like so many torn shreds. Pinnae with entire margins are extremely rare. In many genera, including *Trichomanes*, the fronds are covered in hair.

Hymenophyllaceae produce only one type of frond. The sporangia are combined into sori at the edge of the fronds. Every sorus is enclosed in an indusium whose shape differs from genus to genus. The indusium of *Mecodium* and *Hymenophyllum* has

two flaps; that of *Meringium*, a genus whose main centre of distribution is New Guinea, is funnel-shaped; that of *Vandenboschia* and *Trichomanes* is cylindrical or cup-shaped.

Another characteristic feature of many Hymenophyllaceae is the peculiar structure of the receptacle, the cushion of tissue on which the sporangia develop. In the genera *Vandenboschia*, *Didymoglossum* and

Fig. 354 *Hymenophyllum australe.* Right: entire plant (slightly reduced); left: tip of pinna with sori (slightly magnified)

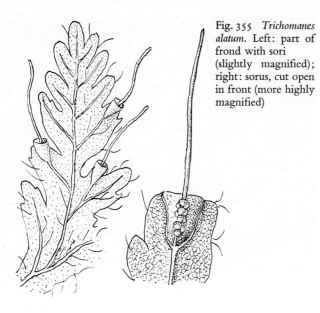

Fig. 355 *Trichomanes alatum*. Left: part of frond with sori (slightly magnified); right: sorus, cut open in front (more highly magnified)

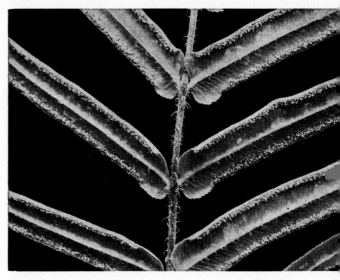

Fig. 356 *Pteris sp.*; the curving margin of the pinnae help to protect the sporangia

Trichomanes, the receptacle takes the form of a long thread protruding from the indusium; at its base, short-stalked sporangia are closely crowded together.

The sporangia of Hymenophyllaceae are small and of spherical to cylindrical shape. They have a closed annulus that runs diagonally or horizontally across their wall. The spores germinate into lobular or filamentous prothalli. Remarkably enough, even the filamentous types have their archegonia embedded in tissue.

The only genus to grow outside tropical rain forests is *Hymenophyllum*, whose 25 species range throughout the world. Four species are indigenous to Britain.

Family
Pteridaceae

This is one of the great fern families, and accounts for much of the fern flora in all parts of the world. With the exception of a few tropical epiphytes, most Pteridaceae live in the soil. Usually only the fronds rise above the surface, while the stem remains hidden below the ground. In a few genera, however, the stem rises above the surface as well; in either case, it is usually covered in scales or hairs.

Most Pteridaceae have pinnate fronds, with a large number of sporangia on their under-surface, usually combined into sori. In most species, the sori occur at fixed distances along the leaf margins; in some species, however, the entire under-surface of the fronds is covered in them. The sori generally lie hidden beneath an indusium. In some cases, however, for instance in *Pteris*, the leaf margin takes over the role of the indusium: it curls up and forms a protective roof over the sori. In a few species, the sori are completely unprotected.

The sporangia of Pteridaceae generally have an incomplete annulus running vertically across the top, and at maturity, tear just beneath its two ends. A few species, however, have a diagonal annulus that forms a closed ring.

The ferns in this family display an astonishing variety of shapes and particularly of fronds. The most imposing species are found in *Dicksonia* and *Cibotium*, two tropical and predominantly arborescent genera. They all have a stout stem which – particularly in *Dicksonia* – can grow to a considerable height. The stem bears a large crown of gigantic, tripinnate leaves. The sporangia are confined to certain pinnae only which, in *Dicksonia*, are easily distinguished from the rest by their strongly reduced blade.

Another important genus in this family is *Lindsaea*, not so much because of its size – all species are herbaceous and have a short rhizome – as because of its great range: it includes 200 species, mainly tropical.

The genus *Pteridium* is a true cosmopolitan. It consists of only the one species, *P. aquilinum*, bracken, which grows over great expanses of forest land, on open heath and moorland, and on many a hedge bank. It has a hairy, stout stem that creeps underground over distances of up to 6 ft. and sends up composite, pinnate fronds every year. The fronds are more or less densely covered in hair. On their underside, they bear sporangia which combine into sori along the edge of the pinnae. The sori enjoy the protection of a double sheath formed by the edge of the curled-over leaf, and by a true indusium. The annulus is diagonal and incomplete; the spores resemble a 4-sided, smooth pyramid.

Bracken owes its specific name (*aquilinus*, eagle-like) to the spread-eagle appearance of its woody tissue (see *Fig. 356*).

Bracken was formerly of some economic importance in the Far East, where its rhizomes used to supply the local population with starch.

Pteris, like the true ferns in this family, has a surface stem. However, none of its species is arborescent – their scaly or hairy stem is exceedingly short, and produces a quick succession of pinnate or multiple composite fronds. The sori are borne marginally on the pinnae and are protected by the down-curling leaf edge. They are built up of sporangia together with sterile paraphyses and have a vertical, incomplete annulus. The genus *Pteris* comprises some 280 species, predominantly tropical. The only European species, *P. cretica*, occurs as far north as the lakes in Upper Italy.

Acrostichum is another genus with a short surface

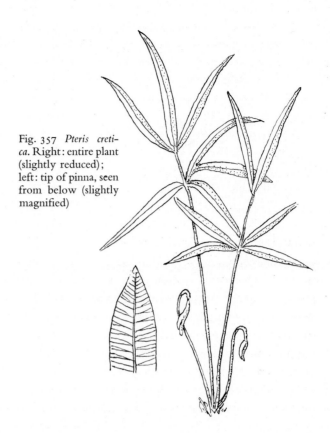

Fig. 357 *Pteris cretica*. Right: entire plant (slightly reduced); left: tip of pinna, seen from below (slightly magnified)

stem. Its only species, *A. aureum*, grows in mangrove formations of tropical coastlands, of which its very large, greenish-yellow fronds are a typical constituent.

Perhaps the most beautiful ferns of all are found in the genus *Adiantum* (*Fig. 361*), many of whose 200 tropical and subtropical species are grown as indoor plants. The decorative, finely divided fronds rise up

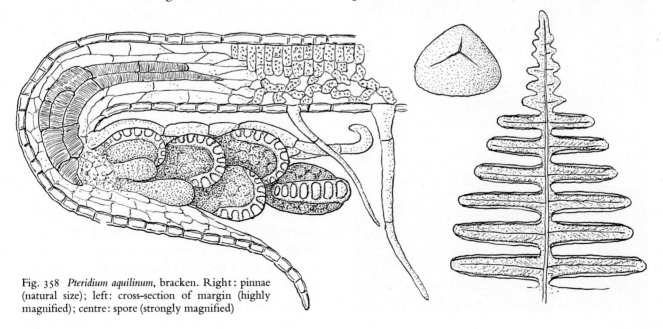

Fig. 358 *Pteridium aquilinum*, bracken. Right: pinnae (natural size); left: cross-section of margin (highly magnified); centre: spore (strongly magnified)

281

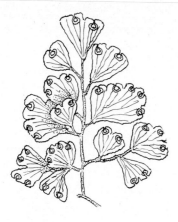

Fig. 359 *Adiantum cuneatum*; part of frond (slightly reduced)

Fig. 360 *Acrostichum aureum*; tip of frond (greatly reduced)

from a creeping or erect rhizome densely covered in dark scales. The blade is divided into numerous, mostly fan-shaped, pinnae whose bright-green colour makes a striking contrast to the shiny black stems. The sporangia are densely grouped round the tips of the veins on the leaf under-side, where they are protected by the curling leaf edge. They have a vertical and incomplete annulus.

A. capillus-veneris, maidenhair fern, is a truly cosmopolitan representative of this species, and in

Fig. 361 *Adiantum cuneatum*

Europe is specially abundant along the Mediterranean. *A. reniforme* (*Pl. 136, p. 264*) is restricted to islands in the Atlantic Ocean, particularly to the Canaries. Its fronds are kidney-shaped and extremely decorative.

Family

Parkeriaceae

This family comprises only the small genus *Ceratopteris*, whose aquatic members are mainly found in the tropics. They either sink their root-like stems into the mud or else float freely on the water surface. Their multipinnate fronds can attain considerable lengths and occur in two forms: as *Fig. 362* shows, the sterile fronds are divided into broad, the fertile ones into relatively narrow and long pinnae with a curling edge under the protection of which the sporangia develop. The sporangia do not combine into individual sori, are borne on short stalks and have a vertical annulus built up of a very large number of relatively thin-walled cells. Every sporangium gives rise to 16 or 32 spores with ribbed walls.

Vegetative reproduction is common in this small family. Young plants grow in the axils of old fronds and later break free.

Family

Davalliaceae

This predominantly tropical family includes *Davallia canariensis*, the only species to occur in more temperate latitudes – it advances as far north as the Iberian peninsula. Most Davalliaceae are epiphytes; only a few genera, including particularly *Nephrolepis*, also live on the ground.

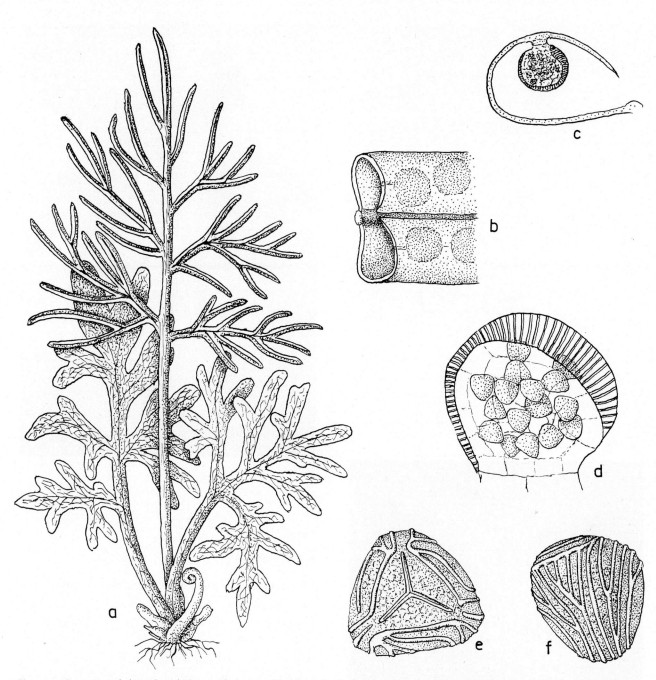

Fig. 362 *Ceratopteris thalictroides.* *a:* Plant with two sterile and one fertile frond (reduced); *b:* part of fertile pinna seen from above (slightly magnified); *c:* cross-section of a fertile pinna (slightly magnified); *d:* sporangium (more highly magnified); *e:* spore seen from above (highly magnified); *f:* spore seen from the side (highly magnified)

Species of *Davallia* have their elongated rhizome hidden in the substrate. The fronds are generally finely divided, as, for instance, in *D. fijiensis* (*Fig. 364*), one of many Asiatic species. The under-side of the fronds bears the sporangia, which cluster round the tips of the veins and combine into sori. Each sorus is protected by an indusium.

In *Nephrolepis*, the stem is short and erect, and in many species forms stolons. The fronds are simply pinnate and sometimes covered in hair. The sori at the tips of the veins are spherical or elongated, and lie hidden beneath an indusium. Several species grow up into bizarre-looking plants, for which reason they are often cultivated in hothouses.

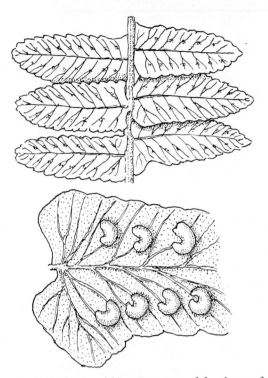

Fig. 363 *Nephrolepis cordifolia*. Top: part of frond seen from above (natural size); below: part of pinna with sori, seen from below (slightly magnified)

Fig. 364 *Davallia fijiensis*

Fig. 365 *Cyathea sp.*

Family

Cyatheaceae

This family of close on 800 species constitutes the main body of tree ferns, all of which are now treated as members of the genus *Cyathea* (*Pls. 139, 140. p. 265*).

The most striking feature of this group is their usually slender stem, which may rise to heights of up to 65 ft. One of the few species with a stout stem is *C. australis*, which occurs in the tropical forests of Australia.

The stem tapers markedly towards the base, where it is surrounded by a dense web of hard, dark roots, which lend it extra strength. At the tip of the stem rises a rich crown of gigantic fronds, up to 13 ft. in length and multipinnate. The leaf stalk, which can attain a considerable length as well, is studded with sharp spines, and so are the main veins. Some species shed their old fronds as soon as they have concluded

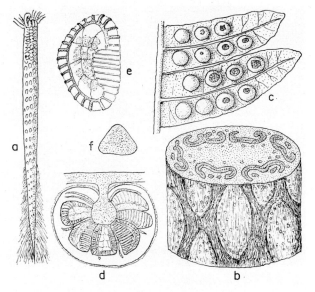

Fig. 366 *Cyathea sp. a:* Stem, with tapering base reinforced by roots (very much reduced); *b:* part of stem (note vascular bundles and elliptical scars left by old fronds; reduced); *c:* two pinnae with sori seen from below (slightly magnified); *d:* sorus in cross-section (more highly magnified); *e:* sporangia (magnified); *f:* spore (highly magnified)

Fig. 367 *Cyathea australis*

their development; in others, the dead fronds continue to hang down for a long time. The shed fronds leave broad scars on the stem.

The fronds have their under-side covered with sori consisting of sporangia and filamentous paraphyses. The sporangia and paraphyses are squashed together into hemispherical or columnar receptacles. From the base of each receptacle rises an indusium which, in most species, surrounds the entire sorus; in others it is notched and open on top; in yet others it is entirely absent.

The relatively small sporangia have a closed annulus running diagonally across their wall. The part of the wall destined to tear open when the sporangia mature, stands out very prominently: it is built up of elongated cells arranged in horizontal rows. Each sporangium gives rise to 64 spores.

Cyatheaceae are distributed in the tropical belt, particularly in tropical rain forests.

Family
Aspidiaceae

This large family of ferns is distributed throughout the world. All are herbaceous, and the great majority have creeping or more or less erect rootstocks. Only the genus *Woodsia*, with two species native to Britain, produces a short surface stem.

The fronds of all Aspidiaceae are more or less clearly divided into pinnae. Most species produce only a single type of frond, but some form sterile as well as fertile ones.

The sori, most of them rounded, are usually scattered over the entire under-surface of the pinnae; only in isolated cases do they congregate near the leaf margins. They generally develop in the protection of an indusium. The sporangia of a number of species do not combine into sori; all have an interrupted annulus running vertically across their top. The spores are more or less kidney-shaped and have their walls covered in nodulous or spinous processes.

The best-known, most common, and most popular British species is the beautiful *Dryopteris filix-mas*, male fern (*Pl. 141, p. 266*), which has been known since antiquity as a remedy against tapeworms.

Another common species is *D. phegopteris*, beech fern (*Pls. 142, 143, p. 266*) which, in Britain, is

285

distributed throughout Scotland and mountain districts of England and Wales.

Closely related to *Drypoteris* is the genus *Lastrea*, so much so that two of its species, *L. oreopteris*, mountain buckler-fern, and *L. thelypteris*, marsh buckler-fern, are often classified as *Dryopteris*. While most of the more than 500 species of *Lastrea* are at home in the tropics, the two we have mentioned are common in temperate latitudes: in Britain, they occur in stations that are often far apart. In their general appearance and in the shape of their fronds, they strongly resemble *Dryopteris*, from which, however, they differ in a number of important respects. Thus many species of *Lastrea* have an erect stem; their fronds are often covered in hair, and the small, mostly round sori on the lower surface of their pinnae often lack a protective indusium.

The small genus *Matteuccia*, distributed in Europe, East Asia and North America, consists of only two species, of which one, *M. struthiopteris*, occurs in Central Europe. It is a herbaceous fern with an underground rhizome. The fronds are of two types – the sterile ones are divided almost from the base into broad, distinctly serrated pinnae; the fertile ones have a relatively long stalk and narrow, undivided pinnae that gradually turn brown. The edge of the pinna curls round the sori, which are further protected by an indusium. The sporangia attain a con-

Fig. 369 *Dryopteris filix-mas*, male fern

siderable size and generally have an open annulus.

Temperate latitudes, and northern regions in particular, are the home of the genus *Woodsia*, all of whose 40 species are low-growing. Their stout rootstock sends up a bunch of pinnate or bipinnate and often hairy fronds, year after year. The fronds are of one type only, and have their under-side covered with numerous sori, protected by a delicate indusium. The sporangia have the vertical annulus characteristic of this family, and the spore walls are strengthened by a latticework of ridges. In Britain, this genus

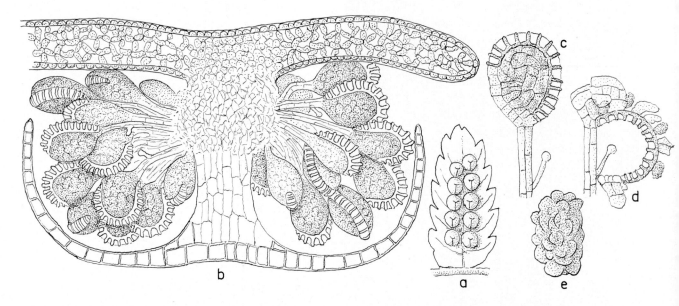

Fig. 368 *Dryopteris filix-mas*, male fern. *a*: Pinnules with sori seen from below (slightly magnified); *b*: cross-section of sorus (magnified); *c*: ripe sporangium (more strongly magnified); *d*: open sporangium; *e*: spore (highly magnified)

is represented by *W. ilvensis*, oblong woodsia, which grows in several scattered stations at altitudes below 2000 ft., and *W. alpina* which grows only at the highest altitudes.

Like so many other genera in this family, *Polystichum*, shield fern (*Pl. 138, p. 265*), is distributed throughout the world. Many individual species enjoy a surprisingly wide range, among them *P. lobatum*, prickly shield fern, which grows in British woodland, above the treeline in the Alps, and even in tropical mountain forests.

The short rootstock of shield ferns is covered in abundant soft, broad scales; the fronds are richly tufted and have short stalks. The sori are usually restricted to the under-side of the topmost leaves, where they develop under the protection of tiny, shield-shaped indusia, to which these ferns owe their popular name. The sporangia have an open, vertical annulus, and contain nodulous or spinous spores.

In moist mountain crevices, on walls and wells we often come across bladder-ferns in the genus *Cystopteris*, all of them low-growing, and with thin, finely divided fronds, bearing indusia and sori on their under-side. This genus, too (18 species), is distributed throughout the world. Three of its species occur in Britain; of these *C. fragilis*, brittle bladder-fern, is the most common.

The genus *Athyrium* is another with a world-wide distribution; among its close on 600 species, *A. filix-femina*, lady fern, is a true cosmopolitan. This splendid plant flourishes throughout moist sites in the British Isles; its large, pinnate, bipinnate or even triply pinnate fronds have a lace-like appearance suggesting feminine grace – whence the name. Lady ferns have a stout rootstock covered with large rusty scales, and rigid, black roots. The elongated sori, protected by indusia, form rows on either side of the veins on the leaf under-surface. The related *A. distentifolium* is chiefly restricted to the Alps.

The genus *Onoclea*, consisting of only the one species, *O. sensibilis*, is at home in North America and East Asia. This fern produces two utterly different types of fronds: the sterile ones are divided into broad pinnae, pairs of which are fused together by small, wing-shaped processes of the stalk: the fertile ones are bare except for pinnae at the very tip. These pinnae are divided into fine lobes that curl up to form

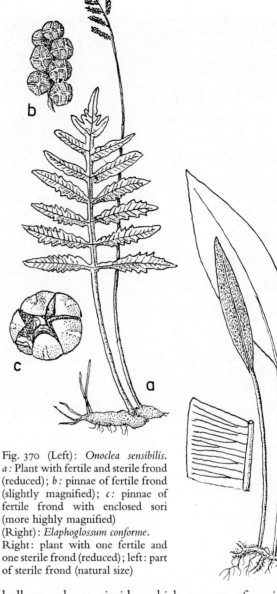

Fig. 370 (Left): *Onoclea sensibilis*. *a*: Plant with fertile and sterile frond (reduced); *b*: pinnae of fertile frond (slightly magnified); *c*: pinnae of fertile frond with enclosed sori (more highly magnified) (Right): *Elaphoglossum conforme*. Right: plant with one fertile and one sterile frond (reduced); left: part of sterile frond (natural size)

hollow spheres, inside which groups of sori lie protected.

A small group of Aspidiaceae is exclusively tropical. The South-East Asian genus *Bolbitis* occupies a special position in this family, because it has no indusia. The main body of tropical Aspidiaceae is combined in the genus *Elaphoglossum*, with 400 species throughout the tropics, particularly in the Andes. Most live on the ground, but some have become adapted to the epiphytic habit. The chief character of these ferns, by which they are easily distinguished from all other Aspidiaceae, is their undivided frond. The fronds are of two types: the fertile ones have a narrower blade and a longer stalk than the barren. Their under-surface is densely covered with countless free-standing sporangia.

Fig. 371 *Blechnum brasiliense*

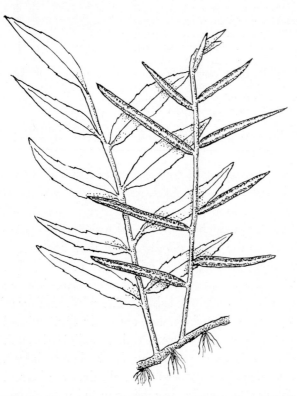

Fig. 372 *Stenochlaena palustris;* plant with sterile and fertile frond (greatly reduced)

Family
Blechnaceae

This family is largely confined to the southern hemisphere – only one species, *Blechnum spicant*, hard fern (*Pl. 146, p. 267*), occurs in the northern hemisphere, including Britain.

Blechnum (with more than 200 species) is a genus of low-growing ferns with a creeping or erect rootstock. The fronds are usually pinnate or at least deeply divided. A number of species produces two distinct types of frond. Thus in *B. spicant*, the fertile fronds are roughly twice the size of the barren, pinnate throughout rather than deeply cut above, with wide spaces between the pinnae, whose edges curl over the sori. The unusually large sporangia contain kidney-shaped or near-spherical spores. In hothouses, we often meet the exotic *B. brasiliense* whose fronds are borne on a woody stem just under 18 ins. tall.

The second genus in this family, *Stenochlaena*, includes only a small number of forms, which some taxonomists treat as a single species and others as several distinct ones. All are ferns of considerable size; some species can attain heights of up to 35 ft. The rootstock of several types is capable of winding round trees. It bears large pinnate fronds of two types: the fertile ones are much narrower than the barren, whose pinnae are relatively broad and have serrated margins. The fertile pinnae have their undersides covered with numerous sporangia. These occupy certain zones only, but do not combine into sori.

The genus *Stenochlaena* is at home in tropical Asia; *S. palustris*, which ranges from India to Polynesia, lives in jungle swamps, but also advances into mangrove formations.

Family
Aspleniaceae

This family plays an important part in the world's fern flora, thanks largely to the genus *Asplenium*, spleenwort, which comprises close on 700 universally distributed species. Their chief characteristic is the structure of their sori: elongated swellings on either side of the lateral frond veins, usually protected by indusia. The sporangia are borne on slender stalks which, in most species, consist of a single row of cells; they have a vertical, open annulus. The spores are elongated or kidney-shaped.

Most species of *Asplenium* live on the ground; a few, however, have turned epiphyte. The best-known epiphytic species, *A. nidus* (*Pls. 147, 150, pp. 268, 269*), which ranges from India to Polynesia, is a common sight in hothouses. It owes its name (*nidus*, nest) to the arrangement of its fronds which, as in many other *Asplenia*, are undivided and combined into a dense rosette – the 'nest'. The rosette forms a funnel in which water and humus can collect; the roots grow into the funnel and obtain nourishment there.

Species with undivided, tongue-shaped fronds include a number of British representatives. One of the most beautiful of these is *A. scolopendrium*, hart's tongue (*Pls. 144, 145, p. 267*), which is often described as *Scolopendrium vulgare* or *Phyllitis scolopendrium*. This species, though widely distributed in Britain, is only locally abundant and does not grow at altitudes above 500 ft.

The genus also includes a large number of ferns whose fronds are more or less clearly divided into pinnae. One of these, *A. trichomanes*, maidenhair spleenwort, is found in Europe, Asia and North America. Like many of its relatives, it likes rocks and walls that offer it moisture and shade. It is easily identified by its delicate fronds, with their shiny, dark-brown rachis bearing pairs of oval pinnae. Perhaps the best-known indigenous species is the small

Fig. 374 *Asplenium nidus*

A. ruta-muraria, wall rue (*Fig. 375*), which grows in rock crevices, where it often forms dense tufts. Its delicate fronds are triangular in shape and dark-green to brown in colour.

Ceterach, the second genus in this family, comprises only three species, distributed in Europe, Asia and North Africa. All are small ferns, anchored to

Fig. 373 *Asplenium scolopendrium*, hart's tongue

Fig. 375 *Asplenium ruta-muraria*, wall rue. Left: entire plant (slightly magnified); top right: pinnae with sori seen from below (more highly magnified); lower right: spore (highly magnified)

Fig. 376 *Ceterach officinarum*, rusty-back fern

the ground or to walls by means of a short, scaly rootstock. Unlike most other ferns, *Ceterach* prefers dry, sunny sites. To cope with this type of habitat, the oval pinnae have a leathery consistency and are densely covered in scales on the underside. In Britain, the genus is represented by *C. officinarum*, rusty-back fern (*Fig. 376*), which is most plentiful on walls and stone dykes in western regions.

Family
Matoniaceae

This family, which comprises only the one species, *Matonia pectinata*, is indigenous to Malacca, Sumatra, Amboina and New Guinea. *M. pectinata* (*Fig. 377*) is an imposing fern; its fronds, which arise from a forking and creeping rootstock, often attain heights of more than $6\frac{1}{2}$ ft. They have a long and stout rachis and apparently palmate leaves. In fact, the rachis forks at the tip, one prong developing into a serrated pinna, while the other remains bare and continues to grow more or less horizontally and to produce fresh forks. The serrated pinnae bear two rows of sori, one on either side of the central vein. The sori contain only a small number of sporangia, crowded round a columnar receptacle, topped with a shield-shaped indusium.

Because of the forking habit, *Matonia* has close affinities with a very important family of ferns: the Polypodiaceae.

Family
Polypodiaceae

This almost exclusively tropical family consists chiefly of epiphytic forms. Since epiphytes have to rely for their water supply on the irregular rainfall, they must protect themselves against excessive evaporation. This the Polypodiaceae achieve by means of leathery fronds, densely covered in scales or hairs. Some species are, moreover, able to store water.

Ground-dwelling Polypodiaceae are the exception – only a single genus contains no epiphytes at all.

The rootstock of Polypodiaceae may be creeping or erect. The fronds are entire or simply pinnate;

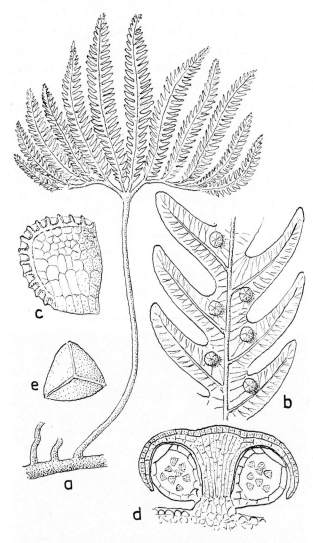

Fig. 377 *Matonia pectinata. a:* Entire plant (much reduced); *b:* part of frond with sori, seen from below (slightly magnified); *c:* sporangium (magnified); *d:* sorus in cross-section (more highly magnified); *e:* spore (highly magnified)

290

only a very few species have more finely divided leaves. In quite a few, the sporangia do not combine into sori, but appear singly on the underside of the fronds. In the majority, however, sori are the rule; they are ranged on either side of the vein and never covered by an indusium.

The only non-epiphytic genus, *Dipteris*, ranges from the Malayan Archipelago to China. All its species are tall plants; their rootstock, covered in dark scales, forks and creeps in the ground, and sends down numerous roots. The upper surface bears fronds at regular intervals. The leaves form two fan-shaped lobes at the tip of a long rachis. The main veins are characteristically forked in all species. The fronds bear numerous sori on their under-side; in some species they arise in the vicinity of the main veins, in others they are scattered over the entire surface. The genus includes 7 species, among them *D. conjugata* from the mountain forests of Indonesia (*Fig. 379*).

Ferns of the most unusual shape make up the genus *Platycerium*, whose fronds resemble the antlers of stags. This shape is particularly pronounced in *P. alcicorne* (*Fig. 378*) and *P. bifurcatum* (*Pl. 149, p. 269*). Sometimes, however, the antlers are less clearly defined, as for instance in *P. angolense* (*Pl. 148, p. 268*) from the tropics of Africa. The fronds, which in some species may attain lengths of up to 17 ft., rise up almost vertically at first, but gradually begin to arch over.

In addition to 'antlers', this family also produces a

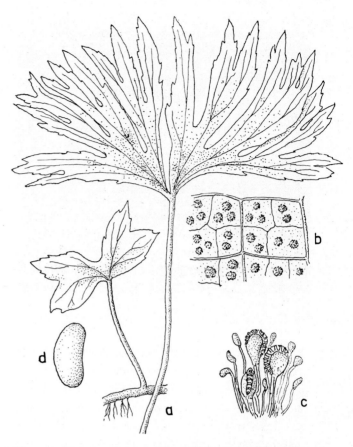

Fig. 379 *Dipteris conjugata. a :* Plant with a young and an older frond (much reduced); *b :* part of frond with sori, seen from below (slightly magnified); *c :* several sporangia and paraphyses (more highly magnified); *d :* spore (highly magnified)

second kind of leaf: rounded, mostly entire, bowl-shaped and attached directly and tightly to the root-stock. Between these leaves and the bark of the host tree an open cavity is formed and gradually fills with considerable quantities of humus from which the plant derives its nourishment.

The 'antlers' serve as combined organs of assimilation and reproduction. Their under-surface is partly covered in dense felt, formed of sporangia and paraphyses. Although the sporangia are restricted to certain zones of the frond, they never combine into sori. In some species, they appear on a special part of the leaf, oval in shape and separated from the rest of the blade by a special stalk.

The genus *Platycerium* comprises some 17 species, ranging from tropical Africa through India to Australia. Many species are cultivated in hothouses where, with proper care, they generally produce luxuriant fronds.

Epiphytic members of this family are often exposed to prolonged spells of drought. They generally

Fig. 378 *Platycerium alcicorne*

Fig. 380 *Polypodium vulgare*, common polypody

survive unhurt, not only because they are able to prevent excessive evaporation, but also because they can store water. In *Pteropsis*, ranging from Madagascar to the South Sea Islands, only the sterile fronds have been transformed into storage organs; in the predominantly South Asian *Pyrrosia* most fronds have been specially thickened.

Another genus capable of storing water is *Lecanopteris*. Here the fronds are fleshy and the long stipe is swollen at the base. The stem, too, is conspicuously thickened and, on closer investigation, proves to be divided into numerous internal cavities inhabited by ants.

One of the chief characteristics of Polypodiaceae is their complete lack of an indusium. Only in *Pleopeltis*, a genus indigenous to the tropics of America, Africa and Japan, are the sori protected in any way – here the paraphyses accompanying the sporangia broaden at the tip into flat shields and form a protective roof over the sporangia.

The only genus in this family to appear in temperate latitudes is *Polypodium* (*Pls. 151–153, p. 270*). Of its 75 species, several are indigenous to Britain, including *P. vulgare*, common polypody (*Pl. 151, 152*), a small fern with oval-oblong, pinnate fronds. It usually creeps over the leaf-mould of old hedgerows, but will occasionally settle on decaying tree stumps.

Unlike most other Polypodiaceae, most species of *Polypodium* have more or less pinnate leaves; the Central American *P. crassifolium* (*Fig. 382*) is a rare

exception. The fronds combine the functions of photosynthesis and reproduction, except in *P. meyenianum* (*Fig. 381*) from the Philippines, whose fronds are divided into a lower sterile and an upper fertile section. The pinnae of the fertile section have become reduced to thin threads with the sori strung upon them like so many pearls.

Family

Vittariaceae

This small family of epiphytic ferns, comprising only the one genus, *Vittaria*, holds a special position in the order Filicales, because its prothalli are elongated rather than heart-shaped. Like all epiphytic ferns, Vittariaceae can withstand prolonged periods of drought: their roots, which are wrapped round the scaly stems, are able to absorb large amounts of water quickly, and to retain moisture for a long time. The fronds, which resemble those of many Polypodiaceae, may be stalked or sessile. The tongue-shaped

Fig. 381 *Polypodium meyenianum*

292

Fig. 382 *Polypodium crassifolium* from Central America

leaves are leathery and hairless; their lower edge is densely covered in sori, consisting of sporangia and paraphyses. There is no indusium. All the 80 or so known species occur throughout the tropics.

HYDROPTERIDALES

Water Ferns

Within the Hydropteridales, which occupy a special position among the ferns, we distinguish two families with so many distinct features that many taxonomists treat them as two separate orders. All are aquatic; some float on the water surface, others live in the bottom ooze of rivers and lakes; all alike produce a rootstock. The fronds are simple or slightly divided, and those of floating species do not curl over at the tip when young, thus differing from all other ferns. The side of the rootstock facing the substrate bears dense bunches of roots or root-like fronds.

Like all ferns, Hydropteridales form true sporangia. They are invariably of two types – microsporangia and macrosporangia – and are unusual in that they do not arise beneath the leaves but develop inside more or less spherical receptacles at the base of the fronds. Such sporangia are known as sporocarps.

In the first of the two families, the microsporangia and macrosporangia are combined into common sori; in the second family, they develop in separate sporocarps. Each microsporangium contains a very large number of spores, which germinate into prothalli with several more or less strongly reduced antheridia; the entire development of the micro-prothallus takes place inside the spore. The macrosporangia form only a few macrospores, each of which develops into a macroprothallus. The macro-prothalli, in each of which several archegonia are produced, protrude from the spore wall; they never completely break free from the spore.

Family

Marsileaceae

This is a family of firmly-rooted water ferns. It comprises the two genera *Marsilea*, clover-fern, and *Pilularia*, pillwort. They grow chiefly in mud, to which they are attached by means of a forking, proliferating rootstock of fantastic growth; quite often a single plant will occupy an area more than 65 ft. in diameter.

The two genera differ markedly in external appearance. The far more imposing clover ferns have very large, conspicuous fronds. These rise alternately from the rootstock on a slender, 8-in. stipe terminating in two pairs of pinnae, placed so close together that they seem to form a single whorl. The pinnae, which are near-triangular, spread out horizontally, thus resembling four-leaved clover plants.

The hard, bean-shaped sporocarps arise on short stalks from the base of the fronds; in some species there are only one or two sporocarps per frond, in others there are considerably more. Every sporocarp contains a fixed number of sori, in which the microsporangia are combined with the macrosporangia. The sporangia are borne on a ring-shaped receptacle which is gelatinous when moist. As the sporangia become mature, the receptacle absorbs water and expands so strongly that it bursts the wall of the sporocarp, whereupon the receptacle and sori break out. The receptacle retains its annular form for some time still, but finally expands completely.

The genus *Marsilea* comprises close on 70 species throughout the world; its main centre of distribution is in Australia and South Africa. The only European species, *M. quadrifolia*, clover-fern (*Pl. 155, p. 271*), occurs in warmer regions only, and is particularly abundant in the Po valley.

The second genus, *Pilularia*, pillwort, includes only 6 species, of which two occur in Europe and the rest in Chile, New Zealand and Australia. Like clover-fern, pillworts live in shallow water and on the moist margins of lakes and bogs. The creeping rootstock is reduced to a mere thread; only a few species produce root fibres. At the upper surface of the rootstock, the fronds arise in quick succession; because they lack a blade and consist entirely of a pointed stipe they are readily mistaken for small bulrushes. At the base of the fronds, the sporocarps are borne singly; the popular name of pillwort refers to their shape and size. The sporocarps are divided into 4 chambers, each bearing a sorus consisting of a microsporangium or a macrosporangium attached to a parietal receptacle. The sporocarps open in much the same way as those of *Marsilea*; the mature sporangia are embedded in a mass of mucilage. In Britain, *P. globulifera* ranges south from Skye and Sutherlandshire to Cornwall. Its wider range is mainly restricted to Europe, north of the Alps.

Family
Salviniaceae

While the Marsileaceae differed noticeably from most other ferns, the floating Salviniaceae are more unusual still. All species are delicate plants floating on the surface of stagnant or slow-moving waters. The stem is much branched and spreads immediately beneath the surface. It is crowded with oval or roundish fronds, which are folded lengthwise in the bud but later spread out horizontally. Their tissue contains a large number of air chambers, to which these plants owe their floating powers. A few species produce roots as well as leaves. Like the last family, Salviniaceae have their sporangia enclosed in sporocarps; however, the microsporangia and macrosporangia develop in separate receptacles. The two

Fig. 383   *Salvinia natans*

genera, *Salvinia* and *Azolla*, differ in a number of respects.

Salviniae are completely devoid of true roots: their branching, hairy stem bears nothing but leaves, arranged in whorls of three on nodes that follow one another in quick succession. Of the three fronds to each whorl, only two are distinguishable as oval, green leaves. They act as organs of photosynthesis and help the plant to swim. The third leaf is split up into a number of hairy threads lacking chlorophyll and drooping into the water: they act as roots and at the same time bear several sporocarps at the base – small spherical bodies with a tough wall built up of two superposed layers of cells. Inside the sporocarps, a columnar receptacle bears numerous small microsporangia or a few macrosporangia. These are released on the decomposition of the sporocarp wall.

Each microsporangium gives rise to 64 microspores which develop into tiny microprothalli. They pierce the wall of the sporangium but never leave it. Every microprothallus produces two strongly reduced antheridia containing 4 spermatozoids each. The macrosporangia bear only a single macrospore each, which germinates into a macroprothallus in the protection of the sporangium. It pierces the wall and pushes its terminal archegonia outside. After fertilization, the egg cell of one of the archegonia develops into an embryo and hence into a new *Salvinia* plant.

Salvinia comprises some 10 species, most of them indigenous to South America and Africa. The only species to occur in Europe, *S. natans* (*Pl. 156, p. 272*), is restricted to warmer regions, particularly to old branches of rivers, which they sometimes cover in a dense carpet of green.

Like *Salvinia*, *Azolla* is a genus of floating ferns; for the rest, the two genera differ markedly. To begin with, the branching stem of *Azolla* bears small fronds as well as true roots. The fronds, which are sessile on the stem and overlap like scales, are divided into two lobes, of which the uppermost contains chlorophyll and thus acts as an organ of assimilation. It also helps to keep the plant afloat by means of large air chambers which, incidentally, harbour the blue-green alga, *Anabaena azolla*, as an endophyte. The lower lobe is thin-skinned, colourless and scale-like. It not only lends extra support to the roots, but also bears the sporocarps, combined in groups of 2 or 4. Usually, each pair of sporocarps consists of a large capsule containing numerous microsporangia and a small one containing a single macrosporangium. As the sporocarps decompose, the sporangia drop to the bottom, where they conclude their development. In the process, the microsporangia release small balls of foam (massulae) in which the microspores are embedded. The outer wall of each massula is armed with countless hooks. The macrosporangia, too, break up, though a small remnant of their sporangial wall persists in the form of a conical cap. From the wall of the macrospore protrude rounded swellings interspersed with hooked threads. These threads become entangled with those of the massulae, thus ensuring the eventual meeting of the mature reproductive cells.

Each microspore gives rise to a strongly reduced microprothallus which, in turn, gives rise to a single antheridium. The macrospores germinate into small macroprothalli, each of which bears a single archegonium. Beneath the cap over the macrospore, the spore wall sends out several processes of the same foamy consistency as the massulae. They gradually lift the cap and thus free the way to the archegonium. Fertilization of the egg cell and the early development of the embryo take place on the bottom of the river, etc. The moment the first leaf is formed, however, its air chamber helps to lift the young plant to the surface.

The genus *Azolla* comprises 6 predominantly tropical and sub-tropical species, one of which, *A. filiculoides*, American water fern (*Pl. 157, p. 272*), made its appearance in a pond in Middlesex in 1899, and has since spread to other parts of southern England. So rapid is its growth that it will sometimes oust duckweeds from ponds where the two plants appear in association. *A. caroliniana*, another American species, has also been recorded, but never properly identified, in England (Surrey and Middlesex).

Index

Figures in italics refer to illustrations

Brucellaceae, 19
brucellosis, 15
Bryophyta, 7, 8, 226–49
Bryopogon, see *Alectoria*
Bryopsis, 43, 66
Bryozoa, 30
Bryaceae, 246
Bryales, 246–7
Bryidae, 239, 240, 241–9
Bryum, 246
bubonic plague, 11
buckler-fern, 286
    marsh, 286
    mountain, 286
budding, 145
Buellia, 224
    canescens, 224
    pulchella, 224
Buelliaceae, 224
Bulgaria inquinans, 124
bunt, 147
Buxbaumia, 204, 242
Buxbaumiaceae, 242
Buxbaumiales, 242

C

cabbage, disease of, 192
Calamites, 251
Caliciales, 217
Calicium, 217
    viride, 217
Callithamnion, 82
Calocera viscosa, 132, 154
Caloplaca, 224
    bracteata, 200, 224
    elegans, 224
    murorum, 224
Caloplacaceae, 224
Caloplacales, 224–5
Calosphaeria, 119
calvacin, 187
Calvatia caelata, 187
    gigantea, 186
    saccata, 187
calyptra, 239
Camarophyllus, 165
    marzuolus, 165
    pratensis, 165
cancer, 9, 16
Candida albicans, 86, 91, 209
candidiasis, 87, 209
    bronchopulmonary, 209
    pulmonary, 209
candle-snuff fungus, 117

Cantharellaceae, 159–61
Cantharellus, 160
    cibarius, 160
    cornucopioides, 160
    friesii, 160
    infundibuliformis, 160
capillitium, 84
Capnodiaceae, 106
Capnodium, 106
capsule, 228
carbon cycle, 12
Carboniferous, 251, 256
carotenoids, 34, 41, 70, 76
Carpenteles, 111, 209
carpogonium, 77–8
carpospore, 77–8
carragheen, 81
Caryophanales, 21
Catenaria anguillulae, 96
Catenariaceae, 96
cattle plague, 9
Caulerpa, 43, 66
cauliflower fungus, 159
Caulobacteriaceae, 19
cauloid, 70, 74
'cedar apple', 151
cell, structure of:
    daughter, 7
    in bacteria, 16–18
    in blue-green algae, 25
    in diatoms, 37–41
    in *Euglena*, 33
    in karyobionts, 26
    in slime moulds, 85
    sexual, 7
    see also under names
    of cell types
Cellulomonas, 20
Centrales, 38–40
cep, 113, 142, 184
Cephaleuros, 30, 216
cephalodial zone, 215
cephalodium, 215
Cephalozia, 236
    byssacea, 236
    pleniceps, 236
Ceramiaceae, 82
Ceramiales, 81–2
Ceramium, 77, 82
    rubrum, 29, 76, 82
Ceratiomyxa fruticulosa, 85
Ceratium, 32
Ceratocystaceae, 112
Ceratocystis picae, 112
    ulmi, 112, 211
Ceratodon, 244

    purpureus, 244
Ceratomycetaceae, 109
Ceratopteris, 282
Ceratostomataceae, 119
Ceratostomella ulmi, 119
Cercospora, 211
    apii, 211
cereals, diseases of, 151–2, 211, 212
Ceterach, 289, 290
    officinarum, 290
Cetraria, 215
    islandica, 216, 223
Chaetophora, 43, 48
Chaetophoraceae, 42, 48
Chaetophorales, 42
Chain, E.B., 89
Chamaesiphonales, 23
champignons, 174
Chantransia, 77
chanterelle, 160
    true, 166
Chara, 55, 68
Characeae, 68
Charales, 42, 43, 68–9
Chariopsidaceae, 35
Chariopsis borzi, 35
cheese and bacteria, 14
    and fungi, 88, 112
chestnut blight, 118
Chilomonas paramaecium, 32
Chlamydobacteriales, 13, 20–1, 22
Chlamydomonadaceae, 44–5
Chlamydomonas, 29, 42, 45
    braunii, 42
    coccifera, 42
    nivalis, 44
    seriata, 44
    suboogonium, 42
chlamydospore, 100, 166
chloramphenicol, 16
Chlorella, 30, 31, 47
Chlorobacteriaceae, 18
Chlorochytridiales, 44
Chlorococcales, 43, 46–7
Chlorogonium oogamum, 42, 44
Chloromonadophyceae, 33
chlorophyll, 8, 24, 34, 41, 70, 86, 226
    a, 34, 41, 70, 77
    b, 34, 41, 70, 82
    c, 70
Chlorophyta, 7, 8, 28–9, 41–70
Chlorosiphonales, 42–4, 65–6
Chlorosplenium, 125
cholera, 11, 16, 19
    of chickens, 15
Chondria, 82

Mucorales, 86, 92, 99–101
mucus, 231
'mummies', 124
mumps, 9
muscaridine, 172
muscarine, 172, 178
Musci, 238–49
mushroom, 127 *ff.*
  cultivated, 175
  field, 89, 173, 174
  horse, 89, *138*, 174–5
Mutinus caninus, 189
Mycelia sterilia, 212
mycelium, 90 *ff.*
  tertiary, 127
Mycena, 168
  galopus, 170
  polygramma, *136*, 170
  pura, 170
  rosella, 170
Mycetozoa, 85
Mycobacteriaceae, 20
Mycobacterium leprae, 16, 20
  tuberculosis, 14, 16, 20
mycobiosis, 213–25
Mycophyta, 8, 86 *ff.*
mycoplasma, 18, 21
Mycoplasmatales, 21
mycorrhiza, 87–8, 164
  ectotrophic, 87–8
  endotrophic, 87–8
Mycosphaerella, 106, 211
  pyricola, 192
  rubi, 192
Myriangiaceae, 106, 108
Myriangiales, 106, 108
Myriangium duriaei, 106
Myriostoma coliforme, 188
Myxacium, see *Cortinarius*
Myxobacteriales, 21
myxomatosis, 9
Myxomycetes, 21

N

Nardia, 236
Navicula, 40
  cardinalis, 40
  oblongata, 39
  ostrearia, 38
Naviculaceae, 38
Naviculineae, 40
Neckeraceae, 247
Neckera crispa, 247
Nectria, 113, 114

  cinnabarina, *63*, 113
  galligena, 114
  haematococca, 114
Nectriaceae, 113–14
Nemalion, 79
Nemalionales, 78–9
Nemataceae, 248
Nematoloma fasciculare, *139*
neomycin, 16
Nephrolepis, 282, 283
Nereocystis, 29, 70, 71
net blotch, 211
Neurospora, 116
  sitophila, 116, 117
Nidulariaceae, 190
Nitella, 55, 68
Nitophyllum, 82
Nitrobacter winogradskyi, 13
nitrogen cycle, 12–13
  fixatoin, 13, 24, 88
Nitrosomonas, 17
  europaea, 13
Nitzschia, 40
Noctiluca, 32
  miliaris, 32
Nostoc, 22, 24, *49*, 83, 218, 219, 237
  commune, 24
Nostocaceae, 218
Nostocinales, 23
Notholaena marantae, *264*
Nowakowskiella, 95
nucleic acid, 9
nucleus, 10
Nyssopsora, 150

O

oarweed, 70, 72, 76
Obelidium mucronatum, 95
Ochromonadaceae, 37
Oedogoniales, 65
Oedogonium, 30, 42, 65
oidium, 91
olive tree, tumour of, 15
Olpidiaceae, 91–2, 94–5
Olpidium, 87
  pendulinum, 94
Oltsmannsiella, 45
onion, disease of, 212
Onoclea, 287
  sensibilis, 287
Onygena, 112
Onygenaceae, 112
Onygenales, 112
Oocystaceae, 47

oogamy, 26, 38, 42
oogoniogamy, 42, 44
Ophiobolus iridis, 211
Ophioglossaceae, 274
Ophioglossales, 274
Ophioglossum vulgatum, *262*, 274
Ophiothea, 85
Orcheomyces, 212
Orchidaceae, 88
Ornithocercus magnificus, 32
orsellic acid, 218
Orthotrichaceae, 246
Orthotrichales, 246
Orthotrichum, 246
Oscillatoria, 24, 25
  caerulescens, 24
  erythrea, 25
Oscillatoriaceae, 22–5
Osmunda, 277
  regalis, *264*, 277
Osmundaceae, 277
ostiolum, 187
Ostropaceae, 126
Ostropales, 126
Otidea, 120
  onotica, 120
oyster mushroom, 168

P

Padina pavonia, 54, 73
Palmella, 216, 217
Palmellaceae, 46, 218–19
Panaeolus, 176
Pandorina, 27, 29
  morum, 45
Panellus, 168
  conchatus, 168
  ostreatus, 168
  stipticus, 168
panther cap, 171, 172
Paramecium, 12, 47
paramylum, 29, 34
Paranema, 34
  trichophorum, 34
Paranemaceae, 34
paraphysis, 105 *ff.*, 238
parasitism, 8
  balanced, 213–25
  in algae, 24, 29, 30, 32, 76, 81
  in bacteria, 12, 15
  in fungi, 86 *ff.*
parasol-mushrooms, 173–4
parasymbiosis, 215
Parkeriaceae, 282